THE SECRET OF CYCLING

Hunter Allen, Legendary Coach and Co-developer of TrainingPeaks' WKO+ software

"When Dr. Coggan and I wrote Training and Racing with a Power Meter, there were some very elite coaches that took this information and became experts around the world. The authors of this book are such experts. They used the laws of nature to describe and calculate the performance in running as well as in cycling. This book will help to take your cycling to the next level and the concepts written inside are foundations to creating success."

Asker Jeukendrup, Sports Nutrition Scientist, Professor of Exercise Science

"One of the best books about endurance performance I have ever seen, with an evidence based analytical approach to performance in cycling. The many practical examples make it easy for the reader to understand and apply this to improve their own performance. The breakthrough of power meters is analyzed critically, including the possibilities to increase cycling economy and cycling performance."

Maria Hopman, Professor of Integrative Physiology, Radboud University, Nijmegen

"I like the quantitative approach to the physics and physiology of cycling in this book. I feel this is important to understand and improve the performance in sports. I believe this book will help coaches and cyclists as theory and practice are combined in a highly understandable way."

HANS VAN DIJK | RON VAN MEGEN | GUIDO VROEMEN

THE SECRET OF CYCLING

MAXIMUM PERFORMANCE GAINS THROUGH EFFECTIVE POWER METERING AND TRAINING ANALYSIS

Meyer & Meyer Sport

British Library Cataloguing in Publication Data
A catalogue record for this book is available from the British Library

The Secret of Cycling
Maidenhead: Meyer & Meyer Sport (UK) Ltd., 2017
ISBN 978-1-78255-108-9

Auckland, Beirut, Dubai, Hägendorf, Hong Kong, Indianapolis, Cairo, Cape Town,
Manila, Maidenhead, New Delhi, Singapore, Sydney, Teheran, Vienna

 Member of the World Sports Publishers' Association (WSPA)

Manufacturing: Print Consult GmbH, Munich, Germany
ISBN 978-1-78255-108-9
E-mail: info@m-m-sports.com
www.m-m-sports.com

Contents

WHY DID WE WRITE THIS BOOK?

In theory, there is no difference between theory and practice. In practice, there is!

The Success of Our Books on the Dutch Market

Our previous Dutch books[1,2,3] were an instant success in the running and cycling communities in the Netherlands and Belgium. Apparently many thousands of runners and cyclists share our passion to understand, quantify and optimize the power of our human engine and to calculate and predict our attainable performance in sports. More than 10,000 copies of our books have already been sold in the (relatively small) Dutch market. We get tons of enthusiastic reactions from fans, who call our quantitative approach "a revelation in sports books." The calculators at our websites www.thesecretofrunning.com and www.thesecretofcycling.com are visited by many thousands of runners and cyclists, who enjoy calculating how they can optimize their performance.

How to Get Fitter and Faster

We share a lifelong passion for running, cycling and science. The remarkable story of our books starts in 2011 when Hans retired (at the age of 57) from his position as full professor at Delft University of Technology. Hans decided to devote his time to running and studying the science of running to see if he could get fitter and faster. Hans has been a committed runner since 1980, but over the years his race times had declined slowly as shown in the figure below. Obviously, the decline in performance with age will not surprise our readers, but the fact that he got significantly faster after 2011 should! From 2013 onwards he even managed to become a multiple Dutch Masters Champion (M60)! The reasons for this amazing improvement are the topic of our books. You will gain insights into the factors that determine your performance and how you can get fitter and faster.

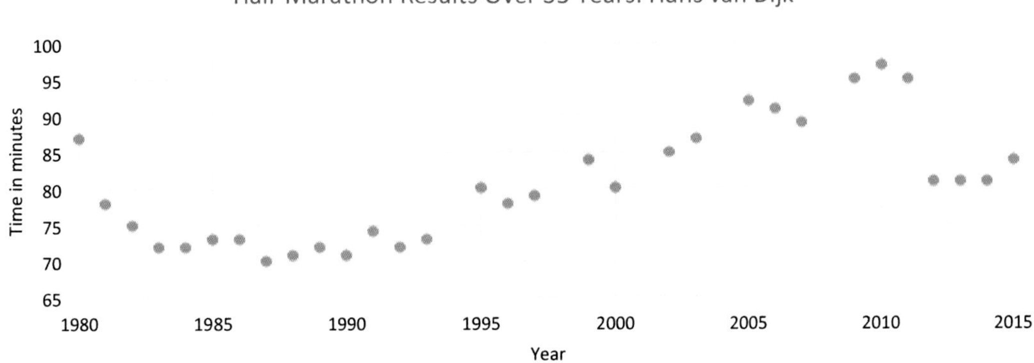

The Quantitative Approach to Sports

As scientists, we were not satisfied with the traditional handbooks on running and cycling which are based mostly on the experiences of athletes and coaches. They do describe the factors which influence the performance, but only in a qualitative way. We were interested in hard numbers and formulas that would enable us to calculate the performance exactly. We also wanted to differentiate between scientific proof and the opinions of athletes and coaches, so we have set out to develop science-based models for all factors influencing the running and cycling performance and to test these models with hard data from measurements

Cycling Science: The Laws of Physics and Physiology

We have developed a complete cycling model based on the laws of physics and physiology. The figure below illustrates the model, which enables us to calculate the race time exactly.

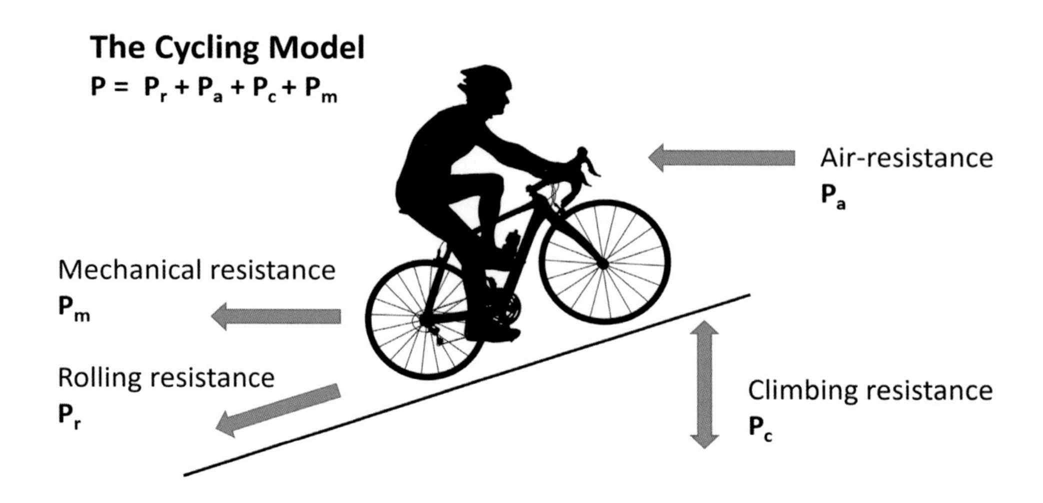

The model is based on the fact that your muscles and your cardiovascular system form your human engine. Your human engine has a certain capacity, which can be described in terms of the traditional notion of oxygen uptake capacity (VO_2 max), but better in terms of the amount of power (P, in watt). Obviously, the power (P) depends as factors such as talent, training, endurance time or distance, altitude, tapering and so on.

In the equilibrium condition, the power of your human engine (P) is used to surmount the rolling resistance (P_r), the air resistance (P_a), the climbing resistance (P_c) and the mechanical resistance (P_m). Consequently, we can calculate your cycling speed and race time when the conditions of the race (such as distance, pavement, wind, temperature, hills, and altitude) are known.

We believe that our cycling model is a major step forward as it is based on the laws of physics and physiology. This applies particularly to our model of the human power. Based on the biochemistry of the four energy systems of the human muscles, we managed to calculate the ultimate limits of human power as a function of time, as illustrated in the figure below.

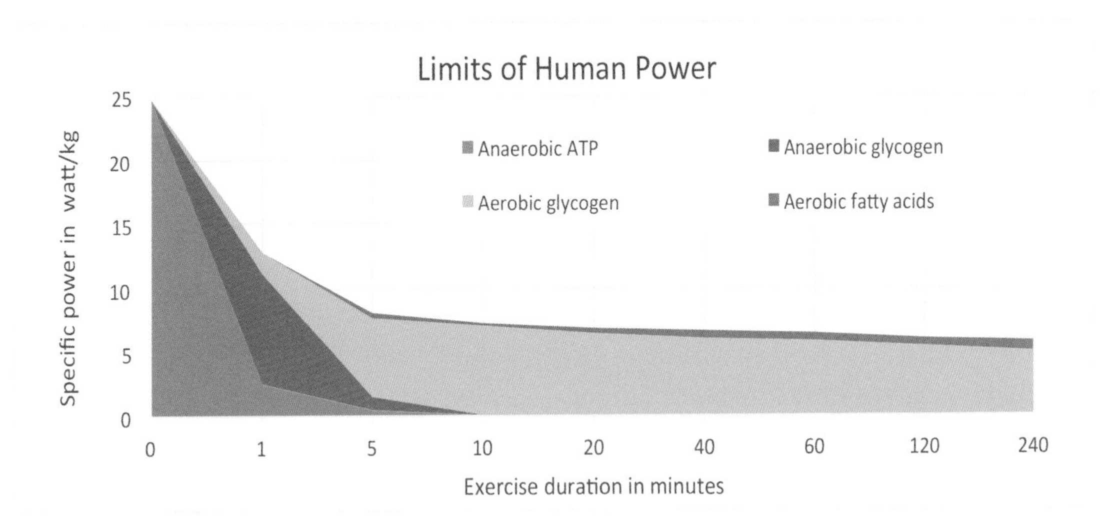

Our calculations show that these ultimate limits of human power match perfectly well with the current world-class performances in cycling and in other sports, including running.

The Theory of Nearly Everything: How to Calculate and Optimize Your Race Time

We have never met a cyclist that did not want to get faster. Moreover, most cyclists are keen to learn the impact of all factors that may affect their performance. Consequently, in this book we have systematically analyzed the impact of nearly everything on your cycling performance. In 66 chapters, you will find the answers to questions like:

- How big is the power of your human engine?
- How fast can you race with your human engine (both at the flat and uphill)?
- How much slower do you get with age?
- How much faster can you get by shedding body fat?
- How much faster can you get from training?
- How can you optimize your training?
- How much time can you gain from a perfect bike position?
- How much time can you gain from an aero bike?
- How much time can you gain from a lightweight bike?
- How much time can you gain from better bearings and gearing?

- How much time can you gain from high-performance tubes?
- How much time do you lose on account of the wind?
- How much slower do you go uphill and how much faster downhill?
- How can you use power meters?
- How can you optimize your pedaling efficiency?
- What is the ultimate limit of the world hour record?
- What is the ultimate limit of the clean climbing time to the Alpe d'Huez?
- How big is the impact of the air pressure on your race time?
- How big is the impact of the temperature?
- How big is the impact of altitude and training at altitude?
- How much time can you gain from riding together or in a pack?
- How big is the impact of nutrition and carbo-loading?

Who Are the Authors?

Hans van Dijk is a lifelong runner and scientist. Since retiring from a full professorship at Delft University of Technology, he has devoted his time to studying the laws of sports, developing new concepts and models and writing books and columns on running, cycling and other endurance sports. Hans has also developed the running and cycling calculators, enabling the readers to analyze and calculate their own performances. As an added bonus, his research has led to a spectacular improvement in his race times at the age of 60!

Ron van Megen is a lifelong runner, engineer and managing director. He has been a friend and running mate of Hans for over 30 years. He enjoys quantifying his running results and using new running technologies, including power meters. Just like Hans, he is also keen on improving his race times, and was happy to see them go down by 20% at the age of 55! He has organized the production of the book and provided many of the photographs.

Guido Vroemen is a cyclist, triathlete and sports physician. He is the team physician and trainer and coach of the Dutch Pro-Continental Cycling Team Roompot-Nederlandse Loterij. He is the owner of a sports medical and performance centre and combines this with many coaching activities (e.g., elite cyclists, ironman triathletes, the Dutch Triathlon Association). His expertise is in the field of exercise physiology and in training and racing with power meters.

Hans van Dijk (right), Ron van Megen (left) and Guido Vroemen (middle), authors of this book.

Website and Calculators

The website www.thesecretofcycling.com contains many columns, papers, media reports, Q&As and our calculators, which the readers can use to calculate and predict their own race times, depending on many variables. The authors welcome reactions from readers and cyclists around the world, and hope that the readers will enjoy the calculators and give us their feedback!

Hans van Dijk, Ron van Megen and Guido Vroemen

Leusden, the Netherlands, September 2016

PART I

THE BASICS OF CYCLING

1. CYCLING IS GOOD FOR YOU!

I have two doctors, my left leg and my right.
—George M. Treveyan

A Dutch magazine once summarized the advantages of cycling with the headline "Miracle cure within reach!" A daily routine of exercise and cycling indeed provides a miracle cure. The best thing you can do if you want to improve your fitness and health is to become a biker.

A daily ride has an amazing positive impact on your physical and mental health, while a lack of exercise is the single largest health risk in Western society—even larger than the risk of smoking! A paper in The Lancet of July 2012[4] concluded that presently 1 out of 10 people die from insufficient exercise. This adds up to 5.3 million premature deaths worldwide as opposed to 5.1 million from smoking.

Anima Sana In Corpore Sano

The importance of physical fitness has been known through the ages, as evidenced by the above Roman proverb which translates to "A healthy mind in a fit body." Cycling improves your fitness and health in many ways:

1. The daily training has a direct and large positive impact on your physical fitness. Your body will slowly be transformed into that of an athlete.
2. Your habits will automatically become healthier. You will start to eat and drink less and more healthily, you will stop smoking and you will drink only the occasional glass of alcohol.
3. Your blood values and other health indicators will change for the better.
4. Your disease risk will decrease and your resistance to diseases will increase.

Cycling also has a big positive impact on your mental health, as millions of cyclists experience every day. This will be discussed in the next chapter.

Medical professionals and sport coaches know that the human body has a tremendous capacity to adapt to training. By training on a daily basis, you can gradually transform your body. On a long-term basis, your body gets fitter. Your body is then able to achieve better results with less effort. Many aspects of fitness respond to training, such as endurance, speed, strength, agility and coordination. The box summarizes this miracle of training.

Positive Impact of Training on Physical Fitness

1. The oxygen transport capacity of your heart–lung system increases substantially.
2. Your heart rate drops (both at rest and during exercise).
3. Your heart gets stronger and more efficient.
4. Your blood pressure lowers and your blood vessels become more flexible.
5. Your lungs get stronger and more efficient.
6. Your muscles become stronger (particularly the muscles of the legs, heart and lungs).
7. Your bones become stronger.
8. Your joints stay agile and flexible.
9. The energy production in your muscles becomes more efficient.
10. You lose weight and become leaner.

We have not found any scientific papers detailing why cyclists automatically change their lifestyle, but this is by no means less certain. We have never met a serious cyclist who smokes, and almost all cyclists change their eating and drinking habits after some time. They realize that their fitness and performance will improve when they eat and drink less and healthier. Cyclists are aware of their body and the need to take care of it. You are what you eat!

If You Could Stuff the Impact of Cycling in a Pill, You Could Make a Fortune!

The positive impact of cycling is really amazing. Obviously, you get fitter and your body looks much better. Additionally, many processes in your body change with the result that many blood values and other health parameters get better. The box summarizes the positive impact of training on health parameters.

Positive Impact of Training on Health Parameters

1. Your cholesterol levels change for the better (LDL lower, HDL higher).
2. Your insulin values get better (lower).
3. Your blood glucose values get better (lower).
4. Your bone density increases.
5. Your body fat percentage (BFP) decreases markedly.
6. Your blood volume increases.
7. The level of hemoglobin and myoglobin in your blood increases.
8. The buffer capacity of your blood increases.
9. Your immune system becomes more effective.
10. The hormone levels in your brain change for the better (adrenalin lower, serotonin higher).
11. The enzymes in your muscles become more efficient.
12. The level of uric acid in your blood decreases.

Prevention Is Better Than Cure

Proverbs like "Good health is above wealth" and the above "Prevention is better than cure" sum up the importance of the positive impact of cycling on the risk of disease, as indicated in the box below. No wonder that some health insurance companies offer cyclists a rebate on their premium! In the Netherlands a discount is offered on the use of health centers. Cycling is also used as a therapy in the treatment of mental health issues. In general, cycling is considered to be an excellent therapy for many physical and mental complaints.

Physical and Mental Complaints Positively Affected by Training

1. Heart and coronary diseases
2. Diabetes
3. Osteoporosis
4. Stroke
5. Certain types of cancer (colon, uterus, breast)
6. Certain lung diseases (bronchitis, emphysema and asthma)
7. Depression, fears and stress
8. Rheumatoid arthritis
9. Cystic fibrosis
10. Aging problems
11. Gout

Of course, cycling should not be seen as a panacea to all problems for all people. However, we feel that cycling has strongly improved the quality of our own lives and many others. We hope that you will have the opportunity to try it and experience the advantages for yourself, just like we have.

The best thing you can do if you want to improve your fitness and health is to become a cyclist. Enjoy a workout in the great outdoors, take a shower and feel fit and strong!

2. CYCLING IS FUN!

Every day is a good day when you bike!

Cyclists are positively addicted; they enjoy their sport and rejoice in life and cycling outdoors, preferably in nature. During these rides, you enjoy the splendor of the landscape, which may include stunning heath fields, mysterious forests and historical landmarks. You may spot deer, squirrels, woodpeckers and buzzards, while talking about work and life. When you return home after a couple of hours, you feel tired, but happy and full of beans!

Enjoy the splendor of the landscape, which may include mysterious forests.

Positive Impact of Training on Mental Health and Well-Being

1. You feel better.
2. You sleep soundly and wake up smiling.
3. You become more calm and relaxed.
4. You enjoy your body and your performance.
5. You feel younger and fitter.
6. Your concentration improves.
7. You get good ideas and see things more clearly.
8. You enjoy life and feel more energetic.
9. You feel free and in control of your life.
10. Your willpower increases.
11. You become more resistant to stress.
12. The quality of your life increases.

These are the moments when life is lived most intensely. You experience strong feelings of freedom, happiness and power. Most probably, this is related to some subconscious memories of prehistoric man, who roamed the landscape in search of his prey. The positive impact of cycling on our mental health and well-being is very broad and diverse. They are summed up by the ancient Roman proverb Anima sana in corpore sano, meaning "A healthy mind in a fit body." The box gives an overview of these positive effects and experiences.

Somebody who does not cycle may find it hard to believe all these advantages. But they are experienced by almost everybody who starts cycling! You leave your home, meet the elements and enjoy cycling in the great outdoors. Soon, your body becomes your friend and you feel fitter and happier. Even beginners soon become ambassadors of the sport and advocate the many advantages.

Scientific research has established that the natural hormones endorphin and serotonin are produced during cycling. These are the hormones that stimulate a euphoric senses of happiness, often called a biker's high. Unfortunately, not everybody produces the same amount of these hormones and it may take some time before you feel more happy than tired. But research has shown that the level of endorphin in our brain is definitely statistically increased by cycling. Our ancestors may have needed this in order to escape predators and survive in the prehistoric landscape. We can enjoy the feelings of happiness without the use of drugs. As a matter of fact, most cyclists are pleasantly addicted to their sport.

Cycling can be done at any available time slot and you can do it by yourself, relaxing or meditating, and listening to the birds. It is also great fun to cycle with some friends and chat and exchange ideas. The most serious cyclists join a cycling team. Together with their comrades they travel to the great races, telling tall stories en route and celebrating their performances and successes. One of the nicest things about cycling is that everybody is a winner. You mainly compete with yourself, trying to improve your performance and race times. Once you have made your first progress, your sense of pride and self-esteem will only grow.

There is also a belief that cyclists enjoy happier marriages and do not divorce. Althouigh this has not been studied scientifically, it is true in our own circle of cycling friends!

Finally, cycling is a tested cure for aging problems and guaranteed to improve the quality of the life of the elderly. In many places, cycling therapy is used to improve the mental well-being of senior citizens.

Youngsters and seniors enjoy their sport and rejoice in life and cycling outdoors, preferably in nature.

Former elite cyclist Michael Boogerd, famous for his big smile.

3. SPORTS PHYSIOLOGY

The heart of a cyclist is a superior and more efficient organ.
–Cardiologist Dr. J. Wolffe, MD

In this chapter we will give some background information on the human engine. In short, the human engine comprises of the leg muscles and the cardiovascular (or heart–lung) system, which ensures the supply of oxygen to and the disposal of metabolites from the muscles.

Which factors determine the capacity of the human engine? Which fuels are used by the muscles and how much power can be produced? And what is the impact of training? Training leads to huge adaptations in our body as a result of which we become fitter. In many handbooks[5,6] and papers, this miracle of training has been described. Below, we present a summary of the most important aspects of the human engine.

Training Effects

Consistent and balanced training leads to the following adaptations of the muscles and the cardiovascular system:

1. **Muscles**

   The leg muscles become stronger. There is an increase of:

   - the number of mitochondria (the energy producers of the cells);
   - the number and size of the muscle fibers;
   - the number of capillaries and the blood flow through the capillaries;
   - the stockpile of ATP (adenosine triphosphate) and glycogen;
   - the number and activity of enzymes (improving the breakdown of glycogen and fatty acids).

   Recent research has shown that training can even lead to a modification of the ratio of fast-twitch (FT) muscles to slow-twitch (ST) muscles. As a consequence, both speed and endurance can be improved by training. Such training should be continuous and focused. As a result of the training stress, initially some muscles will be damaged. You can feel this, as your muscles may ache the first days after the training. However, in time your body will react by strengthening the muscles. Consequently, they can better cope with the training load. Training your leg muscles is a protracted process and you have to put many miles in the tank to get the best results. The majority of the training can be done at an easy pace, but in order to develop the FT muscles it is necessary to do some speed work as well.

2. **Heart**

The adaptation of the heart to the training is most remarkable. The number of heart muscle fibers increases and so do the number of the capillaries and the blood flow through the capillaries, in particular those of the left heart chamber. As a result of this, the sports heart is much more efficient than the heart of untrained, sedentary people. We can illustrate this by considering the heart as a pump. The discharge of this pump (called cardiac output or heart minute volume) is the number of liters of blood pumped per minute. This equals the stroke volume (in liters) times the heart rate (HR, in beats per minute). The stroke volume of a trained cyclist can be twice as large as that of an untrained person. Consequently, at rest the heart of a trained cyclist has a large spare capacity and the HR can be quite low. It is quite common for well-trained cyclists to have a resting heart rate (RHR) of 40 or even lower! During exercise, the sports heart is capable of pumping much more blood, leading to an increased oxygen transport to the leg muscles. As the muscles need oxygen to produce energy, this oxygen transport capacity is the single most important factor to determine the performance in sports in general and in cycling in particular. The increase in stroke volume and the corresponding decrease of the RHR are important physiological adaptations of the heart. These adaptations increase the capacity of the heart. The sports heart is able to increase the blood flow during exercise from 5 l/min to 40 l/min, thus by a factor of eight. This is achieved by a combination of the increase in the stroke volume and the HR. The adaptation of the sports heart depends mainly on the intensity of the training (a high HR and thus a high intensity of the training is required) and can occur relatively quickly. It is possible to achieve a significant reduction in the RHR in as little as six weeks.

3. **Blood**

The blood volume of a well-trained cyclist is some 10% larger than that of an untrained person. This is mainly caused by an increase of the plasma volume. Of course this increase has a positive impact on the oxygen transport capacity. Another important adaptation is an increase in the flexibility of the blood vessels, leading to a decrease in blood pressure. The blood composition also changes: the cholesterol levels decrease, in particular those of the bad LDL and the total cholesterol. The good HDL increases. The level of hemoglobin may increase as a result of altitude training. Hemoglobin is vital for the oxygen transport by the blood. One gram of hemoglobin can transport 1.34 ml oxygen (O_2), so an average hemoglobin level of 15 g/100 ml blood leads to an oxygen transport capacity of 15*1.34 = 20 ml O_2/100ml blood or 20%. A low level of hemoglobin may indicate an iron deficiency in the nutrition or increased iron loss. A high level of hemoglobin may be the result of blood or EPO doping. Finally the blood vessels dilate during exercise, leading to a reduction of the peripheral resistance and an automatic increase of the blood flow to the leg muscles. Less blood is diverted to nonessential body parts, such as the digestive system.

4. **Lungs**

As a result of training, your breathing muscles become stronger and the tidal volume (functional lung volume) increases. We illustrate this in the same way as we did for the heart: by considering the lungs as a pump. The capacity of this pump (called respiratory minute volume) is the tidal volume (in liters) times the breathing frequency (in breaths per minute). At rest, we breathe around 10-15 times per minute and the tidal volume is around 0.5 liter, so the respiratory minute volume is 5-7.5 l/min. During exercise, the respiratory minute volume can increase dramatically to 180-200 l/min for well-trained athletes. This is the result of an increase of both the breathing frequency (to 60 breaths per minute) as well as the tidal volume (to 3-4 liters). The increase in the capacity of the lungs is even larger than that of the heart, so the lungs are usually not the limiting factor. Consequently, we can conclude that normally the oxygen transport capacity of the cardiovascular system is the main factor that determines the performance in endurance sports. However, we should remark that the breathing muscles themselves need a significant amount of oxygen. This can amount to some 10% of the maximum oxygen transport capacity or VO_2 max.

Energy Systems

In order to cycle we need energy. This energy is produced in our muscle cells, to be precise in the mitochondria. The cells can do this by using any (or a combination) of the four following energy systems:

1. **ATP**

   Adenosine triphosphate (ATP) is the primary fuel for sprinters. ATP can be transferred to ADP very quickly, releasing a large amount of energy and thus providing the muscles with the largest amount of power. Moreover, the process does not require oxygen. However, the stockpile of ATP in the muscles is extremely small, lasting only for a short sprint of some 10 seconds. During recovery, the muscle cells are able to regenerate the ATP from the ADP. This process requires energy, which has to be supplied by the aerobic (using oxygen) breakdown of glycogen. The amount of oxygen needed to regenerate the ATP is called the oxygen debt. So, the energy debt is created during exercise and needs to be redeemed during recovery. As a result of training the efficiency of the stockpiling and the use and recovery of ATP can be increased. This requires many repetitions of short sprints at top speed.

2. **Anaerobic glycolysis**

   The anaerobic breakdown of glycogen or glycolysis is the most important energy system for breakaways and prologues, lasting a few minutes. Glycogen is composed of large chains of glucose (sugar) units. Glycogen is stored in the muscles and the liver. The blood also contains a small amount of glycose. Glycogen can be broken down anaerobically (without the use of oxygen) into lactic acid. This lactic acid may accumulate and cause exhaustion and pain in the muscles. During recovery, the lactic acid can be broken down using oxygen, thus redeeming another oxygen debt. With training the efficiency of the glycolysis can be improved. This requires training at a high intensity so that lactic acid is accumulating. This occurs only at a high HR, around 85-90 % of the maximum HR (MHR). This is called the anaerobic limit or threshold limit. The anaerobic breakdown of glycogen produces less power than the ATP system, but it is somewhat more durable. The time to exhaustion is a few minutes, depending on the speed and fitness.

3. **Aerobic breakdown of glycogen**
   The aerobic breakdown of glycogen is the main energy system for endurance athletes, including cyclists. Glycogen is broken down into carbon dioxide and water, using oxygen. The carbon dioxide is removed from the muscles by the blood and the lungs. The oxygen is supplied to the muscles by the lungs and the blood. This is a very durable process that can be maintained for a very long time when the oxygen transport capacity of the cardiovascular system is large enough. This oxygen transport capacity can be increased by training at an intensity just under the anaerobic or threshold limit. Training at a lower intensity (e.g., 70% of MHR) is also useful as it stimulates the muscles themselves. The aerobic breakdown of glycogen produces less power than the glycolysis, but the stockpile of glycogen lasts for at least 1.5 hours. With training and optimized nutrition (e.g., carbo-loading), this period can be increased to 2-3 hours.

The Dutch time trial king Tom Dumoulin in the Grande Partenza (prologue) of the 2016 Giro d'Italia in Apeldoorn.

4. **Aerobic breakdown of fatty acids**

The aerobic breakdown of fatty acids is the main energy system for cyclists and triathletes. Fatty acids are broken down into carbon dioxide and water, using oxygen. Consequently, this system is quite comparable to the previous one (the aerobic breakdown of glycogen). The main drawback is that it produces less power. This is the reason for the well-known phenomenon of hitting the wall. This happens when the stockpile of glycogen in your muscles is exhausted, so the muscles have to transfer to the breakdown of fatty acids. From that moment onwards, your power output is greatly reduced and your speed drops dramatically. The main advantage of the breakdown of fatty acids is that the stockpile is extremely large and sufficient to cycle for many days. We use this system during rest and when exercising at low intensities. When the exercise intensity increases, our muscles switch to the other systems. This depends on the required amount of power: so first fatty acids, then glycogen, then glycolysis and finally ATP. The efficiency of the fatty acid system can also be improved by training. This should be done by long rides at low intensity (less than 70% of your MHR). Eating less carbohydrates may also help, as well as early morning trainings prior to breakfast. We should realize that the fatty acid system is used by all cyclists at low and moderate intensities. When we ride slowly, the amount of fatty acids in the fuel mix of our muscles may be as high as 90%. At threshold pace this percentage may be only 25%.

The box summarizes some important aspects of the 4 energy systems of the human engine.

1. **ATP**

ATP → ADP + energy

Small stockpile, 10 seconds, sprint, maximum power and speed

2. **Glycolysis**

Glycogen → Lactic acid + energy

Limited time to exhaustion, few minutes, breakaways, high power and speed

3. **Aerobic breakdown of glycogen**

Glycogen + $6O_2 \rightarrow 6CO_2 + 6H_2O$ + energy

Large stockpile, 1.5 hours, long distance, endurance power and speed

4. **Aerobic breakdown of fatty acids**

Fatty acids + $23O_2 \rightarrow 16CO_2 + 16H_2O$ + energy

Very large stockpile, many days, ultra-distance, low power and speed, higher oxygen use

The theory on the human engine applies to all endurance sports. The performances of elite cyclist Robert Gesink (left) and multiple world champion speed-skating Sven Kramer (right) can be compared with our unified model

4. TRAINING PRINCIPLES

Listen to your body!

Many textbooks[5,6] describe the principles and practices of training. However, it is not easy to distinguish the scientific research and facts in these writings from the practical experiences, hearsay and personal opinions of cyclists and coaches. Moreover, we should realize that most scientific studies have a limited scope in terms of the number of athletes (usually no more than 20) and the timespan (usually no more than a few months). Obviously, it is hard if not impossible to draw statistically sound conclusions from these limited studies. In practice, we want to know how we can optimize our training with subtle variations (with relatively small effects of each variation) and on a long-term basis (over many years). This problem is further complicated by the variability of the impact on training: what is good for one person may not be good for someone else.

Nevertheless, some training principles have been well studied. They are based on the science of sports physiology and have a general validity. Coaches and cyclists should use these training principles to design a training program and—even more importantly—to modify the program based on the actual results. In this chapter we will give a review of these nine training principles, including some practical applications.

1. **Principle of stress and recovery**
   This is the most essential training principle. Our body has the unique capacity to strengthen itself when exposed to cycles of stress and recovery. This principle was first studied by the Hungarian physician and endocrinologist Hans Selye (1907-1982). He found that a training impulse will initially lead to fatigue, strain and some damage to muscles and cells. After sufficient recovery time, the fatigue disappears and the cells adapt and get stronger. As a result, they are better able to cope with the next training impulse. After a workout, the damaged cells are broken down by enzymes and replaced by new and stronger cells. This means that the pain that we sometimes feel after a hard workout is actually a good sign as it means this process is taking place ("No pain, no gain"). It is essential to time the cycle of work and recovery accurately. If we do not allow sufficient recovery time, the body will be overloaded and the cyclist may get overtrained (stress on top of stress equals breakdown). If we allow too much recovery time, the impact of the training will be small. The goal is to find a perfect match of training impulses and recovery time, so an optimal progress is achieved (super compensation).

Consequently, the training should be composed of the right combination of work and recovery to get the best training impact. Rest and recovery are an essential part of the training program (stress followed by recovery equals progress). In practice this means that hard days and easy days should always be sandwiched. Which training load should be considered hard and which easy depends of course on the quality of the cyclist and his training status.

2. **Principle of sufficient intensity and variation**

   This is an important principle, which is too often neglected. In order to get the best training results, it is necessary not to limit the training to one aspect (e.g., long, slow rides). Instead you have to make sure to incorporate enough other training forms so that all relevant muscles are trained (when you do what you have always done, you will get what you have always gotten). Also you have to do part of your training at high intensity in order to develop all energy systems. Consequently, in practice you have to pay attention to both volume and intensity. Many miles are required to develop your leg muscles (building the muscles) and high speed is required to develop your VO_2 max and the four energy systems (the aerobic breakdown of fatty acids, the aerobic breakdown of glycogen, the anaerobic glycolysis and the anaerobic conversion of ATP). Many cyclists neglect the speed work, but this is not wise as only the aerobic energy systems are developed with such training. In order to make progress, the high intensity speed work is by far the most effective! Finally, it is important to try to consistently incorporate new impulses in your workouts. Remember that effective training impulses are always out of your comfort zone, so it is necessary to dig deep in part of your training ('no pain, no gain').

3. **Principle of moderation and consistency**

   Don't increase your training too fast or too much or you will suffer with injuries. In practice you should increase the work load by no more than 5-10% per month. Listen to your body! Pay attention to signs of overtraining and avoid injuries as these will set you back severely. In general it is wise to maintain a training impulse for six weeks. During this period, your body will be adapted and you will be ready for the next step, either in volume or in intensity. Try to incorporate sufficient variation in the training (e.g., repetitions of sprints can be useful to allow the body to get used to high speeds).

4. **Principle of diminishing returns**

   For novice cyclists, the training will have a large effect. Both endurance and speed will increase rapidly and to a large degree. Unfortunately, the training effect will become smaller and slower as we train more. Elite cyclists have to train extremely hard—both in terms of volume and intensity—to achieve a gain of a few seconds. Normal cyclists will experience a rapid improvement until the moment that they train almost daily and achieve a volume of 200-400 kilometers per week, including at least one high-intensity (interval) session. From then on, progress will be slow and small. The good news is that even after many years of consistent training you may still progress further; often the best results are achieved after 5-10 years of training.

5. **Principle of specificity**
   This principle implies that you will see the effects of training specifically on the muscles and energy systems that have been stressed in the training. In cycling mainly the leg muscles and the muscles of the heart are developed, while the arm and other muscles are hardly affected. There is even a difference between the development of the leg muscles in runners and cyclists. In cycling the quadriceps are tested more, whereas the hamstrings are the main muscles of the runners. The practical consequence of this principle is that a cyclist should bike during the vast majority of his training program. This is the best way to prepare his body for the race. Fitness and strength training in a gym are of limited value to a cyclist, and should only be used as a supplementary training. Another consequence of this principle is that it is wise to focus the training on the race distance as well. This applies mainly to the development of the energy systems. A sprinter will have to develop his ATP system and a GC cyclist his aerobic systems. Of course, it is always good to vary the training somewhat, as GC cyclists also face a sprint finish sometimes.

6. **Principle of periodization**
   This principle was developed by Arthur Lydiard (1917-2004), the New Zealand runner and coach of Olympic champion Peter Snell. Based on his experiences, Lydiard concluded that many athletes could not maintain a continuous high-level training program. After some time, his athletes petered out and their performance dwindled. Consequently, he was the first to develop a cyclic training program. His training plans distinguish the following periods:

   - **Base period:** building aerobic endurance by increasing mileage with limited intensity
   - **Building period:** increasing speed while maintaining volume
   - **Peak period:** reducing volume, focusing on high-intensity speed work
   - **Race period:** mainly speed work with low volume
   - **Transition period:** allowing the body to recover and to start a new cycle

Nowadays, almost all training programs of elite cyclists are based on this structure. Usually, within the annual or macro cycle they also incorporate smaller (meso- and micro-) cycles of work and recovery (e.g., a building block of three weeks followed by a recovery block of one week).

7. **Principle of reversibility**
   The effects of training are highly reversible. The bad news is that you may lose the gains of years of training within a short period of illness or overtraining. One month without training may lead to some

10% loss in performance ("Use it or lose it"). The good news is that retraining also proceeds quickly. Within a month you may regain most of what was lost.

8. **Principle of individuality and flexibility**

   This is a very important principle which underlines that people react very differently to training. Obviously the training program of a sprinter has to include much more speed work as compared to the program of a GC cyclist. But some GC cyclists gain a lot from speed work, whereas others benefit more from endurance rides. This is related to genetic differences and the trick is to find out what works best for you. That is also why you need to be flexible in adapting the program to the results. Make sure you avoid overtraining and injuries! In general it is wise to use your natural abilities ("Go with your strengths").

9. **Principle of maintenance**

   Once you have reached a high level of fitness, it is possible to maintain a good performance over a longer period with only limited training. During this period you should keep up the speed work, but you can reduce the volume to a minimum without much negative effects. Arthur Lydiard used this principle to strongly reduce the training of his runners in the race period, so they were always fresh and hungry for the speed sessions and the races.

Lanzarote training week builds aerobic endurance and focuses on speed and cycling technique.

5. TRAINING PLANS

Keep varying the program. Your body will tell you what to do.
–Joan Benoit-Samuelson

This chapter deals with the most popular topic in the literature on cycling. No wonder, as training is (next to losing weight) is the most effective way to get better and faster. Many books and papers have been written on training plans, including such aspects as training goals, training modes, training paces and training mileage. Almost all writings are based on the experiences of coaches and cyclists in the daily practice of training and racing. Scientific reasoning and support is usually limited.

Fortunately, some high-quality scientific textbooks[5,6,7,8,9,10] and papers have also been published on the topic. They all conclude that intensity is the most important factor of training. Most progress can be made when at least part of the training is performed at a high intensity. This means that the training should be done at a high speed, high heart rate (HR) and a high percentage of the VO_2 max. Of course a cyclist must have a sufficient base before he can train at a high intensity. This means he will already have completed a proper base training with sufficient mileage at low intensity. It also goes without saying that a high-intensity training can only be maintained for a short period. This means the training will always be done in intervals: short blocks at high speed sandwiched between short blocks at low speed, during which the cyclist can recover. The reason for the effectiveness of high-intensity training is the fact that all energy systems are stressed and developed in this way. Next to the aerobic breakdown of fatty acids and glycogen, the anaerobic glycolysis and the direct conversion of ATP are stressed at high intensity. The aerobic energy systems are also trained during the recovery parts of the training. As these parts are biked at low speeds, interval training also fulfils the requirement of sufficient variation.

Training Goals

The following training goals can be distinguished:

1. **Building the muscles and stamina**
   The body of the cyclist will slowly adapt to the daily work load. Both the leg muscles and the heart–lung system will get stronger. As a result of the training, part of the cells will be broken down by enzymes and replaced by stronger cells, which will form stronger fibers and stronger muscles. In order to fully achieve this adaptation, it is necessary to ride many miles on a long-term basis (to put sufficient mileage in the bank). This training should be done at an easy pace, approximately 50-70% of the maximal heart rate (MHR) and the VO_2 max. A trained cyclist can maintain such a pace for some four hours and the risk of injuries is small.

2. **Increasing functional threshold power (FTP)**
   The goal of this training is to adapt the body to cycling at the functional (lactate) threshold level (i.e., the level at which the anaerobic glycolysis starts to kick in and lactate starts to accumulate). We can feel this accumulation of lactate as an acute fatigue in our legs, which limits our performance. The training is focused on the capability of the body to cope with some lactate. This means that the intensity should be high, around 85-90% of the MHR and VO_2 max. Well-trained cyclists can maintain this level for about one hour during a race, so the speed is around that of a one-hour time trial. In a later chapter, we will discuss more details of this level, which we will call the Functional Threshold Power (FTP). In training, a few intervals of 5-10 minutes are usually biked at this level, sandwiched between low-speed blocks to allow recovery and to limit the training stress. At this intensity, mainly the aerobic systems are stressed.

3. **Increasing VO_2 max**
   This is a very important goal, as the VO_2 max is an essential factor in determining the performance in cycling. In order to increase the VO_2 max, it is necessary to train at an even higher intensity than the FTP level, around 90-100% of MHR and VO_2 max. In practice the speed will be around that of prologue. Training at such a high intensity, work can only be done at intervals of 2-4 minutes at high speed, sandwiched between low-speed recovery blocks of a few minutes. At this high intensity, both the aerobic and the anaerobic systems are stressed severely. Such training is hard and should only be done once or twice a week.

4. **Increasing speed**

   This is an essential training for sprinters. It requires training at such a high speed that the anaerobic systems are fully tested. The intensity should be above 100% of the VO_2 max and the HR will be 100%. In practice the speed will be near maximum. In training such intensity can only be done at short intervals of around one minute, again sandwiched between low-speed recovery blocks of some minutes. At this very high intensity, the anaerobic systems need to supply the power required above the capacity of the aerobic systems. This training should also be limited to once or twice a week. A good combination would be to do one speed training and one VO_2 max training weekly.

5. **Increasing pedaling economy (PE)**

   This training is focused on adapting the body to bike efficiently at race speed. Pedaling economy (PE) is a complicated phenomenon. The biking style includes many factors, such as cadence, bike position, bike design and many more. In later chapters we will discuss the biking style and the PE in much more detail. In order to bike economically at race speeds, you need to train many repetitions at race speeds. Consequently, the intensity of this training will depend on your race distance and goals.

Training Modes

1. **Recovery ride**

   This is the easiest training and is meant to improve recovery after a race or hard training. Fatigue disappears faster when you ride at an easy pace. Waste products such as lactic acid are removed faster, so your recovery will be swifter. The intensity should be low, around 55% of the FTP.

2. **Endurance ride**

   This is definitely the most popular training mode. Worldwide millions of cyclists ride at an easy pace in their neighborhood or nearby forest, enjoying their fitness and the world outside. Meanwhile, they develop their stamina and muscles. The short endurance ride lasts around two hours and can be done daily as it not stressful. When preparing for longer races, it is wise to incorporate a longer endurance ride of some 4-6 hours in your weekly schedule. The intensity of an aerobic endurance ride should be limited to 55-75% of the FTP. It is wise to include some hills, a few accelerations or a climax finish in your endurance ride. This will provide some variation, which is desirable.

3. **Tempo ride**

   This training is used to increase the aerobic–anaerobic efficiency. It consists of fast rides of 5-20 minutes. The intensity should be around 75-90% of the FTP. The fast blocks should be alternated with slow recovery parts lasting five minutes, during which your HR will drop to below 70% of the MHR. The total volume will be around 1-2 hours. Once a week is sufficient for most bikers.

4. **Interval training**

   Interval training can be considered the holy grail of competitive training. It is by far the best way to improve race performances in almost all races. It became well known by the example of Olympic champion Emil Zatopek, who pushed the limits of interval training to 50 times 400 meter at blistering speed. His famous quote was "Why should I practice running slow? I already know how to run slow. I want to learn to run fast."

   We can distinguish two interval modes:

   - **Threshold intervals**

   These longer intervals should be done at an intensity of 90-105% FTP. They are focused on increasing the VO_2 max and aerobic capacity. They consist of a limited number of repetitions of 3-10 minutes (e.g., 5 x 5 minutes at 90% FTP with three minutes of recovery).

   - **VO_2 max intervals**

   These are the shorter intervals which should be done at 105-120% FTP. They are focused on increasing the anaerobic capacity and speed. They consist of many repetitions of intervals ranging from 30 seconds to 3 minutes (e.g., 10 x 45 seconds at 110% FTP).

The total volume of interval sessions is always limited to 60 minutes. Interval sessions are hard, so they should be only be done once or twice a week. Recovery periods should be timed to allow the HR to drop to below 70% of the MHR.

A popular alternative interval mode is high-intensity interval training (HIIT), in which short, 20-second blocks of sprinting are sandwiched between 10 seconds of recovery. As a result of the high intensity, HR will approach the MHR during the sprints. During the recovery the HR will remain quite high, making this a very effective training mode which can be completed in 30 minutes.

5. **Sprint training**

   This is an intensive interval training in which short intervals are used and the maximum power is determined (e.g., 10 x 10 seconds maximum sprint, recovery 3 minutes). After 10 seconds, the average power is determined. Sprint intervals can range from 5-30 seconds.

6. **Time-trial training**

   This interval training is executed around FTP. For short time trials it is necessary to execute more anaerobic intervals at 100-110% FTP. For longer time trials, it is better to use intervals just below the FTP (95-100%).

7. **Bike strength training**

   The goal of bike strength training is to increase the power of the relevant leg and gluteal muscles (gluteus maximus, quadriceps, hamstrings, gastrocnemius, soleus). It is also important to pay attention to the core stability in order to prevent injuries. Strength training can best be started in pre-season and may be continued in a maintenance program during the season. Examples include riding against a gradient or viaduct, biking at a large gear, biking at a low cadence (50-75 rpm) or explosive (15-20 seconds) standing starts from standstill. The latter may also be done sitting with a longer duration (1-5 minutes).

8. **Training behind a moped**

   Most people enjoy training behind a moped, scooter, motor or car. In this way, it is possible to train at high speeds and at high cadences. The body will thus learn to cope with the high race speeds. This training mode can also be combined with intensive intervals by occasional jumps from the wheel of the moped.

9. **Training on a roller bank**

   This can be done as a recovery training. It is also useful to improve the control of the bike position. The resistance is not very high, but it is easy to pedal at high frequencies.

10. **Training indoor or on an ergometer**

    This type of training can be used for different modes (e.g., interval training). By controlling the resistance it is possible to set up an efficient program with an array of intervals and recovery. In bad weather, it can often be preferred over outdoor training.

In summary, we conclude that it is very important to train with sufficient variation. Make sure that all energy systems and muscles are stimulated and developed. In order to get faster, it is essential to do enough speed work ("Riding slow will make you slow"). Provide sufficient recovery time between workouts so you are always fresh and ready to perform high-intensity work.

The Dutch Pro-Continental Cycling Team Roompot-Nederlandse Loterij during a training session in Spain.

6. SPORTS NUTRITION

Let food be thy medicine and medicine be thy food.
–Hippocrates

A great many books have been written on the topic of food and most of them sell well! Many books detail a specific diet with the promise to lose body fat and gain fitness and health, but a scientific base for the claims is usually lacking. Nevertheless, our food has a big impact on our health, as Hippocrates already stated in the above quote. What can science tell us about the effects of nutrition on health in general and on our performance in cycling in particular?

You Are What You Eat

Our body is made of and maintained by the elements in our food. If our diet lacks certain elements, we can get a deficiency disease like scurvy from lack of vitamin C and rickets from lack of vitamin D. Other examples are goiter from lack of iodine and anemia from lack of iron.

These deficiency diseases have all been documented scientifically. Based on the acquired knowledge, we have modified our diet with the result that these diseases do not occur anymore in most Western countries. A proper and varied diet nowadays contains sufficient trace elements, minerals and vitamins, so in general we don't have to fear deficiency diseases anymore.

Our modern problem is actually the opposite: our health suffers from too much food. On average we eat too much and too fat, as a result of which obesity, diabetes and coronary diseases abound. These problems are caused primarily by the fact that we simply eat more energy (calories) than we use for our base metabolism and our physical activities. The result is that the surplus is stored in our body in the form of body fat. So our body weight increases and in time we develop Western diseases. Many scientific studies have proven that eating too much is bad for your health. Obesity was found to decrease the life expectancy by 2.5 years. Presently 60% of the U.S. population is considered to be overweight or obese. Consequently, if we want to become healthier our first priority should be to eat less and be more active. The goal should be that our daily energy balance stops being positive. As a result our body weight will no longer increase.

In later chapters we will discuss in more detail the energy balance and the impact of your body weight on your performance in cycling. We will also detail how you can achieve an optimal racing weight.

Sources of Energy in Our Food

The main sources of energy in our food are carbohydrates, proteins and fats. The boxes below give some information on these compounds[11,12]. The ratio of these compounds in our food may vary to a large degree, depending on diet and tradition. An example are the Inuit, who eat mainly fish and seal, a diet consisting primarily of proteins and fats. The traditional foodstuff of the Kenyan athletes is ugali, which consists mostly of carbohydrates. Various theories exist on what is best for your health. The high life expectancy of the Japanese has been attributed to the fact that they eat a lot of fish. It has also been suggested that the Mediterranean kitchen has a positive health impact because of the widespread use of olive oil.

In the animal world, classic examples exist of species that live either on a fat diet (the Inuit sled dog or husky) or on a protein diet (African wild dogs) or on a carbohydrate diet (thoroughbred horses).

One author[13] has hypothesized that bread and other grain products are less healthy because prehistoric man was a hunter-gatherer and did not yet eat grain. However, these theories have not been proven scientifically. Of course, many other factors have an impact on health such as smoking, physical activity, environmental pollution and professional diseases.

The one thing that all scientists agree on is that the average Western diet contains too much fat and proteins, as indicated in the table below.

Proteins

» Small energy source for endurance cyclists (4 kcal/gram, 5% of total energy intake)
» Essential for the production of cells and muscles
» Present in meat, fish, chicken, dairy products, legumes, tofu
» Found in a varied diet so vegetarians can meet the daily requirement

Fats

- Second energy source for endurance cyclists (9 kcal/gram, 10-35% of total energy intake)
- Stored in the body as fatty acids and triglycerides (a few to many kilograms)
- Risk factor for increased cholesterol levels in the blood and for vascular diseases
- Present in meat, sausages, butter, oil, cookies, French fries, cheese, chocolate
- Also a source of vitamins
- The intake of saturated fatty acids should be limited (butter, sausage, cookies, French fries).
- Unsaturated fatty acids are less harmful (olive oil, sea fish, nuts).

Carbohydrates

- Main energy source for endurance cyclists (4 kcal/gram, 60-90% of total energy intake)
- Stored in the body as glycogen. The muscles contain 300-600 grams, the liver 100-130 grams. The blood also contains a little glucose (5 grams).
- Present in vegetables, fruit, potatoes, whole-wheat pasta, whole-wheat bread, oatmeal
- Generally a healthy source of energy
- Single, refined sugars such as glucose, syrup, soda and white bread are less healthy. They contain less minerals and vitamins and are considered empty calories.

Main Energy Sources in Diet

	Carbohydrates (%)	Proteins (%)	Fats (%)
Average Western diet	45	20	35
Recommended for endurance athlete	70	15	15

The endurance athlete should limit the percentage of fats and proteins in his diet. This will also have a positive impact on the energy balance and thus on his weight. A reduction in the percentage of fats and proteins in the diet can easily be achieved with a heathy diet. Such a diet should have a base of:

1. Vegetables and fruit
   - Three portions of each daily are recommended.

- They consist mainly of carbohydrates and contain fibers, vitamins, minerals and water (a limited amount of calories).

2. Whole-wheat bread, potatoes, pasta and oatmeal
   - Six portions daily are recommended.
   - They also consist mainly of carbohydrates and contain fibers, vitamins and minerals.

Additionally the athlete can use some (no more than three portions daily) low-fat dairy products such as cheese, milk and yoghurt. He should eat meat in moderation and try to replace it partially with fish, chicken or tofu (no more than two portions daily). Butter, soda, beer, French fries and cookies should be avoided and replaced by low-fat products. Water and tea (no sugar!) may be consumed as desired, coffee in moderation. No snacks! In later chapters we will discuss in much more detail the impact of nutrition, vitamins, minerals, antioxidants and supplements on the performance of the athlete.

Carbo-Loading

It has become good practice to eat a lot of carbohydrates during the final three days before a big race. Many scientific studies have proven that this leads to an increased level of glycogen in the muscles and the liver. These levels are vitally important to prevent hitting the wall (caused by a low blood glucose level or hypoglycemia) in the later part of the race, as we will see in later chapters. During these final three days the athlete should strongly reduce his training (called tapering) and eat mainly carbohydrates, the so-called carbo-loading. Carbo-loading can be characterized by the absence of meat and the presence of carbohydrates like pasta, bread, honey, raisins, bananas and oatmeal. In a later chapter we will discuss carbo-loading in more detail. There we will also elucidate the use of a sports breakfast (necessary to compensate for the reduction of the liver glycogen level during the night) and the use of sports drinks during the race (necessary to compensate for the losses of water, minerals and glycogen during the race).

Nothing is tastier than a homemade pasta party on the eve of the race.

PART II

THE PHYSICS OF CYCLING

7. ENERGY

Look deep into nature and then you will understand everything better. –Albert Einstein

In this book we will use the laws of physics to study cycling, so we can understand the fundamental factors that determine our performance. Cycling costs a certain amount of energy (E), which of course is larger for a six-hour cycling classic than for a one-hour time trial. In cycling we use our muscles and our heart–lung system; we will refer to this combined system as our human engine. Our human engine has a certain capacity or power (P), which is the amount of energy per unit of time. Elite cyclists obviously have a human engine with a larger capacity than ordinary people, so they can ride faster. The general relationship, which we will use frequently in this book, is that you can calculate your race time (t) for a certain distance if you know the power (P) of your human engine and how much net energy (E) is required to ride that distance:

$$t = E/P$$

Example for a one-hour time trial:

E = 1080 kilojoule (net)

P = 300 watt

t = 1,080,000/300 = 3,600 seconds

= 1 hour

Of course, the trick is to know the numerical values of E and P. Once you know these, you can calculate your race time easily. In later chapters we will elucidate how you can determine the numerical values of E and P and on which factors these values depend. With this new knowledge, you will be able to understand which factors determine your race performances so you can also make a more informed decision on what you can do to improve your performance. We will also prove that the numbers in the example are exactly right for Fast Eddy, our hypothetical cyclist. We called him Fast Eddy in honor of the great Eddy Merckx. Fast Eddy is a hypothetical 40-year-old man who weighs 75 kg and can sustain a power output of 300 watt during one hour. In this book we will use Fast Eddy frequently to illustrate the impact of various factors on his race times.

In this chapter, we will first discuss the concept of energy (E). We will give some examples from daily life and illustrate how you can use the concept of energy to make useful calculations.

Energy in Our Food

The concept of energy is best known in daily life from the amount of kilocalories (kcal) in our food. Most readers will be aware that we consume some 2,500 kcal daily (of course heavyweight champion Tyson Fury will consume much more than supermodel Naomi Campbell). As 1 kcal is equivalent to 4.184 kilo Joule (kJ), we can calculate that 2,500 kcal equals 10,460 kJ.

Weight Loss Resulting From the Marathon

We should note that the efficiency of our human engine (the metabolic efficiency) is around 25%. This means that the gross energy consumption of our body is four times the net energy use of running. Consequently, Fast Eddy uses a total of 4*1,080 = 4,320 kJ of metabolic energy to ride the one-hour time trial. When we compare this to his daily food consumption of 10,460 kJ, we can calculate that the energy requirement of the time trial is only 4,320/10,460 = 41% of the daily energy (calorie) intake with his food. Obviously, riding a one-hour time trial will not result in a large weight loss (apart from the weight loss through sweating which will be quickly replenished by drinking water).

How much weight do you actually lose from riding such a time trial? We can calculate this when we realize that our body fat has an energy density of 9 kcal/gram or 37.6 kJ/gram. Consequently, Fast Eddy will lose 4,320/37.6 = 115 grams of body fat. A modest amount which may not inspire heavyweights to ride a time trail as a means to lose body fat! Of course, in the long run daily training will definitely lead to a sizable and stable weight loss, as many cyclists have experienced.

Energy in Our Daily Life

At home, the concept of energy is best known to many of us from the electricity consumption (in kWh) for lighting, the fridge and other household uses. When we realize that 1 kWh is equivalent to 3,600 kJ, we can calculate that the amount of energy in our daily food is equivalent to 10,460/3600 = 2.9 kWh. A very small number indeed, in particular when we consider that 1 kWh costs only some US$0.12. In theory, we would thus need only 2.9*0.12 = US$0.35 to provide the daily energy for our metabolism. It is a pity that we cannot eat electricity as this would be a lot cheaper than our groceries!

Another example from daily life is the gas consumption of our cars. The energy density of petrol is 28,800 kJ/l, so if we could eat petrol we would need only 10,460/28,800 = 0.4 liter per day! With a gas price of some 0.6 US$/l, our daily cost would be as low as 0.4*0.6 = US$0.24, so even cheaper than electricity! Of course the energy density of petrol is quite high, which we can see when we calculate that the energy content of a small tank of 40 liters is equivalent to 40*28,800 = 1,152,000 kJ. This is the same amount of energy that we consume with our food in 1,152,000/10,460 = 110 days! Apparently, the gas mileage of our body is far superior to that of our car!

How Much Energy Do We Use for Cycling?

In later chapters, we will discuss the physics of cycling. There we will show that you need energy to overcome a total of four resistances: the rolling resistance of the wheels, the air resistance, the hill resistance and the mechanical resistance of chain and gear. There we will also calculate that Fast Eddy can ride 40.41 kilometers in a one-hour time trial with the power of his human engine (300 watt). For now, we will simply make the assumption that he can sustain his 300-watt power indefinitely (in practice this is not true; the power decreases with time). With this assumption, we can calculate the energy cost of cycling with the formula:

$$E = Pt$$

The formula simply says that in one hour (3,600 seconds), Fast Eddy will use 300*3,600 = 1,080,000 J or 1,080 kJ.

The figure shows the total energy cost of cycling as a function of time.

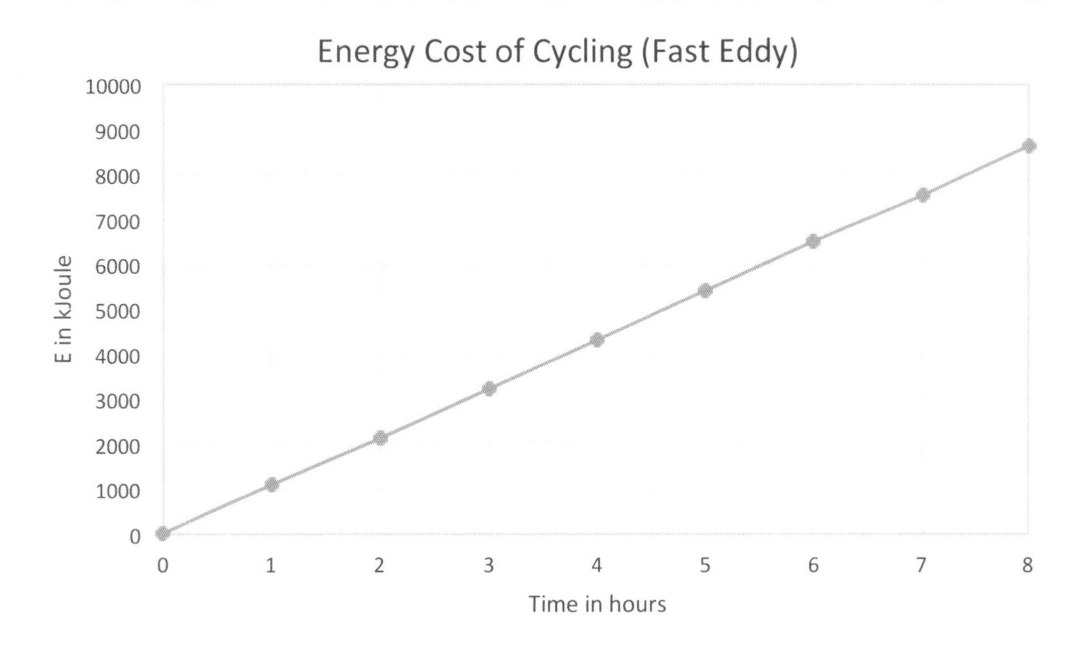

How long do you need to bike in order to lose 1 kg of body fat? We can calculate that easily as 1 kg of body fat is equivalent to 37,600 kJ. Taking into account the metabolic efficiency of 25%, Fast Eddy needs to bike t = E/P = 37,600,000/(4*300)/3,600 = 8.7 hours to burn 1 kg of body fat! This seems quite long, but with regular training you will reach this easily, so you will definitely lose body fat (provided you do not increase your food consumption of course).

We called our hypothetical cyclist Fast Eddy in honor of the great Eddy Merckx. Eddy Merckx (born June 17, 1945) won 525 races and is regarded by cycling connoisseurs as the most successful cyclist of all time.

8. POWER

Knowledge is power. –Sir Francis Bacon

In the previous chapter, we discussed the general relationship which you can use to calculate your race time (t) for any distance, once you know the power (P) of your human engine and the energy cost (E) of cycling that distance:

$$t = E/P$$

Example for a one-hour time trial:

E = 1,080 kilo Joule

P = 300 watts

t = 1,080,000/300 = 3,600 seconds

= 1 hour

In this chapter, we will look more closely at the concept of power (P). Once again, we will give some examples from daily life and illustrate how you can use the concept of power to make useful calculations.

The Average Power of the Human Engine

One way to approach this is by simply dividing the daily energy intake from our food (E = 10,460 kJ) by the number of seconds in a day (t = 86,400 sec). The result is an average power (P) of 121 watts, about equivalent to an old-fashioned lightbulb. However, we should realize that this is just a theoretical calculation of the average thermal power. In practice, we need to take into account that the metabolic efficiency is only some 25%, so the average mechanical power of the human engine is just 121*0.25 = 30 watts.

Of course our human engine is quite capable of supplying more power during a short time. As an example we mention the fact that professional cyclist Chris Froome pushed 415 watts during 39 minutes while climbing to the summit of the Alpe d'Huez in the Tour de France of 2015.

We can appreciate the meaning of 30 watts by considering that we use it to produce electricity with a home trainer. If we would cycle an entire working day (8 hours), we would produce 8*30/1,000 = 0.24 kWh of electricity, with a monetary value of just 0.24*0.12 = US$0.03!

Other Examples of Power

In 1777, James Watt defined the unit of horse power (HP) as the amount of power that a horse produces by hoisting a weight of 150 kg up a height of 30 meters in one minute. The energy cost of this can be calculated as:

$$E = mgh$$

With the gravity constant $g = 9.81\ m/s^2$, E becomes 150*9.81*30 = 44,145 joules.

Consequently, the HP is equivalent to:

$$P = E/t = 44{,}145/60 = 736 \text{ watts}$$

As we know that a horse can easily maintain this power, we may conclude that the endurance power of the horse engine is substantially larger than that of the human engine.

The power of modern cars is much higher still. Many a car is equipped with an engine of 100 HP or 73,600 watts. In the previous chapter, we saw already that the energy content of a small 40-liter tank of petrol is equivalent to 40*28,800 = 1,152,000 kJ. Consequently, we can conclude that the tank will be empty after a time t = E/P = 1,152,000/73,600/3,600 = 4.3 hour drive at full power.

How Can You Calculate Your Race Time in Cycling?

In the previous chapter we already mentioned that Fast Eddy can ride 40.41 kilometers in a one-hour time trial with his power output of 300 watts. Again we make the simple assumption that his power output will remain constant at 300 watts. With this assumption, we can calculate the race time as function of the distance:

$$t = d/v$$

Of course this simple formula just says that his race time (t) will be one hour to cover a distance (d) of 40.41 kilometers with his velocity (v) of 40.41 km/h. The figure below gives the race time as a function of the distance.

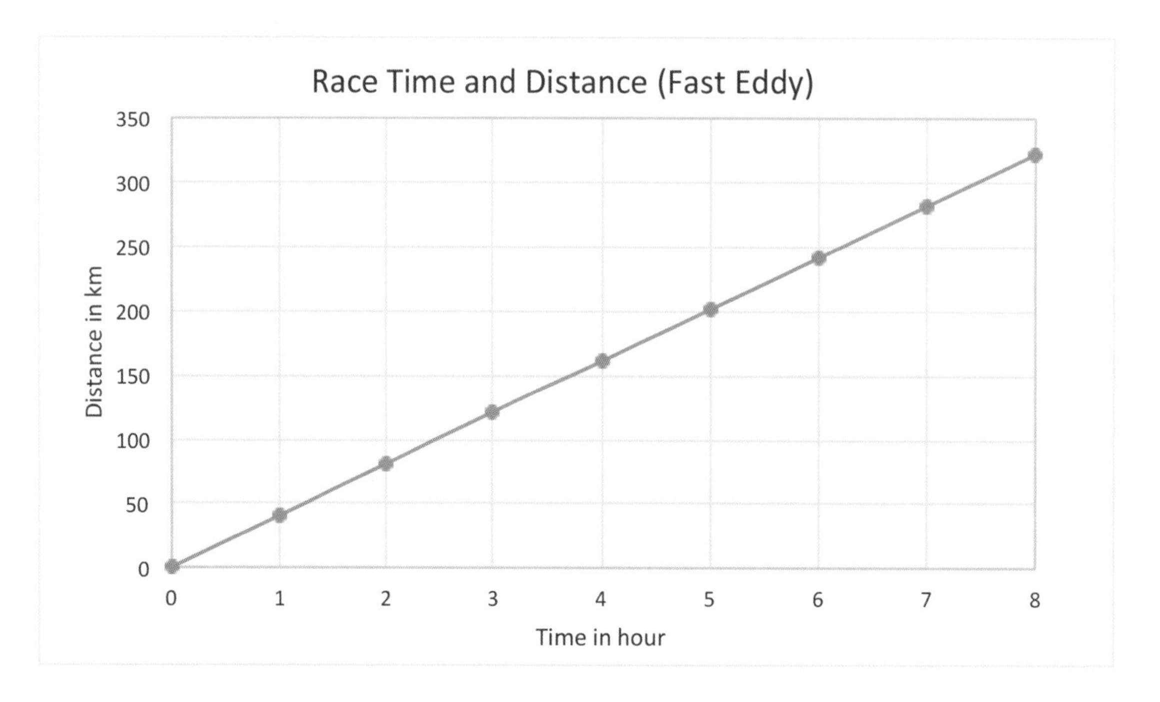

We have to make two comments on this figure:

1. We have yet to explain why his distance in a one-hour time trial will be 40.41 kilometers.
2. In real life his power output will not be constant at a 300 watts, but will decline with time. As a result of this, the race times at distances shorter than 40 kilometers will be less than calculated, whereas for distances longer than 40 kilometers his race times will be more.

In later chapters, both aspects will be dealt with, so exact race times can be calculated.

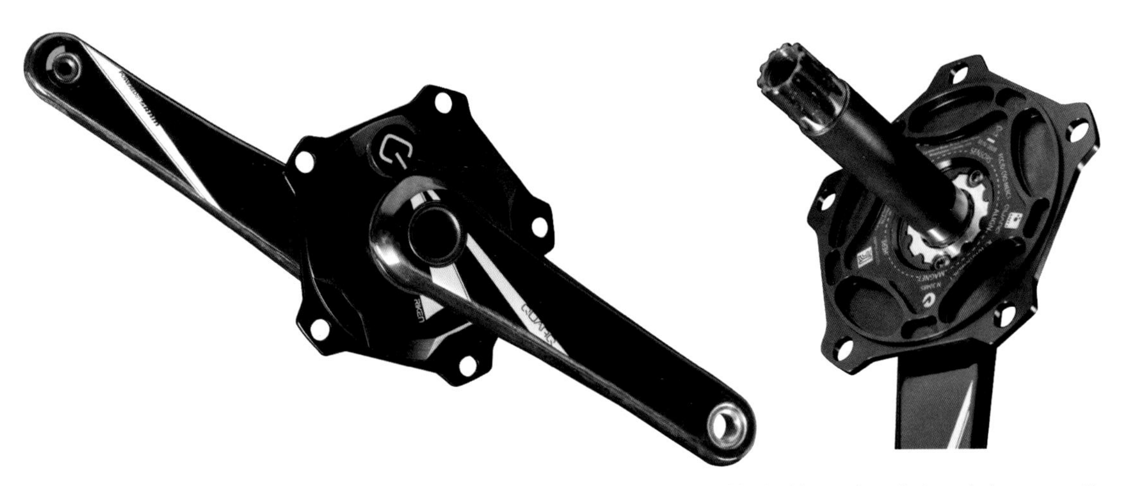

Most cycling power meters use strain gauges to measure torque applied and, when combined with angular velocity, calculate power. The technology was adapted to cycling in the late 1980s. Power meters have revolutionized the world of cycling.

9. POWER REQUIREMENTS FOR SPORTS I

Study the past to succeed in the future!

In this chapter and the next, we will make some simple calculations to illustrate how the power of the human engine determines your performance in various sports. One of the nice things about our theory is that it can be applied to many endurance sports. Once you know the power of your human engine, you can calculate your approximate race times in different sports. In this chapter, we will use the examples of stair climbing and cycling. In the next chapter we will discuss speed skating and running.

We will show that in some sports (like speed skating and cycling at a flat course) your performance is determined by the total power (P, in watts) of your human engine. In other sports (like running and cycling uphill), the specific power (P/m, in watts/kg body weight) is the decisive factor.

Before we start the calculations, we should make one comment. Our calculations are based on the assumption that the power of your human engine is the same in different sports. This does not mean that a cyclist can automatically run or skate as well as he can cycle. Of course he will have to train for this and even then it may appear that he is less talented in the other sports. But we do believe that in general the power of your human engine gives a pretty good indication of what you could achieve in other sports as well, provided you have trained for it!

How Fast Could You Run Up the Stairs of the Empire State Building?

The annual Empire State Building Run-Up has become an elite bucket list item that the general public vies to be included in. Thousands of runners from around the world enter, all seeking one of a select few spaces. The ESBRU includes climbing 1,576 steps to a height of 320 meters. The record time of 9 minutes 33 seconds was set by Australian Paul Crake in 2003.

We can calculate the energy cost of the ESBRU with the formula:

E = mgh

As we know that g = 9.81 m/s^2 and h = 320 meter, we can calculate the race time as:

t = E/P = mgh/P = m*9.81*320/P = 3139/(P/m)

The result is quite interesting; we see that the race time depends inversely on the specific power (P/m, in watts/kg) of the human engine. So far, we have neglected the running resistance. To compensate for this, we have added a 25% margin to the theoretical formula. The figure below shows the resulting relationship between the climbing time and the specific power.

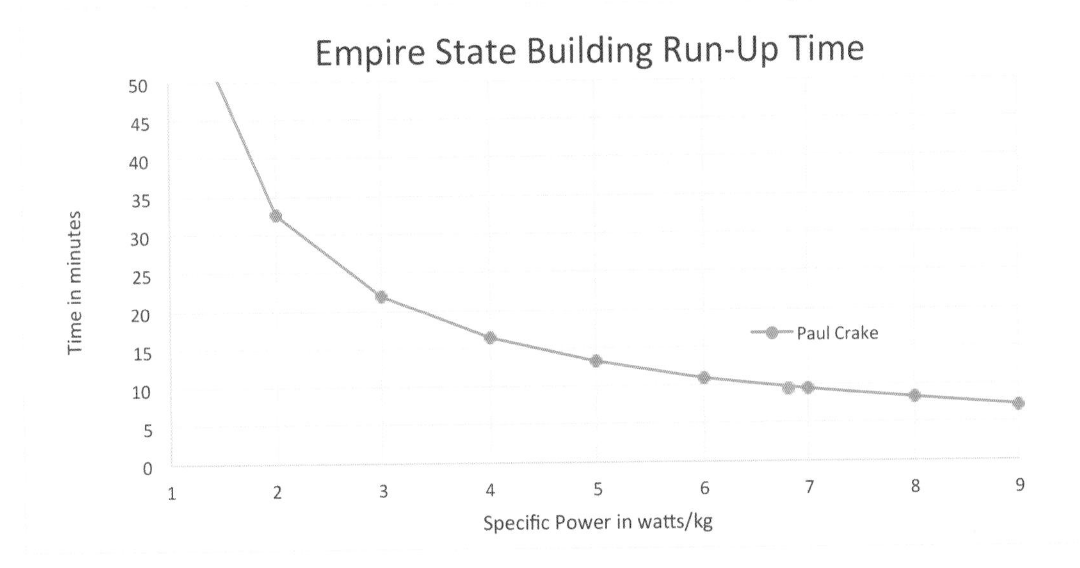

This relationship makes sense as a heavyweight has to carry much more weight upstairs, so he uses more energy for the climb. In comparison to a featherweight, the total power (P, in watts) of his human engine should be much higher in order to reach the top at the same time.

The record time of 9:33 means that the specific power (P/m) of Paul Crake must have been 6.8 watts/kg. We don't know his body weight, but at 60 kg he would have needed a total power (P) of 6.8*60 = 408 watts. If his body weight was 80 kg, he would have needed a total power (P) of 5.48*80 = 544 watts. This last number is even higher than the 415 watts that Chris Froome pushed on the climb to the Alpe d'Huez, as we saw in the previous chapter. Of course, we should remark that Chris weighs only 67 kg, so his specific power was also quite high at 415/67 = 6.2 watts/kg. Moreover, he did this in the third week of the Tour de France and at the end of a tough stage, so some fatigue will definitely have been there already. Also he did this in the thin mountain air (which has a negative impact on human performance) and he maintained this power for 39 minutes instead of 9.5 minutes. In later chapters, we will discuss the impact of all these factors in more detail.

Finally, we can now calculate the race time that we may expect from our Fast Eddy. His power output is 300 watts and his body weight is 75 kg, so his specific power is 300/75=4 watts/kg. This means he will reach the top after 16 minutes. He might even be a little faster as his power output during these 16 minutes can be somewhat higher than the 300 watts which is his power output during the one-hour time trial. This will also be discussed in later chapters.

The Empire State Building Run-Up includes the climbing of 1,576 steps to a height of 320 meters.

How Fast Could You Bike on a Flat Course?

For now, we will assume that in this case the power of the human engine is used completely to overcome the air resistance. This means we have neglected all other losses in cycling (the rolling resistance of the wheels, the climbing resistance of hills and the mechanical resistance of chain and hubs). Without wind, we can then use the following formula:

$$P = 0.5 \rho c_d A v^3$$

In this formula ρ is the air density (1.205 kg/m^3 at 20°C), c_dA is the air-resistance coefficient (0.21 m^2 for a streamlined cyclist) and v is the velocity in m/s. Consequently, we can calculate the attainable velocity as a function of the total power (P) in watts. To compensate for the other losses, we have added a 10% margin to the theoretical formula. With this, we have determined the power–speed relationship as shown in the figure below.

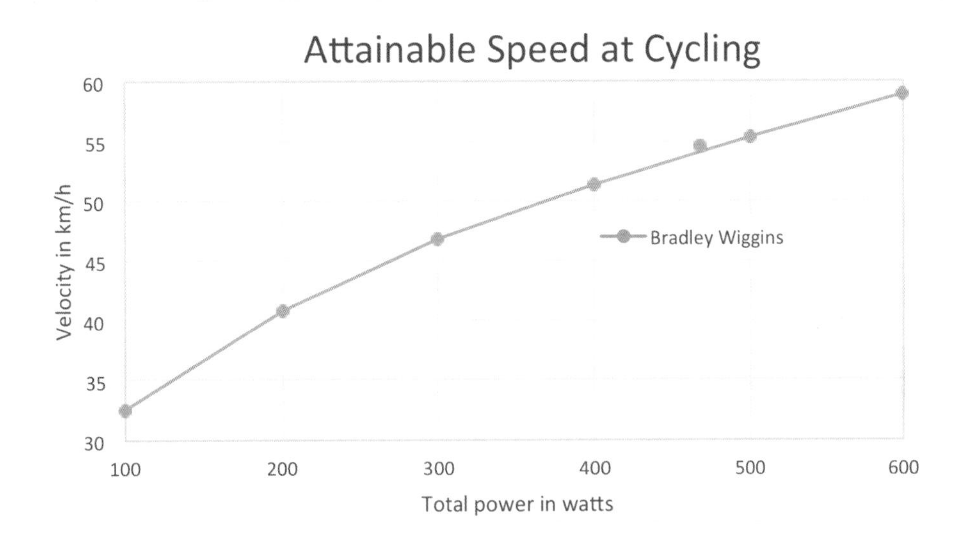

In spite of the simplifications that we used, the graph appears to be pretty good. We have indicated the recent world hour record by Bradley Wiggins[15]. In 2015 he set the record at 54.526 km/h. His power output during this race has been calculated at 468 watts or 6.1 watts/kg as Bradley weighs 77 kg.

Our Fast Eddy could attain a speed of 46.8 km/h with his total power of 300 watts, provided of course that he would be able to ride with the same perfect aerodynamics as Sir Bradley did.

In summary, we conclude that in cycling on a flat course your total power output (P, in watts) is the decisive factor and not the specific power (P/m, in watts/kg). Consequently time-trial specialists are usually somewhat heavier and more powerful than the lightweight climbers.

Bradley Wiggins wins gold in the 4000-meter pursuit at the 2004 Athens Olympic Games.

How Fast Could You Bike to the Top of the Alpe d'Huez?

Here we can use the following formula to calculate the cycling time to the summit:

$$t = E/P = mgh/P = 9.81 * 1071 * (P/m)$$

We know that the summit is at an altitude (h) of 1,071 meters[16]. Just like in the run up the Empire State Building, we find that the specific power (P/m, in watts/kg) is the decisive factor. In climbing every kilogram that you have to carry to the top weighs heavily! As a result, the top climbers are always featherweights with as little body fat as possible.

The figure below gives the attainable climbing times as a function of the specific power in watts/kg. In preparing this figure, we have added 40% to the theoretical formula to compensate for the weight of the bike and the other losses (rolling resistance, air resistance and mechanical resistance).

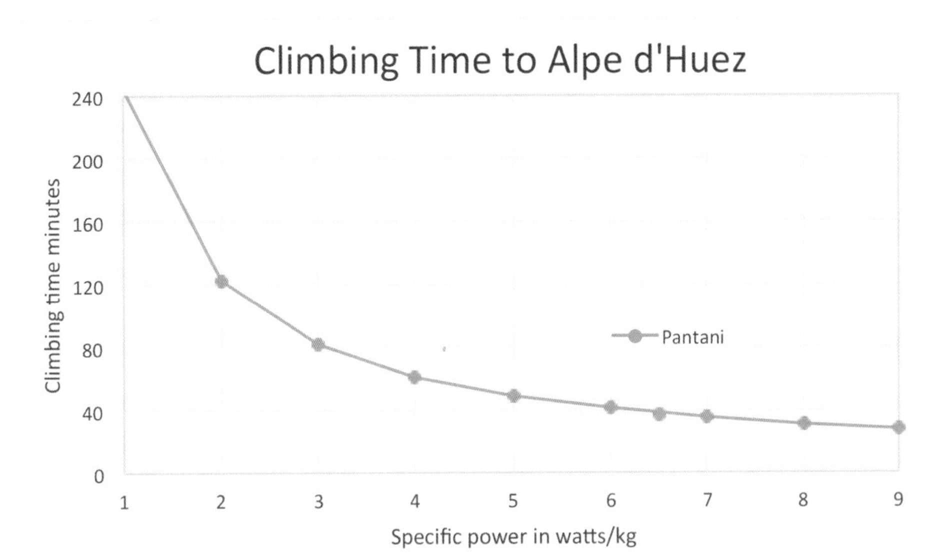

We can see that a specific power output of 6.5 watts/kg is required for the record of Marco Pantani (37:35). This is higher than the 6.2 watts/kg that Chris Froome pushed and it should be considered with suspicion, particularly as Pantani did it in the thin mountain air. In a later chapter, we will discuss these factors in more detail. Here, we remark that Pantani weighed considerably less than Froome (57 kg vs 67 kg), so his total power output was lower than that of Froome (370 watts vs 415 watts). With only 370 watts Pantani climbed almost three minutes faster than Froome would with 415 watts. This corroborates the fact that in climbing the total power output in watts is not the decisive factor, the specific power in watts/kg is!

Finally, we have calculated that our Fast Eddy could reach the top after 61 minutes with his specific power output of 4 watts/kg.

10. POWER REQUIREMENTS FOR SPORTS II

Life is lived forwards, but understood backwards.

In this chapter, we will investigate how fast you can skate and run with the power of your human engine. We will show that in speed skating the total power (P, in watts) is the decisive factor, whereas in running the specific power (P/m, in watts/kg) determines how fast you are. Consequently, speed skaters are usually somewhat bigger and more powerful: the Dutch multiple Olympic and World Champion Sven Kramer weighs 84 kg! Runners on the other hand benefit from being skinny: Haile Gebrselassie weighs only 56 kg!

Before we start the calculations, we should make the same remark as in the previous chapter: you are not automatically as good in speed skating as in running. You should definitely train sufficiently in order to perform up to the potential of your human engine!

How Fast Could You Skate?

We can compare speed skating with cycling on the flat. In both sports the air resistance is the main factor that determines the attainable speed. Consequently, we can use the following formula, neglecting the sliding resistance of the skates with the ice:

$$P = 0.5\rho c_d A v^3$$

In this formula ρ is the air density (1.293 kg/m^3 at 0°C), $c_d A$ is the air-resistance coefficient (0.28 m^2 for a speed skater) and v is the velocity in m/s. Consequently, we can calculate the attainable velocity as a function of the total power (P, in watts). To compensate for the sliding resistance, we have added a 35 % margin to the theoretical formula. With this, we have determined the attainable speed and the race time at the 10,000 meter, the domain of Sven Kramer. The result is shown in the figure below.

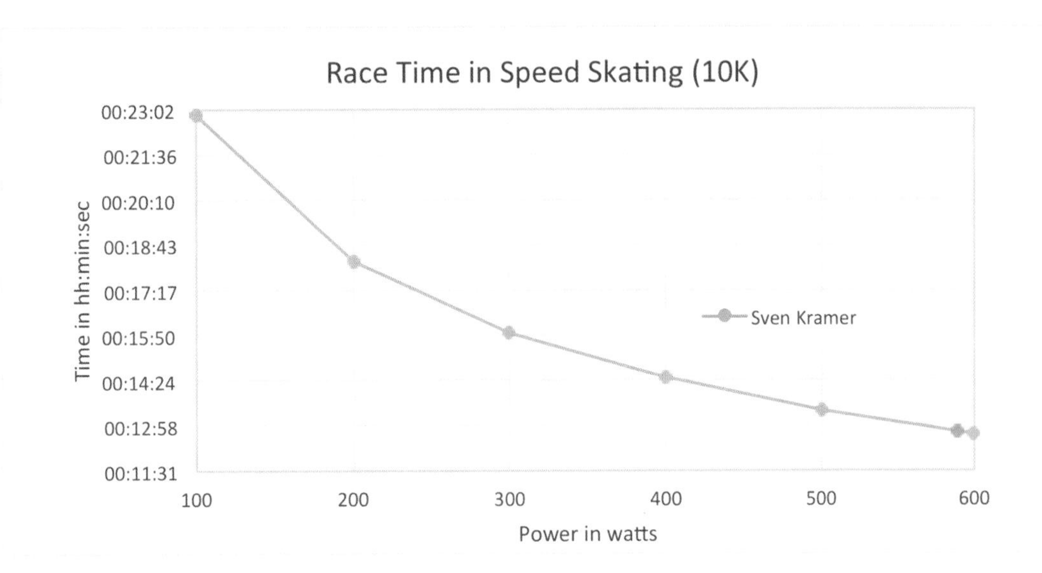

In spite of the simplifications that we used, the graph appears to be pretty good. We have indicated the track record of 12:45 that Sven Kramer set at the Thialf Centre in Heerenveen, the Netherlands[3]. According to our calculations, his power output during this race was 589 watts or 7.0 watts/kg. These numbers are quite high, but we should remember that he only had to maintain this effort for less than 13 minutes.

Our Fast Eddy could skate a time of 15:56 with his power of 300 watts, provided of course that he has trained sufficiently and has the same perfect skating technique that Sven has.

In summary, we conclude that in speed skating the total power output (P, in watts) is the decisive factor and not the specific power (P/m, in watts/kg).

Sven Kramer wins the European Speed Skating Championships Allround 2016 in the Belarus city of Minsk.

How Fast Could You Run?

When we neglect the air resistance and consider running on a flat course, we can use the formula:

$$P = E/t = cmd/t = cmv$$

The numerical value for the specific energy cost of running (c) can be set at 0.98 kJ/kg/km. Consequently, we get an interesting result:

$$v = (P/m)/0.98$$

This means that your speed is directly proportional to your specific power (P/m, in watts/kg). Because we are used to expressing the speed in km/h and not in m/s, we need to multiply with a factor of 3.6. The result thus becomes:

$$v = 3.67*(P/m)$$

This is a simple and very powerful formula for the relationship between specific power and speed. In order to compensate for the air resistance, we have added a factor of 10%. With this assumption, we have calculated the attainable speed and converted it to the race time at the 10,000 meter. The result is shown in the figure below.

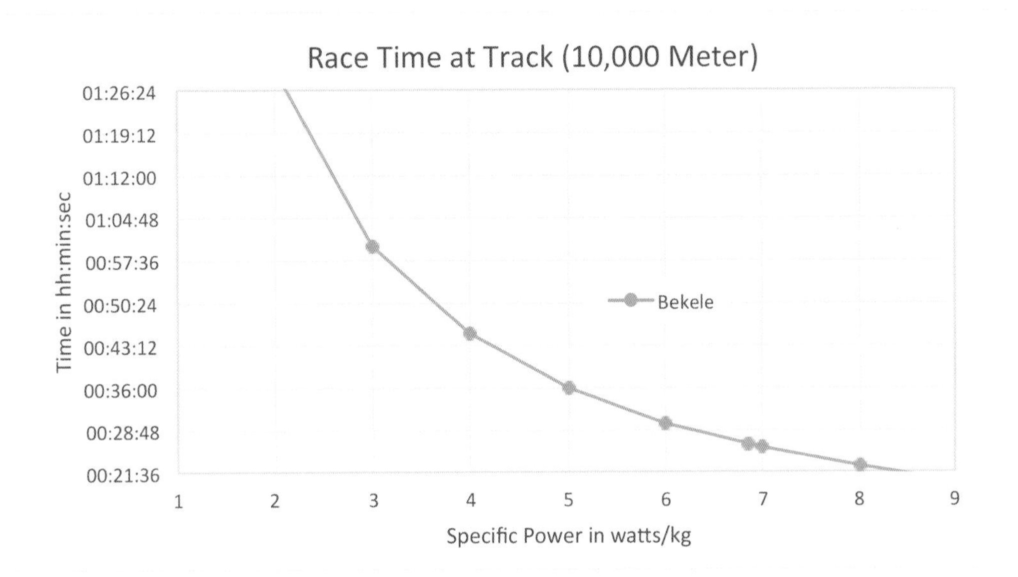

In spite of the simplifications that we used, the graph appears to be pretty good. We have indicated the world record of 26:17 of Kenenisa Bekele[3]. According to our calculations, his specific power output during this race was 6.8 watts/kg. Bekele weighs 56 kg, so his total power output was 383 watts. We see that his total power output (in watts) is much less than that of Sven Kramer and Bradley Wiggins. However, his specific power (in watts/kg) is quite high, considering the fact that he had to maintain this for more than 26 minutes. In later chapters we will give more details on the power–time relationship. There we will also show that the limit of human power can be set at a value of 6.4 watts/kg for an endurance time of one hour. In general the power that you can maintain for one hour is called the functional threshold power (FTP). With the abovementioned formula, we can calculate that the attainable speed for an FTP of 6.4 watts/kg equals (3.67/1.10)*6.4 = 21.35 km/h. Presently, the world hour record on the track is held by Haile Gebrselassie at 21.285 km, which is quite close.

Our Fast Eddy could run a time of 44:58 with his specific power of 4 watts/kg, provided of course that he has trained sufficiently.

In summary, we conclude that it is possible to make simple and interesting calculations on the attainable performance in all kinds of endurance sports. The total power (in watts) is the decisive factor in sports where the air resistance is important, like speed skating and cycling on a flat course. The specific power (in watts/kg) is the decisive factor in sports where gravity is important, like stair climbing, cycling uphill and running (also on a flat course as your legs have to lift your body weight each step).

So far, we have made simplified calculations in which several factors have been neglected or estimated, like:

1. The impact of the endurance time on the power output of the human engine
2. Various losses, like the air resistance, the climbing resistance, the rolling resistance, the gliding resistance and the mechanical resistance
3. The impact of the thin air in the mountains on the human engine
4. The impact of training and other factors (like age, sex and gear) on the power output of the human engine

In the next chapters, we will derive a complete model of the physics of cycling and of the human engine. In the remainder of this book, we will then use this model to calculate the impact of many factors on the attainable race time. We hope and expect that the reader will be able to use this knowledge to assess the power of his own human engine and to see what performances he could reach (e.g., at different distances or under different circumstances). Finally, the reader may then evaluate the options that are available to him to optimize his performance (e.g., training, losing weight and optimizing his bike and aerodynamics).

Multiple Olympic and World Champion Haile Gebreselassie (left) still holds the world hour track record of 21.285 km.

11. THE CYCLING MODEL

Everything should be made as simple as possible, but not simpler. –Albert Einstein

So far we have used very simple models to calculate the race times based on the available power (P, in watts) of the human engine. This has already given promising and interesting results. Now we want to make a complete model of the physics of cycling. In order to do this, we need to know how much power is needed to overcome the resistances in cycling.

In the equilibrium situation (ignoring accelerations and decelerations) we can distinguish four resistances:

1. The rolling resistance (of the tires and pavement)
2. The air resistance (due to the wind and your own speed)
3. The climbing resistance (uphill and downhill)
4. The mechanical resistance (of chain and hubs)

In the equilibrium situation, the available power of the human engine (P) should be equal to the sum of the powers needed to overcome these four resistances: the rolling resistance (P_r), the air resistance (P_a), the climbing resistance (P_c) and the mechanical resistance (P_m):

$$P = P_r + P_a + P_c + P_m$$

We call this the cycling formula. In this chapter we will analyze the four resistances that define the cycling formula. The figure illustrates our cycling model.

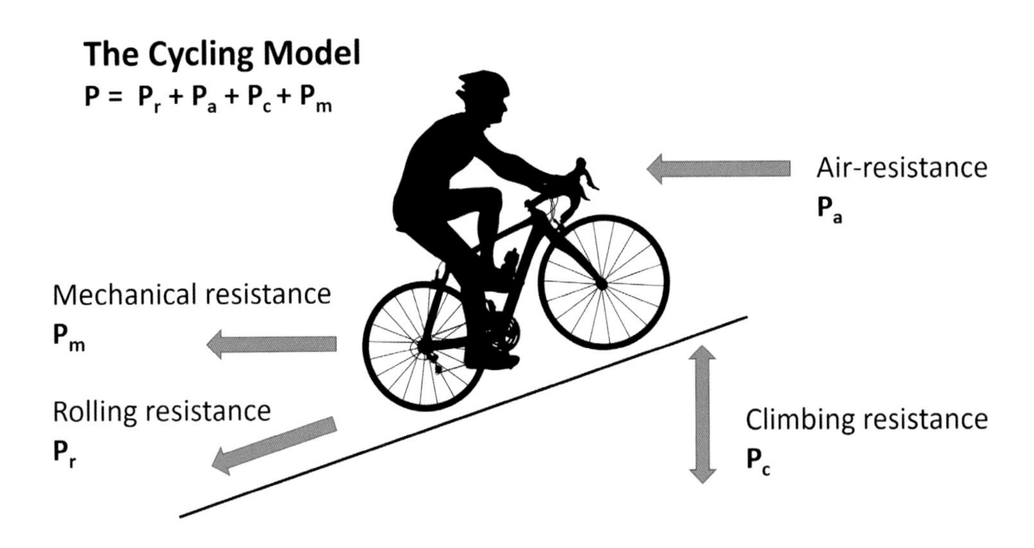

The Rolling Resistance

Theoretically, we can calculate the power (P_r, in watts) required to overcome the rolling resistance from the rolling resistance factor (c_r, dimensionless), the combined weight (m) of cyclist and bike (in kg) and the speed (v, in m/s) of the cyclist, as given in the box.

The Rolling Resistance

$$P_r = c_r mgv$$

Example:

$c_r = 0.004$, m = 83.8 kg (75 kg+8.8 kg bike), g = 9.81 m/s^2, v = 40 km/h

$P_r = 0.004*83.8*9.81*40/3.6 = 36$ watts

The example is valid for our Fast Eddy, who weighs 75 kg and has a bike weighing 8.8 kg. His available power (P) is 300 watts, so the rolling resistance (P_r) at a speed of 40 km/h is only 36/300 = 12% of his available power. The formula for the rolling resistance shows that the required power is directly proportional to the weight and the speed (see the figure below). The figure shows that the rolling resistance of Fast Eddy will be only 18.3 watts at a low speed of 20 km/h.

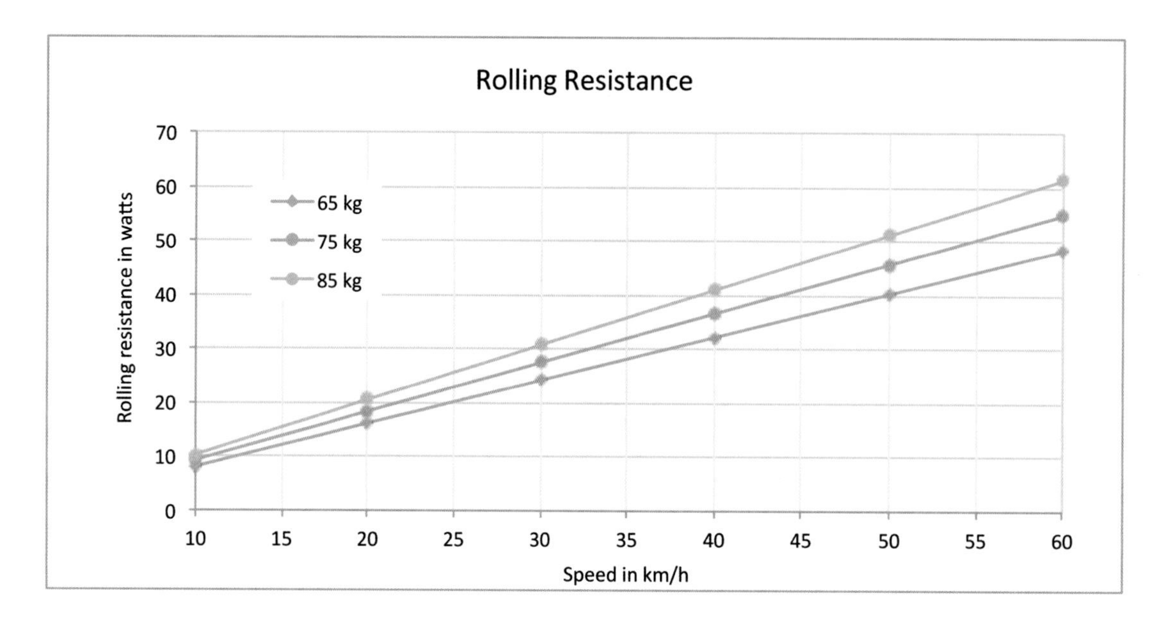

For completeness we have to remark that we should have included a factor cos(arctangent (i/100)) in the formula, i being the gradient (in percent). In practice this factor is very close to 1, even at steep hills (at an extreme gradient of 20%, the factor is 0.98). Consequently, we did not include it in the box. However, we have included it in our model calculations in this book and in our calculator.

The Air Resistance

The power (P_a, in watts) required to overcome the air resistance depends on the air density (ρ, in kg/m³), the air-resistance factor (c_dA, in m²), the speed (v, in m/s) and the wind speed (v_w, in m/s), as shown in the box.

The Air Resistance

$$P_a = 0.5\rho c_d A(v+v_w)^2 v$$

Example:

$\rho = 1.205\ kg/m^3$, $c_dA = 0.30\ m^2$, $v = 40\ km/h$, $v_w = 0\ km/h$

$P_a = 0.5*1.205*0.30*(40/3.6)^3 = 248$ watts

The example is again valid for Fast Eddy, who cycles in an aero position ($c_dA = 0.30\ m^2$), at a temperature of 20°C (at this temperature the density of the air is 1.205 kg/m^3) and in ideal, windless conditions. We see that the power (P_a, in watts) required to overcome the air resistance due to his own wind is 248 watts or 248/300 = 83% of his available power. Moreover, the formula also shows that P_a increases to the third power of the speed. As can be seen in the figure below, the power required to achieve a speed of 60 km/h is as high as 837 watts! This makes it easy to understand that sprinters can maintain such speeds for a few seconds only.

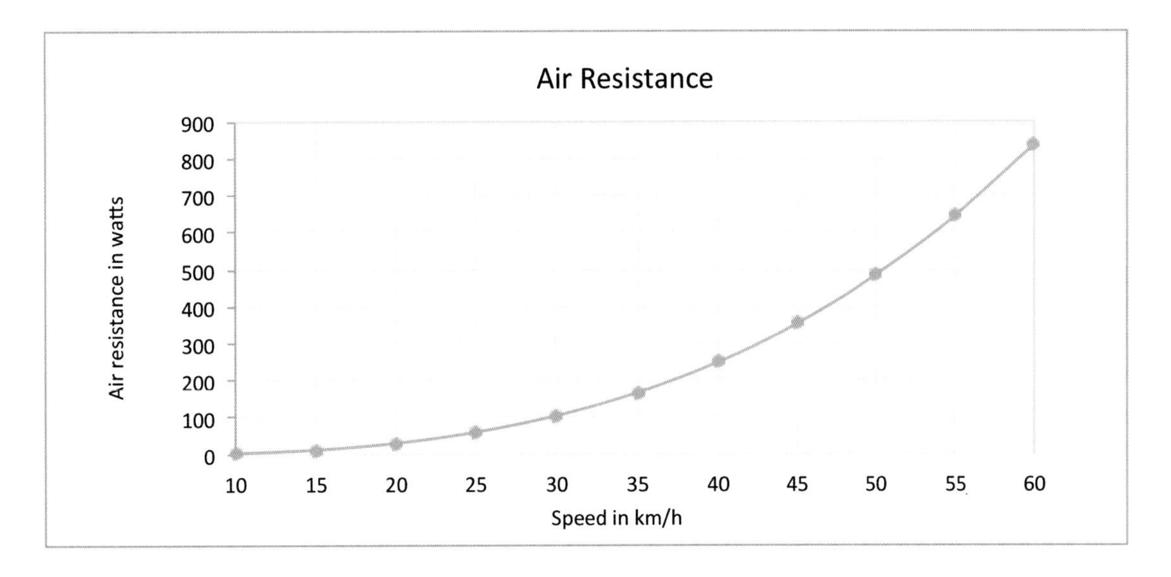

In later chapters we will also show the impact on the attainable speed and race times of the other factors that impact P_a, such as the wind conditions and riding in the pack.

The Climbing Resistance

The climbing resistance depends on the gradient (i, in %), the combined weight of cyclist and bike (m, in kg) and the speed (v, in m/s), as shown in the box.

The Climbing Resistance

$P_c = (i/100)mgv$

Example:

$i = 7.4\%$, $m = 83.8$ kg, $v = 40$ km/h, $g = 9.81$ m/s^2

$P_c = 7.4/100*83.8*9.81*40/3.6 = 677$ watts

The example is again valid for Fast Eddy, who attempts to climb to the top of the Alpe d'Huez. The numbers show that uphill he cannot maintain a speed of 40 km/h, as this would require a climbing resistance of 677 watts on top of the 248 watts that he needs for the air resistance and the 36 watts for the rolling resistance. So he will have to reduce his speed until the sum of the resistances equals the power of his human engine (300 watts).

The climbing resistance (P_c, in watts) increases proportionally with the speed (v) and the gradient (i), as can be seen from the formula. The figure below gives the climbing resistance at a speed of 40 km/h. Obviously such a speed cannot be maintained uphill; at steep gradients even elite cyclists have to reduce their speed to a pedestrian pace in order to limit their climbing resistance.

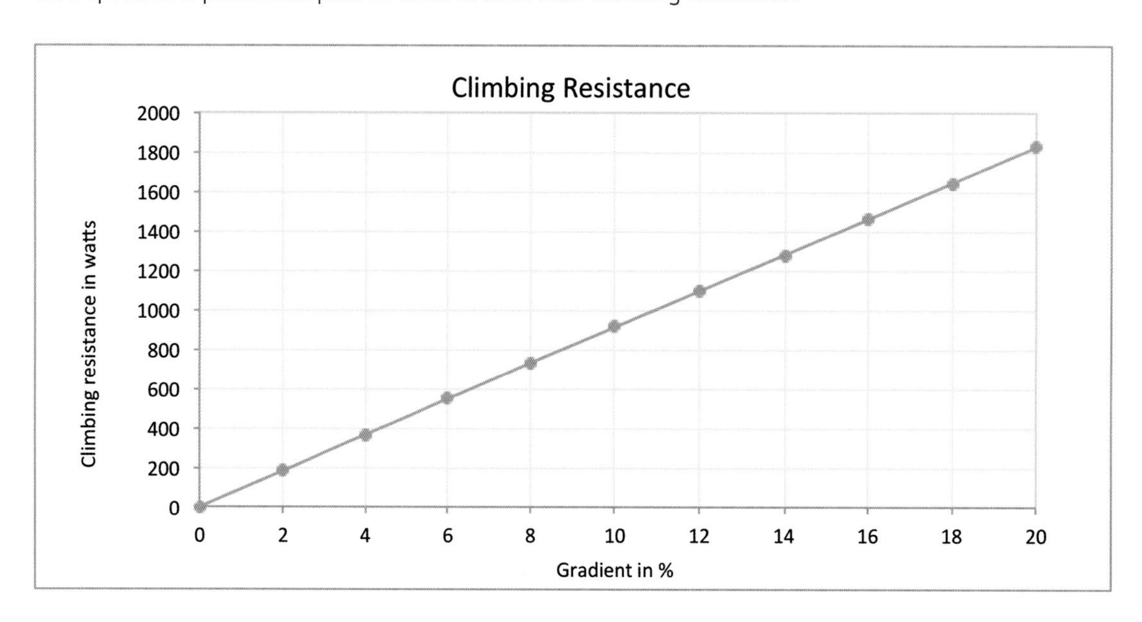

In later chapters we will discuss all factors that impact the climbing resistance and the attainable speed uphill and downhill. For completeness we have to remark that we should have included a factor sin(arctangent (i/100)) in the formula. In practice this factor is also very close to 1, even at steep hills (at an extreme gradient of 20%, the factor is 0.98). Consequently, we did not include it in the box. However, we have included it in the model calculations in this book and in our calculator.

The Mechanical Resistance

The mechanical resistance of chains and hubs is generally expressed as a percentage of the total power. The mechanical efficiency (η) of the bike is in the order of 97.5%, which means that the losses due to the mechanical resistance are in the order of 2.5%. Consequently, the mechanical resistance of Fast Eddy is 0.025*300 = 7.5 watts. So it certainly makes sense to keep your chain and hubs in optimal condition to minimize these losses!

In later chapters we will discuss all factors that impact the mechanical resistance and the impact on the speed.

The authors of this book want to verify experimentally as much as possible by themselves, so Ron cycled the climb to the Alpe d'Huez and checked his race time with our model.

Conclusions

The physics of cycling comprises the formulas that describe the power to overcome the four resistances. In the equilibrium situation, the power output of the human engine will be equal to the sum of the power needed to surmount these resistances: the rolling resistance, the air resistance, the climbing resistance and the mechanical resistance:

$$P = P_r + P_a + P_c + P_m$$

The final result is the fairly complicated third-power formula given in the box below. In the next chapter we will explain how we have solved this equation. There we will also show how you can use the formula to calculate the attainable speed and race times depending on the power of the human engine and the race conditions.

The Physics of Cycling

Rolling resistance: $P_r = c_r mgv$

Air resistance: $P_a = 0.5\rho c_d A(v+v_w)^2 v$

Climbing resistance: $P_c = (i/100)mgv$

Mechanical resistance: $P_m = (1-\eta)P$

Cycling formula:

$$\mathbf{P\eta = c_r mgv + 0.5\rho c_d A(v+v_w)^2 v + (i/100)mgv}$$

Alberto Contador in Le Grand Départ (prologue) of the Tour de France 2015 in Utrecht, the Netherlands. With the cycling formula race times can be calculated on the basis of available power (P, in watts) of the human engine.

12. THE CYCLING FORMULA AND THE STANDARD CONDITIONS

One cannot say that one model is more correct than the other, just more useful. –Stephen Hawking

In the previous chapter we have derived the cycling formula, which we can use to calculate the attainable speed and race time as a function of the power of the human engine, as shown in the box:

$$P\eta = c_r mgv + 0.5\rho c_d A(v+v_w)^2 v + (i/100)mgv$$

With the cycling formula, we can calculate the speed when all other parameters are known. We can also use it to make sensitivity analyses to see the impact of all the parameters. By doing this, we can answer many relevant questions, including:

- How much faster do you get when your power (P) increases as a result of training?
- How big is the advantage of aero gear and an aero bike position?
- How much slower do you get when you get older?
- How big is the advantage of cycling in the pack?
- How much time do you lose in windy conditions?
- How much slower do you bike uphill and how much faster downhill?
- How much faster do you get when you lose body fat?
- How much time can you gain from improving your pedaling economy?
- How big is the advantage of a lightweight bike?
- How big is the advantage of altitude training?
- What is the physiological limit of the world hour record?
- How big is the advantage of a velodrome at altitude?
- Is it possible to climb clean to the top of Alpe d'Huez in 37 minutes?

In part IV of this book, we will systematically analyze all parameters and show the impact on the speed. But first we need to discuss how we have solved the cycling formula. This is not a trivial matter, as it is a cubic function of the speed (v).

The Solution of the Cycling Formula

In literature, several methods can be found to solve cubic functions[17,18,19]. We have chosen to use the universal solution given in the box below. Although it requires some elaborate calculations, it has the advantage that it is robust and will give the correct result in all possible conditions (including head wind and tail wind). We have programmed the solution in an Excel spreadsheet and into our calculator.

The Solution of the Cycling Formula

$$v = \sqrt[3]{\left(\frac{-b^3}{27a^3} + \frac{bc}{6a^2} - \frac{d}{2a}\right) + \sqrt{\left(\frac{-b^3}{27a^3} + \frac{bc}{6a^2} - \frac{d}{2a}\right)^2 + \left(\frac{c}{3a} - \frac{b^2}{9a^2}\right)^3}}$$

$$+ \sqrt[3]{\left(\frac{-b^3}{27a^3} + \frac{bc}{6a^2} - \frac{d}{2a}\right) - \sqrt{\left(\frac{-b^3}{27a^3} + \frac{bc}{6a^2} - \frac{d}{2a}\right)^2 + \left(\frac{c}{3a} - \frac{b^2}{9a^2}\right)^3}} - \frac{b}{3a}$$

$a = 0.5\rho c_d A$

$b = 2 * 0.5\rho c_d A\, v_w$

$c = 0.5\rho c_d A v_w^2 + c_r mg\cos(\text{arctangent}(i/100)) + \eta mg\sin s(\text{arctangent}(i/100))$

$d = P\eta$

The Parameters of the Cycling Formula

The achievable speed depends on many parameters, including:

1. The available power (P, in watts) of the cyclist. This depends on many other factors, including talent, age, sex, training and fitness, time and distance and specific aspects, such as tapering, altitude training, nutrition and so on.

2. The rolling resistance factor (c_r, in kJ/kg/km). This depends on the wheels (type and air pressure) and the pavement.
3. The combined weight of the cyclist and his bike (m, in kg). This is influenced by his preparation (nutrition and training) and his bike.
4. The temperature (T, in °K). Obviously, this depends on the weather conditions.
5. The air pressure (p_0, in Pa). This also depends on the weather conditions.
6. The altitude above sea level in meters. This is determined by the race location.
7. The air-resistance factor (c_dA, in m^2). This depends on aero gear and position and on the body stature of the runner.
8. The wind direction and speed (v_w, in m/s). This depends on the weather conditions and the race course.
9. The gradient (i, in %). Obviously, this depends on the race course.
10. The mechanical resistance (η, as a fraction). This depends on the bike (type and maintenance) and the cyclist (it is somewhat higher at higher power and speed).

Moreover, we should realize that the air density (ρ, in kg/m^3) depends on three parameters: the temperature, the air pressure and the altitude, as shown in the box below.

Calculation of Air Density

$$\rho = (p*M)/(R*T)$$

$$p = p_0*e^{(-Mgh/RT)}$$

Example:

h = 0 m, p_0 = 101,300 Pa, R = 8.314 kJ/kmol/°K, T = 293°K, M = 28.97 g/mol, g = 9.81 m/s^2

p = 101,300*e^0 = 101300 Pa

ρ = 101,300*28.97/(8314*293) = 1.205 kg/m^3

The Standard Conditions and Fast Eddy

As many parameters influence the results, we saw the need for a systematic analysis of the impact of all parameters. Consequently, we have chosen to use a set of standard conditions throughout this book. In later chapters, we will look at the impact of changing the parameters, one by one. Our standard conditions and the data of our hypothetical cyclist Fast Eddy are shown in the tables below:

Standard Conditions		
η	0.975	-
c_r	0.004	-
c_dA	0.3	m^2
i	0	%
v_w	0	km/h
T	20	°C
h	0	m
p_0	101,300	Pa
ρ	1.205	kg/m^3

Fast Eddy		
FTP	4	watts/kg
Body weight	75	kg
Bike weight	8.8	kg
Age	40	years

With our calculator, we have calculated that at his FTP Fast Eddy can achieve a speed of 40.41 km/h on a flat course and in windless conditions. Consequently, he can ride a 40-kilometer time trial in 59 minutes and 23 seconds. At the climb to the Alpe d'Huez his speed will drop to 15.58 km/h. Consequently, his race time on the 14.45-kilometer climb will be 55 minutes and 59 seconds. These race times are the exact results of the cycling formula, contrary to the simplified calculations we used in previous chapters.

In part IV of this book, we will analyze how much faster or slower Fast Eddy will ride if the conditions change and the parameters deviate from the standard conditions.

But first, we will study the human engine in some more detail in part III. How does the human engine function and how can we determine the available power (P, in watts) and the specific power (P/m, in watts/kg)?

The Calculator and Some Examples of Calculations

At www.thesecretofcycling.com, the reader can access our calculator. There you can make your own calculations and see how fast you can bike in different conditions. We have set the standard conditions as default values, so you can start immediately and get realistic results. As your knowledge increases and you gain more information about your human engine and the conditions of the race, you can change the standard conditions as needed.

In order to introduce the reader to the calculator, we have prepared some examples of calculations. The graphs give the result of the combined effect of the rolling resistance, the air resistance, the climbing resistance and the mechanical resistance.

The first graph shows the relationship between power and speed on a flat course in windless conditions. You can see that the speed depends on the power to an exponent of 0.357. This is close to the theoretical value of 0.333, which is valid for the air resistance, so we can conclude that the rolling resistance plays only a very small role (as the rolling resistance would lead to a relationship to an exponent of 1.0). The graph shows power up to 900 watts, but in practice such values can only be maintained for a short time (seconds), even by the elite professionals.

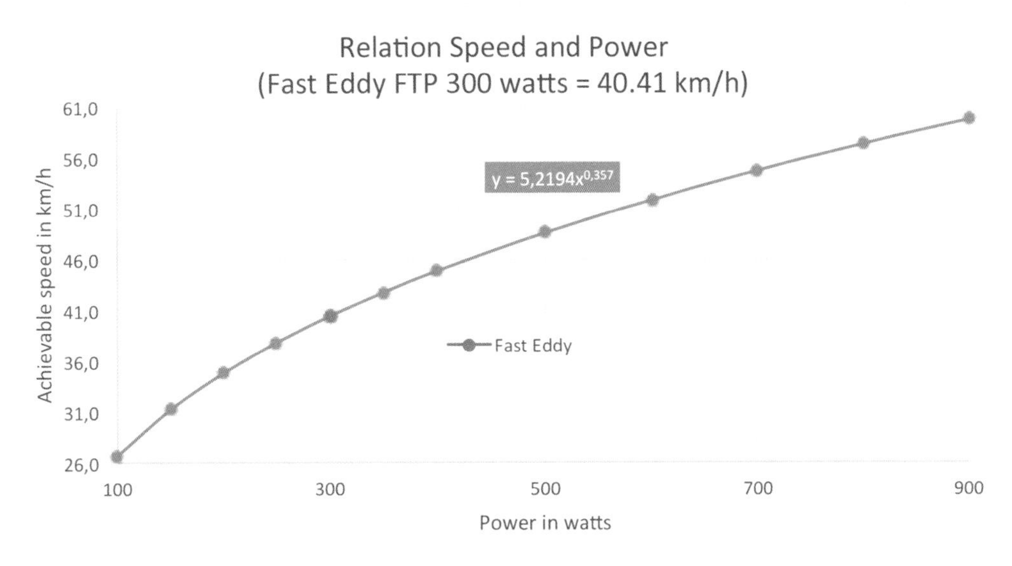

Author Guido Vroemen verifies in practice that the speed depends on the power to an exponent of 0.357 on a flat course in windless conditions.

The second graph shows the impact of the time on the speed. During one hour Fast Eddy can ride 40.41 km, so he can maintain a speed of 40.41 km/h. However, during one minute he can mobilize more power and attain a speed of 52.32 km/h.

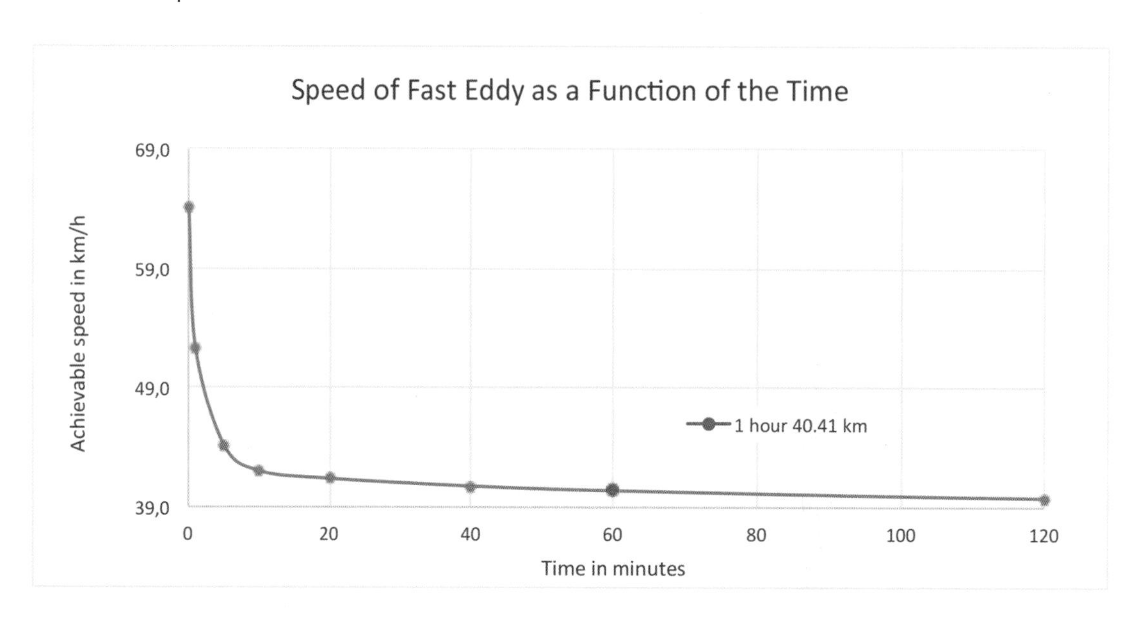

The last example shows the climb to the Alpe d'Huez. We see that the speed is almost linearly dependent on the FTP (the exponent in the relation is 0.940, so almost 1). This confirms that the climbing resistance is indeed the decisive factor and the air resistance plays only a small role. With his FTP of 4 watts/kg, the climbing speed of Fast Eddy is 15.58 km/h, whereas world-class cyclists with an FTP of 6.4 watts/kg can attain a speed of 23.44 km/h.

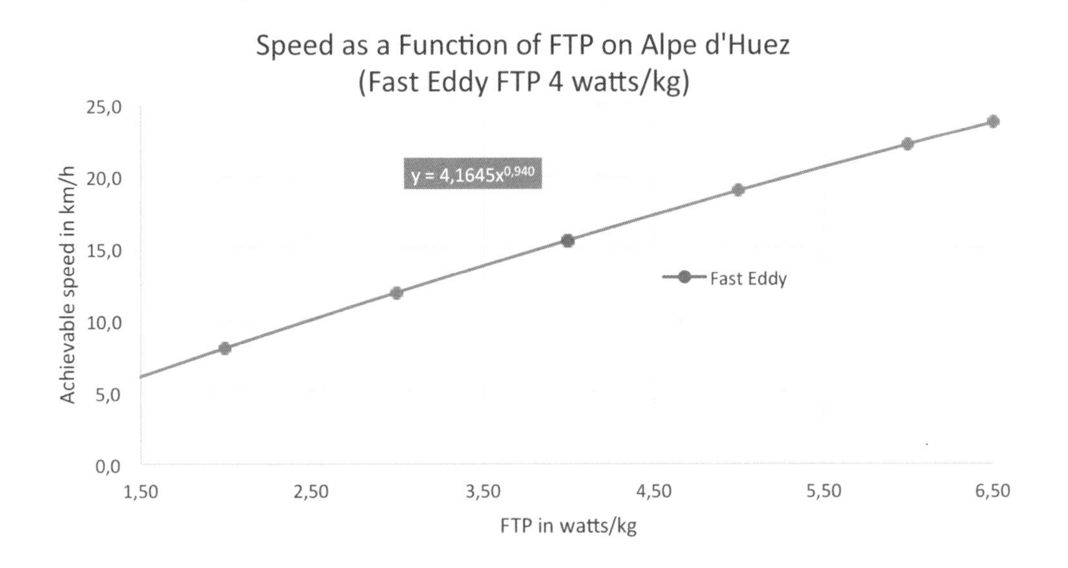

PART III

THE POWER OF THE HUMAN ENGINE

13. THE POWER–TIME RELATIONSHIP

I have never met a cyclist that did not want to go faster.

In order to make calculations on the available power of the human engine, we first need to consider the power–time relationship. In the cycling literature, the CP-AEWC model by Monod & Scherrer[20] is frequently used to describe this. CP stands for the critical power, the power output (in watts/kg) that can be maintained indefinitely (theoretically, obviously). AEWC stands for anaerobic work capacity (in kJ/kg), a limited energy reserve that can be used during a time period (t). The available power thus becomes:

$$P = CP + AWC/t$$

Although the CP-AEWC model is used by many authors, it has some serious drawbacks. The most obvious ones are that P becomes infinite for a very small t and P becomes always equal to CP for a very large t. Both consequences are not realistic.

We have chosen to use a different approach, which originates from our experiences in running. In running, it is well known that the pace decreases with time. As pace in running is determined by power, this means that the power of the human engine apparently decreases as time increases. In this chapter, we will analyze this power–time relationship for running in detail. How can we calculate the power decline as a function of time? What is the cause of this decline? We will show that the power–time relationship is actually determined by the four energy systems of the human engine that we discussed in an earlier chapter. We will see that as time increases gradually the share of the four energy systems in the total power output will change. As the energy systems of the human engine are the same in cycling and in running, we believe that our findings can also be used to describe the power–time relationship in cycling.

Pete Riegel's Famous Formula

The relationship between speed and distance was first investigated by Pete Riegel. He was a mechanical engineer and marathon runner and, as he put it himself, nuts about numbers. He compared his race times at various distances with the world records and concluded that the speed declined exponentially as a function of the distance. He found the same exponential relationship for his own times as well as for the world records! He published his results on running in 1977[21]; later he published a paper on other sports as well[22]. Pete Riegel's formula is simple and straightforward:

$$v_2/v_1 = (d_2/d_1)^{-0.07}$$

In his formula d represents the distance and v is the speed. So the formula says quite simply that as the distance increases by a factor of two, the speed decreases by 5% ($2^{-0.07} = 0.95$).

Pete Riegel's formula is very powerful and is used in many running calculators on the internet. In Pete's papers and in literature by others, there has been some debate on the value of the exponent -0.07. Sometimes -0.06 or -0.08 is also mentioned. As we will see in a later chapter, these differences are related to the fatigue resistance. A runner with a very good fatigue resistance will have an exponent of -0.06, so his speed will only decline 4% as the distance doubles. However, for most runners -0.07 is the most realistic number. This exponent is also valid for the world records of both men and women, as can be seen in the graph below.

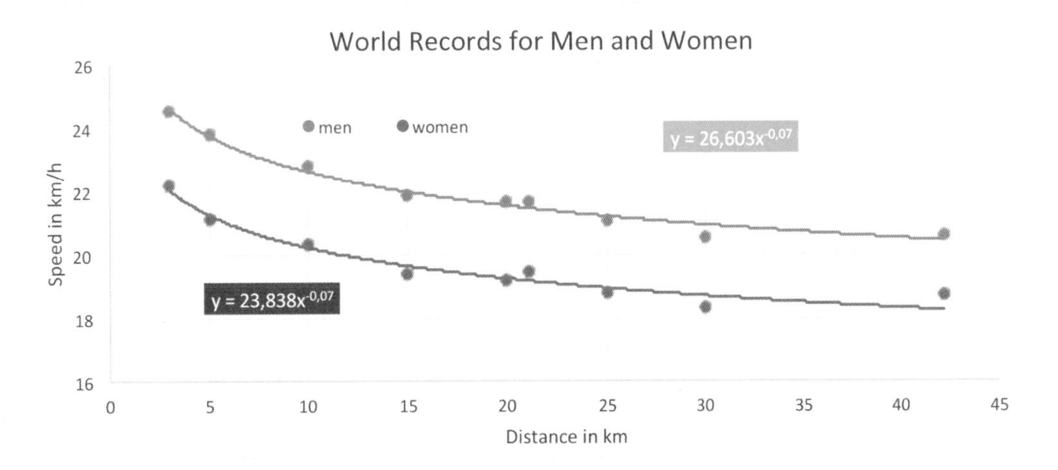

For both men and women the data points are quite close to the regression line with an exponent -0.07. As we will discuss later, Riegel's formula works less well for short distances (less than 1,500 meter), so we have excluded these from the graph.

As the running power depends linearly on the speed ($P_r = cmv$), we can use Riegel's formula to describe the power–distance relationship. Apparently, we can conclude that as the distance doubles, the power decreases by 5% ($2^{-0.07} = 0.95$) as well. As the distance is proportional with time, we can finally conclude that Riegel's formula can also be used to describe the power–time relationship.

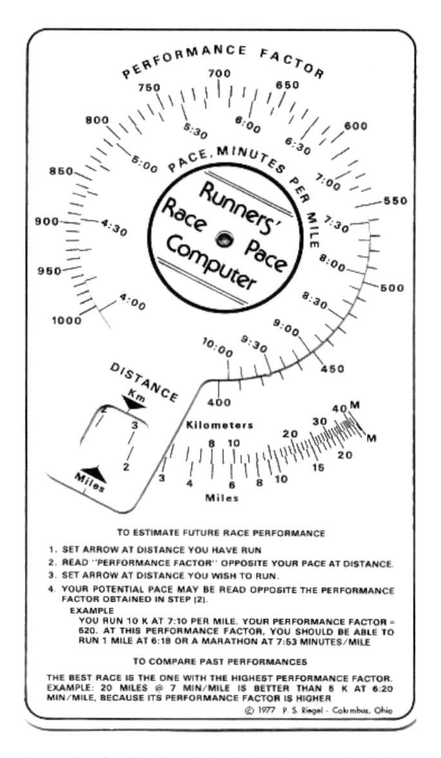

Pete Riegel with the original 1977 artwork of the race pace computer.

How Should We Compare Performances at Different Distances?

In order to make an objective comparison of different performances, we should at least take into account the power–time relationship. A practical way of doing this is to use Riegel's formula to make a table of the power–time relationship. As the base for the table, we chose the power that can be maintained for one hour. We know from literature and experience that at this level the human engine is fueled virtually completely by the two aerobic energy systems, the aerobic conversion of glycogen and the aerobic conversion of fatty acids. These are the two primary energy systems for endurance sports. This level is called the functional threshold power or FTP (in watts/kg). The term threshold is used because at this level the anaerobic systems start to kick in. In a later chapter we will show that the maximum FTP of male world champions in various sports is around 6.4 watts/kg. We consider an FTP of 6.4 watts/kg the ultimate limit of the human performance. However, the FTP is not the maximum power output of the human engine. During a short period, everybody can mobilize more power than his FTP (as the FTP can be maintained for one hour). If you have to run for 10 minutes only, you can mobilize more power (i.e., $(10/60)^{-0.07} * 100 = 113\%$ of your FTP). This means that during 10 minutes you can also run at a 13% higher speed than during one hour. The power–time relationship is given in the table.

Power Ratio With Time	
Time	**% FTP**
(min)	**(%)**
10 (= VO_2 max)	113
20	108
40	103
60 (= FTP)	100
120	95
240	91
300	89

We have set the lower limit of the table at 10 minutes, as during shorter times the anaerobic energy systems (the glycolysis and the conversion of ATP) become too important to be neglected. As we will see in a later chapter, the available power (in watts/kg) that can be maintained during 10 minutes is linearly proportional to the maximum oxygen uptake capacity, the VO_2 max. The table thus shows that the available power at the VO_2 max (duration 10 minutes) is 13% greater than at the power at the FTP (duration 60 minutes). We can say that the available power at the FTP is 100/113 = 88% of the power at the VO_2 max. Another well-known example is that the available power over two hours (which is the approximate marathon time for world-class runners) is equal to 95/113 = 84% of the VO_2 max. As the pace depends linearly on power, this means that world-class athletes can run the marathon at approximately 84% of the pace at their VO_2 max.

What Causes the Decline of Power With Time?

From literature it is well-known that the ratio of the aerobic conversion of glycogen and the aerobic conversion of fatty acids (i.e., the fuel mix) is not constant. During rest, the fuel mix consists primarily of fatty acids. When we start running, the share of glycogen in the fuel mix increases rapidly. At the pace of the VO_2 max, the share of glycogen has increased to 90%. The figure shows experimental findings on the relationship between the exercise intensity and the fuel mix[23]. Looking at the figure, you could also say that as you reduce your pace the share of the fatty acids in the fuel mix increases.

We wondered whether this could be the cause of the decline of power with time as expressed by Riegel's formula. To answer this question, we need to study the biochemistry of the human engine in some detail.

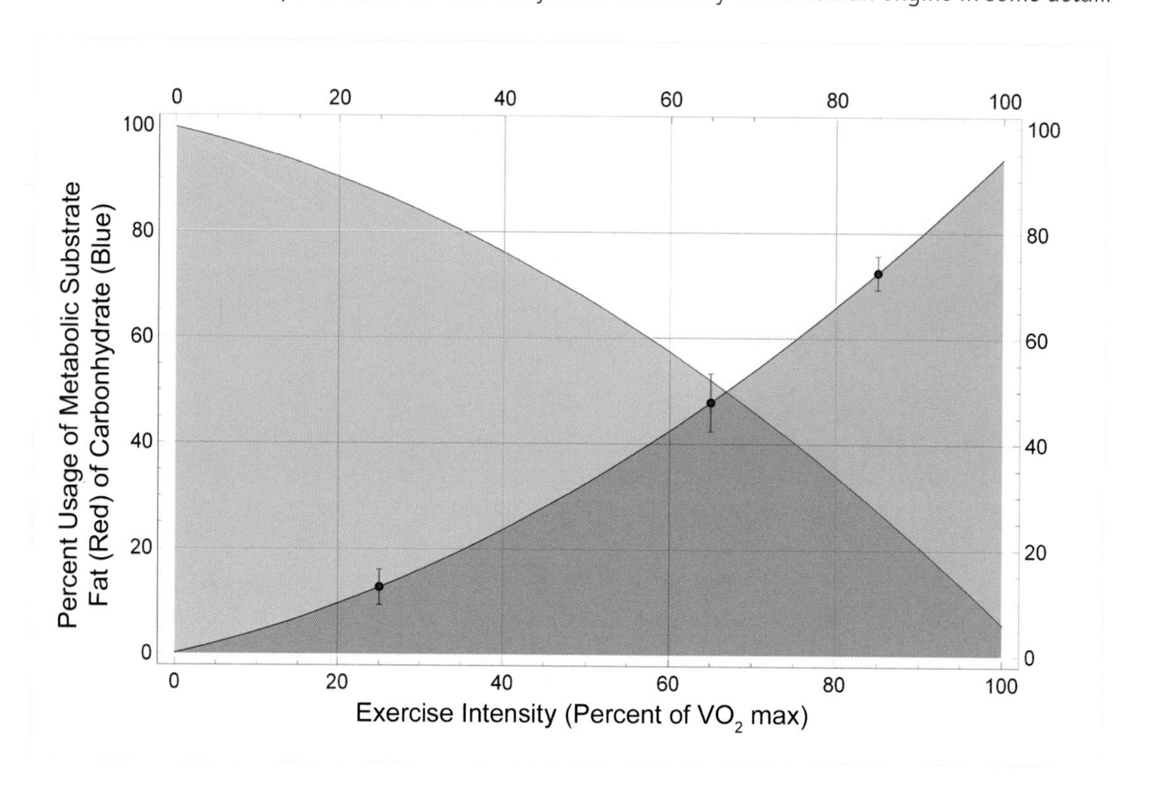

Fuel mix in muscles according to Rapaport[23].

The Power Output of the Four Energy Systems

We have reviewed literature on the biochemistry of the four energy systems of the human engine[31,32,33,34]. The table below gives the theoretical power output of the four energy systems, expressed in the conversion speed of ATP (in mmol/s). In the table we have set the conversion speed of glycogen at 100% and expressed the relative conversion speed of the other systems as a percentage of that of glycogen. From the table we can already see the cause of the phenomenon known as hitting the wall. This is the moment in the marathon (usually after some 30-35 kilometers) when your glycogen reserves are depleted. At this moment, the fuel mix in your muscles switches to fatty acids only. Unfortunately, fatty acids provide only 30% of the power of glycogen. Much to your despair, you will notice that instantly your legs feel empty. Puffing and stumbling, you have no choice but to reduce your speed to embarrassing levels as a result of the reduced power output of the fatty acids.

The Power Output of the Four Human Engines		
	P	%
	(mmol ATP/s)	Glycogen (%)
ATP/CP		
ATP → ADP $C_{10}H_{16}N_5O_{13}P_3 \rightarrow C_{10}H_{15}N_5O_{10}P_2$	73	317
Anaerobic conversion of glycogen		
$C_6H_{12}O_6 + 3ADP \rightarrow 2C_3H_6O_3 + 3ATP$	40	174
Aerobic conversion of glycogen		
$C_6H_{12}O_6 + 6O_2 + 38ADP \rightarrow 6CO_2 + 6H_2O + 38ATP$	23	100
Aerobic conversion of fatty acids		
$CH_3(CH_2)_{14}COOH + 23O_2 + 130ADP \rightarrow 16CO_2 + 16H_2O + 130ATP$	7	30

Is the Decline in Power Caused by the Change in the Fuel Mix?

We have calculated the theoretical share of glycogen and fatty acids in the fuel mix that could explain the decline in power from Riegel's formula. We used the above table, setting the conversion speed of glycogen at 100% and of fatty acids at 30%. In accordance with literature, we set the share of glycogen at the VO_2 max at 90%. The table shows the results, which seem very convincing. The numbers match the experimental findings very well. As an example, we look at the world class athletes at the marathon. They run for approximately two hours, so their power output is 95/113 = 84% of the VO_2 max level and 95/100 = 95% of the FTP level. The share of fatty acids in their fuel mix thus becomes 31% according to the table. The same number was found experimentally, as can be seen in literature[23] and the earlier graph.

Calculated Share of Fatty Acids and Glycogen			
Time	% FTP	Glycogen	Fatty acids
(min)	(%)	(%)	(%)
10	113	90	10
20	108	84	16
40	103	78	22
60	100	75	25
120	95	69	31
240	91	64	36
300	89	62	38

And How About the Anaerobic Systems?

From the above, we believe we can conclude that the change in the fuel mix is indeed the cause of the decline of power with time as expressed by Riegel's formula; however this applies only to the aerobic systems, and thus for time periods of more than 10 minutes. But how about shorter time periods, when the anaerobic systems play a more important role and Riegel's formula is no longer as accurate? We believe that the power–time relationship is then also caused by the change in the fuel mix. Unfortunately, experimental data on the fuel mix during short periods are not readily available in literature. Therefore, we have only made the theoretical calculations of the below table. In the table we have just assumed a certain share of the energy systems at different times and calculated the resulting available power (with the relevant data from biochemistry, so 317% - 174% - 100% - 30% of the power of glycogen). In later chapters, we will show that the calculated power output matches well with the results of the world records in athletics and the measured power profiles in cycling.

Calculated Power (Including Anaerobic Systems)				
Time	Glycogen	Glycolysis	ATP	% FTP
(min)	(%)	(%)	(%)	(%)
5	90	8	2	125
1	50	40	10	201
0	0	0	100	385

Conclusions on the Power–Time Relationship

We conclude that the power–time relationship is expressed accurately by Riegel's formula for time periods of 10 minutes and above. For most runners and for the world records in athletics, an exponent of -0.07 best describes the results at different distances. The decline in power with time as expressed by Riegel's formula can be explained by the change in fuel mix. At the marathon, the pace is slower than at 5K, so the muscles automatically use a fuel mix with more fatty acids.

For time periods shorter than 10 minutes, the pace and the available power is higher than described by Riegel's formula. This is caused by the increasing share of the anaerobic systems in the fuel mix. Unfortunately, only limited experimental findings are available on this. We have calculated that the maximal available power is 385% of the FTP during a short burst, like the 100-meter sprint. In later chapters, we will show that the calculated power values match well with the world records.

Finally, we note that some deviations from the exponent of -0.07 can occur in practice, in particular for:

» Sprinters with a limited fatigue resistance (in this case the factor can be -0.08 or -0.09)
» Endurance athletes with exceptional fatigue resistance (in this case the factor can be -0.06 or 0.05)

Conclusion for Cycling

We believe that these results can be used to describe the power–time relationship in cycling as well as the energy processes of the human engine are the same in running and in cycling. In later chapters we will discuss this in more detail and show that the calculated power output at different times matches very well with the power profiles. In the chapter on fatigue resistance, we will discuss Riegel's factor in more detail and show the impact on the cycling times at different distances.

14. THE LIMITS OF HUMAN POWER

The human body is centuries ahead of the physiologist.
–Sir Roger Bannester

Quite regularly, the media speculate on the limits of human power in sports. Is it humanly possible to run 100 meters in less than nine seconds or to cycle to the top of the Alpe d'Huez in less than 37 minutes? This often also involves debates on doping. Which performances are considered clean and which are suspect? In this chapter, we will analyze this topic, partly based on our experiences in running. Can we calculate the power output during the world record races? And can we calculate the equivalent FTP of the world records at different distances? Does this match Riegel's formula and our theory on the change in fuel mix? And do our calculations provide a sufficient base to come to a conclusion on the ultimate physiological limits of the power of the human engine for cycling?

The Power Output at the World Record Races

With our theory we can calculate the required power to run any pace, including the world records. At a flat track or road race, the power required to overcome the running resistance is equal to:

$$P_r/m = c_v = 0.98*v$$

Usually, we express v in km/h, so we have to divide by a factor of 3.6. The result thus becomes:

$$P_r/m = 0.272*v.$$

The air resistance at 15°C and in windless conditions is equal to:

$$P_a = 0.5*1.226*c_dA*v^3$$

As world records are always run with pacemakers, we have set the c_dA value at 0.20 m^2, except for the sprint events, where we have used the standard value of 0.24 m^2.

Finally, we can calculate the total power output as:

$$P_t = P_r+P_a$$

With these assumptions, we have calculated the required power to run the world records, both for men and women. We used a standard body weight for the men of 60 kg and for the women of 50 kg, in both cases with the exception of the sprint distances. Sprinters are usually significantly heavier, so we surfed the internet to find their real body weight. The results of our calculations are given in the table below.

World Records of the Men

World Records of the Men (September 2016)			v	P_r/m	P_a/m	P_t/m	$P_t/$ FTP	% FTP Riegel
Distance	**Time**	**Name**	**(km/h)**	**(Watt/kg)**	**(Watt/kg)**	**(Watt/kg)**	**(%)**	**(%)**
100 m	0:09.58	Usain Bolt	37.58	10.24	1.78	12.02	**189**	**151**
200 m	0:19.19	Usain Bolt	37.52	10.22	1.77	12.00	**189**	**144**
400 m	0:43.03	Wayde van Niekerk	33.47	9.12	1.53	10.65	**168**	**136**
800 m	1:40.91	David Rudisha	28.54	7.78	1.03	8.81	**139**	**128**
1500 m	3:26.00	Hicham El Guerrouj	26.21	7.14	0.79	7.93	125	122
3000 m	7:20.67	Daniel Komen	24.51	6.68	0.64	7.32	115	116
5000 m	12:37.35	Kenenisa Bekele	23.77	6.48	0.59	7.06	111	112
10,000 m	26:17.53	Kenenisa Bekele	22.82	6.22	0.52	6.74	106	106
15 km	00:41:13	Leonard Komon	21.84	5.95	0.46	6.41	101	103
20 km	00:55:21	Zersenay Tadese	21.68	5.91	0.45	6.35	100	101
21.1 km	00:58:23	Zersenay Tadese	21.68	5.91	0.45	6.36	100	100
25 km	01:11:18	Dennis Kimetto	21.04	5.73	0.41	6.14	97	99
30 km	01:27:38	Emmanuel Mutai	20.54	5.60	0.38	5.98	94	97
42.2 km	02:02:57	Dennis Kimetto	20.59	5.61	0.38	5.99	94	95
100 km	06:13:33	Takahiro Sunada	16.06	4.38	0.18	4.56	**72**	**88**

The table shows a consistent decrease of both total power and the percentage of the FTP as the distance increases. We draw the following conclusions from the table:

1. The limit of the FTP (the power that can be maintained for one hour) is 6.36 watts/kg, as shown by the value of Zersenay Tadese at the half marathon.
2. The percentages of the FTP as calculated with Riegel's formula are quite close to the real percentages as determined from the calculated total power divided by 6.36. The only exceptions are the 100-kilometer races (which is run much less frequently, the record is not very strong) and the 100-800-meter races (in which the anaerobic systems contribute significantly to the power output).
3. When we use the total power at the world records from 5,000 meters up to the marathon to calculate the equivalent FTP of the world record holder with Riegel's formula, we get the figure below. This shows that the equivalent FTP of all world record holders is actually quite close to the value of 6.36 watts/kg. Apparently, the records at 25 and 30 kilometers are somewhat less strong, which is probably caused by the fact that these distances are run less frequently.
4. The maximum calculated power was produced by Usain Bolt at the 100 meter and was calculated at 12.02 watts/kg or 189% of an FTP of 6.36 watts/kg. This 189% is much lower than the maximum output of the ATP system (385%) that we calculated in the last chapter. The difference can be explained by the additional power that Bolt needed to accelerate from the start. In a later chapter, we will show that this acceleration requires an additional 11 watts/kg, bringing his total power output to 23 watts/kg or 363% of an FTP of 6.36 watts/kg.
5. The share of the air resistance in the total required power is 6% at the marathon and even 15% at the 100 meter! This confirms the importance of pacemakers that can reduce the air resistance. For sprinters, this confirms the advantage of running at altitude, where the air resistance is lower.

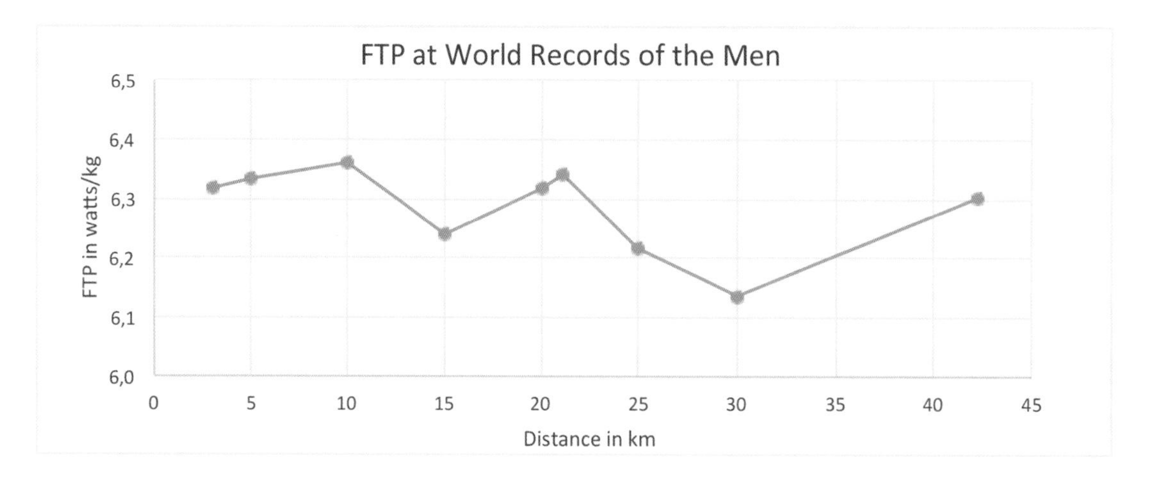

World Records of the Women

World Records of the Women (September 2016)			v	P_r/m	P_a/m	P_t/m	P_t/ FTP	% FTP Riegel
Distance	Time	Name	(km/h)	(Watt/kg)	(Watt/kg)	(Watt/kg)	(%)	(%)
100 m	0:10.49	Florence Griffith Joyner	34.32	9.35	2.16	11.51	**203**	**150**
200 m	0:21.34	Florence Griffith Joyner	33.74	9.19	2.05	11.25	**198**	**143**
400 m	0:47.60	Marita Koch	30.25	8.24	1.41	9.65	**170**	**135**
800 m	1:53.28	Jarmila Kratochvilova	25.42	6.93	0.76	7.69	**136**	**127**
1500 m	3:50.07	Genzebe Dibaba	23.48	6.40	0.68	7.08	125	121
3000 m	8:06.11	Junxia Wang	22.22	6.06	0.58	6.63	117	115
5000 m	14:11.15	Tirunesh Dibaba	21.15	5.76	0.50	6.26	110	111
10,000 m	29:17.45	Almaz Ayana	20.49	5.58	0.45	6.04	106	105
15 km	0:46:14	Florence Kiplagat	19.47	5.30	0.39	5.69	100	102
20 km	01:01:54	Florence Kiplagat	19.39	5.28	0.38	5.67	100	100
21.1 km	01:05:09	Florence Kiplagat	19.43	5.30	0.39	5.68	100	99
25 km	01:19:53	Mary Keitany	18.78	5.12	0.35	5.46	96	98
30 km	**01:38:49**	**Mizuki Noguchi**	**18.22**	**4.96**	**0.32**	**5.28**	**93**	**97**
42.2 km	**02:15:25**	**Paula Radcliffe**	**18.70**	**5.09**	**0.34**	**5.44**	**96**	**94**
100 km	**06:33:11**	**Tomoe Abe**	**15.26**	**4.16**	**0.19**	**4.35**	**77**	**88**

The table shows a similar consistent decrease of both total power and the percentage of the FTP as the distance increases. We draw the following conclusions from the table:

1. The limit of the FTP (the power that can be maintained for one hour) is 5.67 watts/kg, as shown by the value of Florence Kiplagat at the 20 kilometer.
2. The percentages of the FTP as calculated with Riegel's formula are quite close to the real percentages as determined from the calculated total power divided by 5.67. The only exceptions are the 100 kilometer (which is run much less frequently, the record is not very strong) and the 100-800 meter (in which the anaerobic systems contribute significantly to the power output).
3. When we use the total power at the world records from 5,000 meters up to the marathon to calculate the equivalent FTP of the world record holder with Riegel's formula, we get the figure below. This shows that the equivalent FTP of all world record holders is actually quite close to the value of 5.67 watts/kg. Apparently, the records at 25 and 30 kilometers are somewhat less strong, which is probably caused by the fact that these distances are run less frequently. Paula Radcliffe's world record at the marathon was apparently run with an impressive FTP of 5.76 watts/kg!
4. The maximum calculated power was produced by Florence Griffith-Joyner at the 100 meter and was 11.51 watts/kg or 203% of an FTP of 5.67 watts/kg. The same remarks as with Bolt apply here.
5. The share of the air resistance in the total required power is 6% at the marathon and even 19% at the 100 meter! The percentages are slightly higher than for the men as the women have a lower body weight. The total air resistance in watts is independent of the weight, so the specific air resistance in watts/kg is higher for lightweight women.

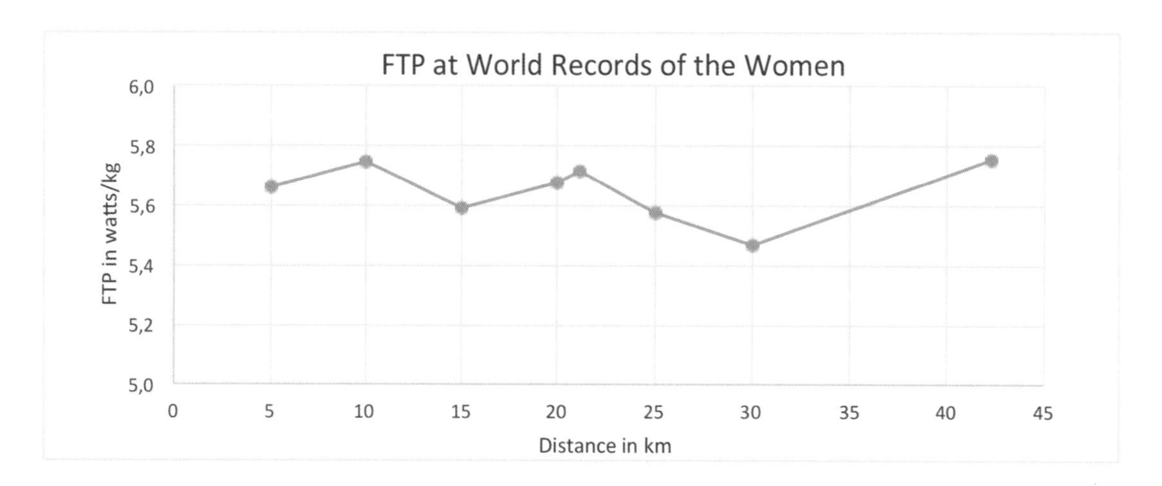

The Limits of the Power of the Human Engine

History has taught us that records are there to be broken, so we need to be humble in our understanding of the limits of human performances. Nevertheless, we feel confident to conclude that the present ultimate limits of the human power are close to an FTP of 6.40 watts/kg for men and 5.70 watts/kg for women. In addition to the above tables and figures, we submit the following arguments to support our bold statement:

1. Athletics is the mother of sports and practiced worldwide by millions. In spite of this, the current world records are broken only rarely and marginally and only in orchestrated races with pacemakers and in ideal conditions. Of course, we cannot rule out that humans will develop further in the future (perhaps as a result of improved training, nutrition or gear or even as a result of DNA engineering). However, we feel that in the foreseeable future significant advances beyond these levels are not to be expected.
2. In cycling, much more data on power output are available as a result of the widespread use of power meters. These data have been analyzed statistically which resulted in the well-known Power Profiles[2]. These data are quite consistent with our numbers. Also in cycling an FTP of 6.40 watts/kg for men and 5.70 watts/kg for women is considered the ultimate limit of human power.
3. We have made many calculations on various world-class performances, including the Tour de France, the climb to the Alpe d'Huez, the world hour record in cycling and also in speed skating. The results always confirmed the FTP values of 6.40 watts/kg and 5.70 watts/kg as the ultimate limits.

What Are the Limits of Human Power According to Biochemistry?

We were curious to see whether the FTP limit of 6.40 watts/kg can also be explained from the power output of the four energy systems of the human motor. Can we calculate the FTP limit from the biochemical data in literature? Therefore, we prepared the table below. In the table, for all four systems we multiplied the conversion speed in mmol ATP/s with the energy value of ATP (81 kJ/mol) and the metabolic efficiency of 0.25 and finally divided the result by 60 kg (which we considered a relevant body weight for a lean athlete with almost no body fat).

Power Output of the Four Human Engines		
	P	P/m
	(mmol ATP/s)	(watts/ kg)
ATP/CP		
ATP → ADP $C_{10}H_{16}N_5O_{13}P_3 \rightarrow C_{10}H_{15}N_5O_{10}P_2$	73	24.64
Anaerobic conversion of glycogen		
$C_6H_{12}O_6 + 3ADP \rightarrow 2C_3H_6O_3 + 3ATP$	40	13.50
Aerobic conversion of glycogen		
$C_6H_{12}O_6 + 6O_2 + 38ADP \rightarrow 6CO_2 + 6H_2O + 38ATP$	23	7.76
Aerobic conversion of fatty acids		
$CH_3(CH_2)_{14}COOH + 23O_2 + 130ADP \rightarrow 16CO_2 + 16H_2O + 130ATP$	7	2.36

The table shows that the power output of the ATP system is 24.64 watts/kg. This should be considered the limit to human power during a very short burst. This number is confirmed by the 5-second value of the power profiles and the data on Usain Bolt.

In the previous chapter, we showed that the fuel mix in our muscles at the FTP level (during one hour) consists of 75% glycogen and 25% fatty acids. This means that the power output can be calculated from the table as 0.75*7.76+0.25*2.36 = 6.41 watts/kg! This matches very well with the limit of 6.40 watts/kg! Of course, we should note that some of our assumptions, such as the metabolic efficiency and the body weight, can also be somewhat higher or lower.

We believe we can explain the lower limit of the women (5.70 watts/kg) by the fact that they have a 10% higher body fat content. Obviously, 10% more body fat will lead to a 10% lower FTP (and also to a 10% slower pace in running).

Conclusions on the Limits of the Power of the Human Engine

We conclude that all four approaches (the world records in athletics, the power profiles in cycling, the calculation of world-class performances in various sports and the biochemical data) lead to the same result: the present ultimate limit of the FTP is close to 6.40 watts/kg for men and 5.70 watts/kg for women. In a later chapter we will show that these values are equivalent to a VO_2 max of 6.40/0.072 = 88.8 ml/kg/min and 5.70/0.072 = 79.2 ml/kg/min.

World-class cyclist Chris Froome in the Grand Départ (prologue) of the 2015 Tour de France in Utrecht. His FTP can be calculated to be around 6.30 watts/kg.

15. THE VO_2 MAX

To be a great cyclist, you have to select your parents carefully.

Back in 1923, the English physiologist and Nobel Prize laureate A.V. Hill found that the oxygen consumption of runners increased with the speed up to a maximum value that could be maintained for a limited time only. Consequently, he postulated that the performance in running is determined primarily by the oxygen uptake capacity of the cardiovascular system. He labeled this maximum oxygen uptake as the VO_2 max[30]. In the past century, many researchers have confirmed that the VO_2 max is indeed a very important parameter for the performance in running and other endurance sports like cycling. As we have seen before, this is caused by the fact that oxygen is needed for the aerobic conversion of glycogen and fatty acids, the two main fuel sources for endurance sports.

The VO_2 max is defined as the maximum volume (V) of oxygen (O_2) that can be taken up by the human body during exercise at sea level. The VO_2 max is expressed as the amount of milliliters of oxygen per kilogram of body weight and per minute (ml O_2/kg/min). From literature and experience it is known that you can maintain exercising at the intensity of the VO_2 max for no more than 10 minutes.

How Can the VO_2 max Be Determined?

In a laboratory, the VO_2 max can be determined experimentally by measuring the oxygen uptake during prolonged and intensive exercise. The VO_2 max is reached when the oxygen uptake does not increase any more in spite of increasing the exercise intensity. The VO_2 max can be measured while running on a treadmill or while cycling on a bicycle ergometer. These tests should be done under medical supervision (e.g., at a sports medical advice center). The authors of this book have taken such tests regularly in the past years. The picture shows author Hans, the treadmill, the breathing measuring equipment and the ECG.

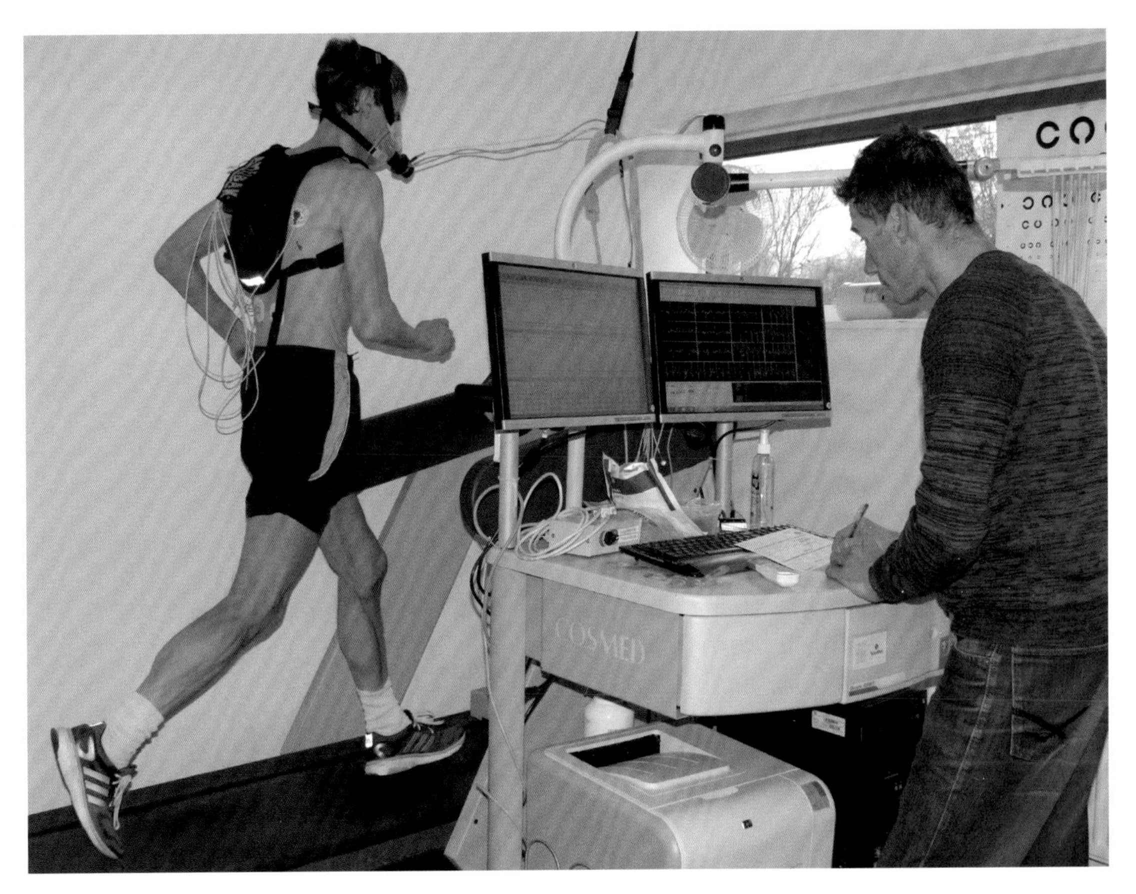

Sports physician Bernard te Boekhorst tests the VO_2 max of author Hans van Dijk on a treadmill.

The box gives the formulas that can be used to calculate the VO_2 max. In the physiological lab, the oxygen uptake is determined from the oxygen balance of the breathing air. During a bicycle test the VO_2 max can also be estimated from the measured maximum power in watts. For a cyclist, the bicycle test is best suited as it is more specific.

As these laboratory tests cannot be performed easily, several field tests have been developed to estimate the VO_2 max. The box gives two of those, including a very simple and crude method to estimate the VO_2 max, based solely on the maximal heart rate (MHR) and the resting heart rate (RHR). This method seems too simple to be true, but it has a certain logic as fit people usually have a high VO_2 max and a low RHR. The second method is frequently used and consists of running as far as you can during 12 minutes (the Cooper test). The distance (d, in meters) can then be used to estimate the VO_2 max.

Methods to Determine the VO_2 max

Lab tests

Oxygen balance: $VO_2 \text{ max} = Q*(c_a-c_v)/m$

Bike ergometer: $VO_2 \text{ max} = (395+11.3W)/m$

Field tests

Rough estimate: $VO_2 \text{ max} = 15*(MHR/RHR)$

Cooper-test: $VO_2 \text{ max} = (d-505)/45$

Q is blood flow or cardiac output (in l/min), c_a and c_v are the concentrations of oxygen in the arterial and venous blood (in ml/l), m is the body weight in kg, d is the distance in meters covered in 12 minutes, W is the maximal wattage during a bike test.

Which factors determine your VO_2 max?

In literature and in practice, it has been established that the VO_2 max mainly depends on:

- Talent (if you want to be a great biker, choose your parents carefully)
- Sex (the VO_2 max of men is 10-15% higher than that of women)
- Age (the VO_2 max decreases approximately 0.5-1.0% per year over the age of 35)
- Training (the VO_2 max can be increased by some 5-25% as a result of training)
- Body weight (the VO_2 max is inversely proportional to the weight, so shedding excess body fat will increase your VO_2 max)

The VO_2 max of the world class athletes is in the order of 88 ml/kg/min, as we will show in a later chapter. Elite cyclists like Eddy Merckx, Chris Froome and Alberto Contador have reached these values as a result of a combination of their talent and years of meticulous training. Normal values for young men are around 40-45, for young women the values are 30-35 ml/kg/min. Consequently, normal persons can never reach the values of Eddy, Chris and Alberto, not even with the most fanatical training.

VO_2 max values in ml/kg/min						
Men						
Age	**Very poor**	**Poor**	**Fair**	**Good**	**Very good**	**Excellent**
13 - 19	< 35.0	35.0 - 38.3	38.4 - 45.1	45.2 - 50.9	51.0 - 55.9	> 55.9
20 - 29	< 33.0	33.0 - 36.4	36.5 - 42.4	42.5 - 46.4	46.5 - 52.4	> 52.4
30 - 39	< 31.5	31.5 - 35.4	35.5 - 40.9	41.0 - 44.9	45.0 - 49.4	> 49.4
40 - 49	< 30.2	30.2 - 33.5	33.6 - 38.9	39.0 - 43.7	43.8 - 48.0	> 48.0
50 - 59	< 26.1	26.1 - 30.9	31.0 - 35.7	35.8 - 40.9	41.0 - 45.3	> 45.3
60+	< 20.5	20.5 - 26.0	26.1 - 32.2	32.3 - 36.4	36.5 - 44.2	> 44.2
Women						
Age	**Very poor**	**Poor**	**Fair**	**Good**	**Very good**	**Excellent**
13 - 19	< 25.0	25.0 - 30.9	31.0 - 34.9	35.0 - 38.9	39.0 - 41.9	> 41.9
20 - 29	< 23.6	23.6 - 28.9	29.0 - 32.9	33.0 - 36.9	37.0 - 41.0	> 41.0
30 - 39	< 22.8	22.8 - 26.9	27.0 - 31.4	31.5 - 35.6	35.7 - 40.0	> 40.0
40 - 49	< 21.0	21.0 - 24.4	24.5 - 28.9	29.0 - 32.8	32.9 - 36.9	> 36.9
50 - 59	< 20.2	20.2 - 22.7	22.8 - 26.9	27.0 - 31.4	31.5 - 35.7	> 35.7
60+	< 17.5	17.5 - 20.1	20.2 - 24.4	24.5 - 30.2	30.3 - 31.4	> 31.4

Above the age of 35, the VO_2 max decreases some 1% annually in untrained persons; with training this decline can be limited to 0.5% annually.

At a very high age, the VO_2 max could decline to such low levels that the life support functions become troublesome. At a level of 10 ml/kg/min or less, the heart is no longer capable of supplying the vital organs with sufficient oxygen. In literature predictions can be found of your lifespan based on your VO_2 max. Endurance runners don't have to worry about this, as we can show from the example of author Hans. His present (2016) VO_2 max is 60 ml/kg/min and his age is 62, so even if his VO_2 max decreased by 1% annually, it would still be 40 ml/kg/min by the time he celebrates his 100th birthday!

In the mountains, the air pressure is lower and consequently so is the VO_2 max. On top of Mount Everest the VO_2 max is only 27% of the value at sea level. When a normal person with a VO_2 max of 40 ml/kg/min tries to climb Mount Everest, his VO_2 max drops to 10.8 ml/kg/min, barely enough to survive. Without oxygen equipment, mountaineers can only progress some 50 meter per hour at great effort!

How Can Your VO_2 max Be Used to Predict Your Cycling Times?

On the internet there are calculators that predict cycling times at various distances as a function of the VO_2 max. In later chapters, we will discuss this in more detail and show exactly what the relationship is between your VO_2 max and your cycling times.

For the moment we will just give a simplified example on how you can calculate your vertical climbing speed (v_v, which is defined as the altitude gained in one hour) in the mountains, based on your VO_2 max. The box gives the formula for this and an example for our hypothetical cyclist Fast Eddy, who has a VO_2 max of 55.4 ml/kg/min. In later chapters, we will derive the equation and discuss it in more detail.

How Fast Can You Climb?

$v_v = 0.030 * VO_2$ max

Example: VO_2 max = 55.4 ml/kg/min

$v_v = 0.030 * 55.4 = 1.66$ km/h (vertical speed)

Another perspective on the VO_2 max is given by the fact that some antelopes are known to have a VO_2 max of 300 ml/kg/min! These antelopes can easily maintain a speed of 65 km/h. Greyhounds and thoroughbred horses also have a very high VO_2 max (respectively 90 and 150 ml/kg/min), so they can easily beat human world-class athletes!

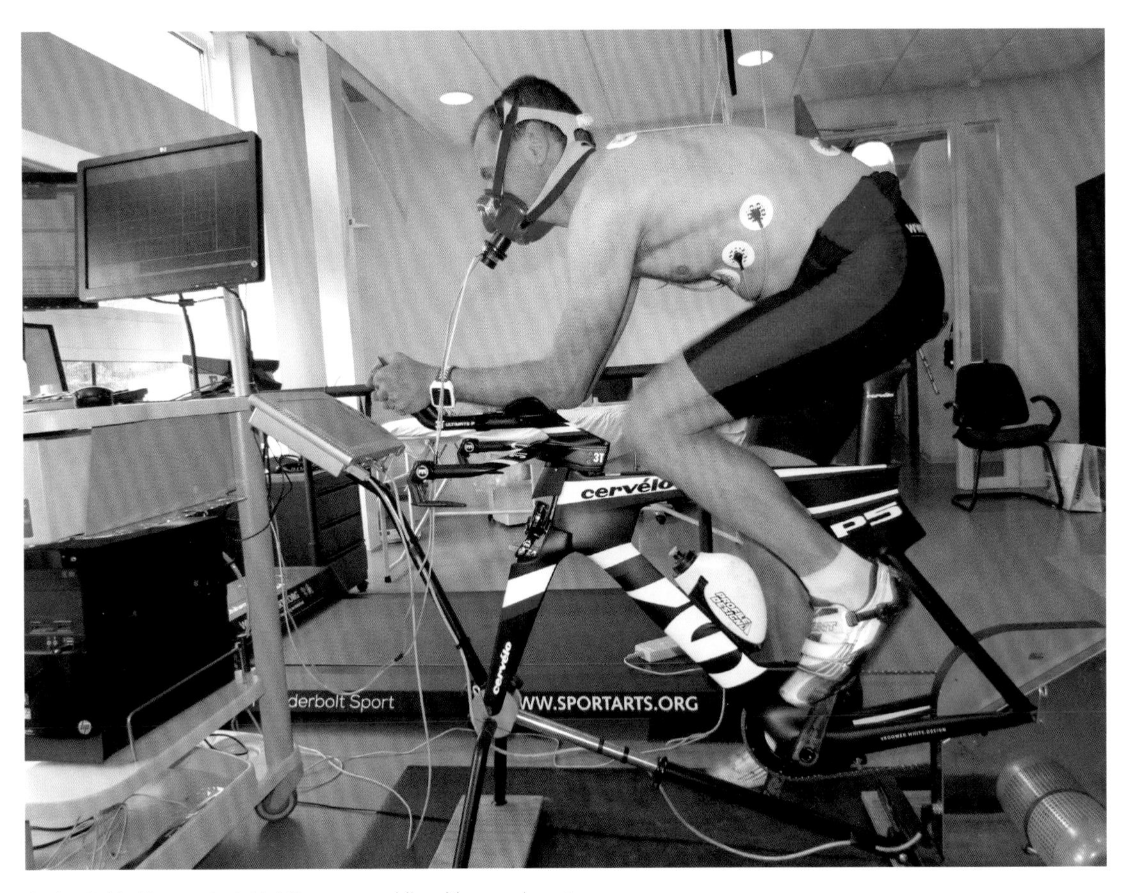

Author Guido Vroemen tests his VO_2 max on a bike with ergospirometry.

16. THE FTP

Biking gives us the evidence we are well.

In cycling, the functional threshold power (FTP) is one of the most important factors determining your performance. The FTP[31] is defined as the power output that can be maintained for one hour and is expressed in watts per kg of body weight. The term functional threshold is used because above this level lactate (lactic acid) starts to accumulate in your muscles. This means that if you go beyond the FTP intensity level, your muscles will start to acidify and you will not be able to maintain your speed. This also means that at the FTP level, your muscles will still produce power with the aerobic energy systems. In practice, the fuel mix at the FTP level will be about 75% glycogen and 25% fatty acids. Consequently, the share of glycogen will be less than at the VO_2 max level, where it is 90%. This also means that your power output and speed will be less than at the VO_2 max level. This makes sense as you can maintain the VO_2 max level for no more than 10 minutes. In the next chapter we will show that there is a fixed relationship between the FTP and the VO_2 max.

How Can the FTP Be Determined?

Traditionally the FTP is determined in cycling. Bikes can be equipped with power meters that enable the determination of the FTP, both in the field and in the lab. A practical problem is that it is not easy to go all out for one hour. This is not something you want to do regularly. Fortunately, we can estimate the FTP from a shorter test as well. As we saw in an earlier chapter, the FTP is equal to 93% of the power that can be maintained for 20 minutes or 88% of the power that can be maintained for 10 minutes. An all-out test of 10 or 20 minutes can be incorporated in most training programs. When executed in the lab (e.g., a sports medical advice center), the FTP test can be combined with additional tests and measurements, like the oxygen uptake and the lactate production, which will give a more complete picture of your fitness and performance level.

Which Factors Determine Your FTP?

In literature and in practice, it has been established that the FTP depends on the same factors as the VO_2 max:

- Talent (if you want to be a great cyclist, choose your parents carefully)
- Sex (the FTP of men is 10-15% higher than that of women)
- Age (the FTP decreases approximately 0.5-1.0 % per year over the age of 35)
- Training (the FTP can be increased by some 5-25% as a result of training)
- Weight (the FTP is inversely proportional to body weight, so shedding excess body fat will increase your FTP)

The FTP of the world class athletes is in the order of 6.4 watts/kg, as we will show in a later chapter. Elite cyclists like Eddy Merckx, Chris Froome and Alberto Contador have reached these values as a result of a combination of their talent and years of meticulous training. Normal values for young men are around 3.1-4.2; for young women the values are 2.6-3.6 watts/kg. The table below gives a classification of FTP levels that is used frequently in cycling.

	FTP Men (watts/kg)	FTP Women (watts/kg)
World top	6.4	5.7
International	5.8	5.1
National	5.1	4.6
Regional	4.5	4.0
Tourist	3.8	3.4
Fair	3.2	2.8
Untrained	2.6	2.3
Poor	1.9	1.7
Very poor	1.4	1.1

How Can You Use Your FTP to Predict Your Cycling Performance?

Your FTP is of vital importance for your performance in cycling. We can illustrate this for uphill races in the mountains. Your race time to the top is inversely proportional to your FTP, as shown in the box.

Calculation of Climbing Time From FTP

$t = 9.81 * h / FTP$

Example: FTP = 4 watts/kg, h = 1071 m

$t = 9.81 * 1071 / 4 = 2627$ sec (43:42)

The example is valid for the climb to the top of the Alpe d'Huez (an altitude gain of 1,071 meters) by our hypothetical cyclist Fast Eddy, who has an FTP of 4 watts/kg. In the example we have neglected the impact of the weight of the bike, the rolling resistance, the air resistance and the mechanical resistance. In the figure below we have assumed that these losses add 30% to the climbing resistance.

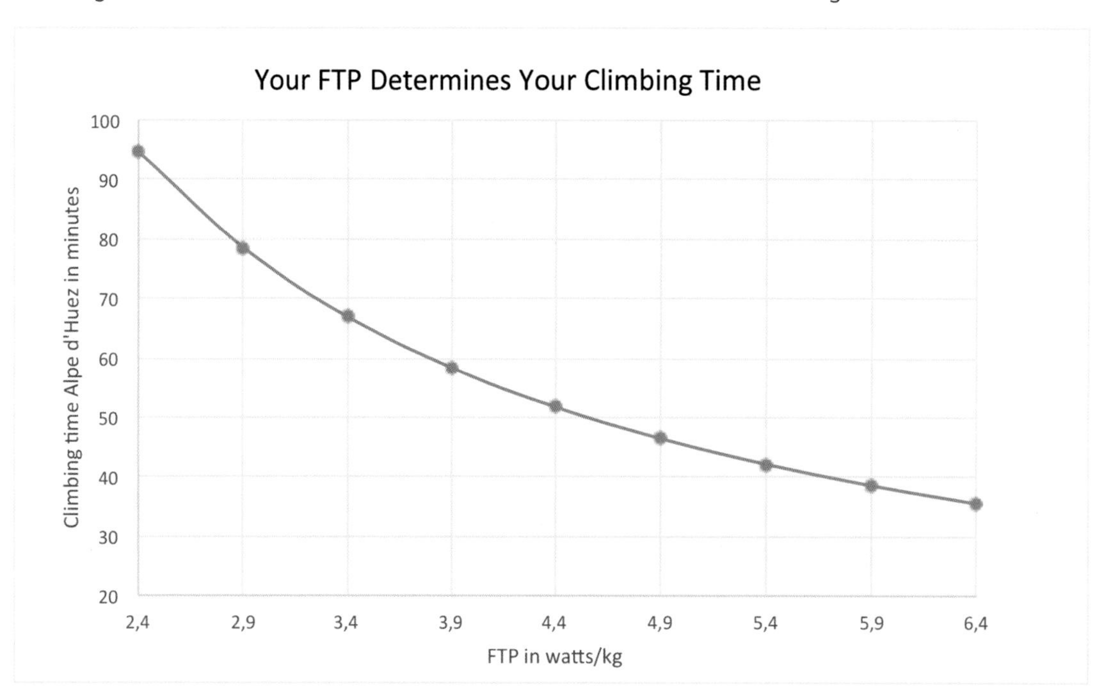

The figure shows that world-class cyclists with an FTP of 6.4 watts/kg could theoretically climb to the top of the Alpe d'Huez in 35 minutes and 34 seconds. This is somewhat less that the actual record of Marco Pantani (37:35), but the time of Pantani includes a 1.2 kilometer flat start of the climb and we should note that he did this is in the thin mountain air. In a later chapter, we will show that this thin air severely limits human performance. Later on in the book, we will also show how to make exact calculations, including the weight of the bike, all losses and the impact of the thin mountain air.

Here we give another illustration of the importance of the FTP. The box shows how you can calculate your vertical climbing speed as a function of your FTP. Please note that this climbing speed is lower than the one we calculated earlier for the VO_2 max. This makes sense as the FTP can be maintained for one hour and the VO_2 max for no more than 10 minutes.

Calculate Vertical Climbing Speed From FTP

$$v_v = 3.6/9.81 * FTP = 0.37 * FTP$$

Example: FTP = 4 watts/kg

$v_v = 0.37*4 = 1.47$ km/h

World-class cyclists can climb to the top of the Alpe d'Huez in less than 40 minutes.

17. THE RELATIONSHIP BETWEEN FTP AND VO_2 MAX

I thought of that while riding my bicycle. –Albert Einstein, on the theory of relativity

In the previous chapter we saw that the FTP is defined as the specific power output (in watts/kg) that can be maintained for one hour. The VO_2 max is defined as the maximum specific amount of oxygen that can be taken up by the body per unit of time (in ml O_2/kg/min). In practice, exercising at the level of the VO_2 max can be maintained for no longer than 10 minutes. Oxygen is used in our muscles to produce energy from the conversion of glycogen and fatty acids. This means that the VO_2 max is actually also a measure of power, as power is the amount of energy per unit of time. So how can we relate the FTP and the VO_2 max? How can we calculate one from the other? In order to understand this, we have to look at the biochemistry of the energy systems of the human engine once more.

Fast Eddy climbs the Alpe d'Huez. His VO_2 max of 55.4 ml/kg/min equals an FTP of 4 watts/kg.

The Energy Production of the Human Engine

In an earlier chapter, we discussed the four energy systems of the human engine. The table specifies the amount of energy (in kJ/mol) that can be produced by the four systems.

Energy Produced by the Four Human Engines	ΔG (kJ/mol)
ATP/CP	
ATP → ADP $C_{10}H_{16}N_5O_{13}P_3 \rightarrow C_{10}H_{15}N_5O_{10}P_2$	81
Anaerobic conversion of glycogen	
$C_6H_{12}O_6 + 3ADP \rightarrow 2C_3H_6O_3 + 3ATP$	227
Aerobic conversion of glycogen	
$C_6H_{12}O_6 + 6O_2 + 38ADP \rightarrow 6CO_2 + 6H_2O + 38ATP$	2,880
Aerobic conversion of fatty acids	
$CH_3(CH_2)_{14}COOH + 23O_2 + 130ADP \rightarrow 16CO_2 + 16H_2O + 130ATP$	9,853

We can convert the amount of energy in kJ/mol to the equivalent amount in kcal/gram by dividing by the molecular weight of the compound and then by 4.184 (the amount of kJ equivalent to 1 kcal). When we do this for the aerobic conversion of glycogen and fatty acids, the result is 3.82 and 9.18 kcal/gram respectively. In the literature on nutrition, these energy values are usually rounded off to 4 and 9 kcal/gram respectively.

The Energy Production Per Liter of O_2

If we want to calculate the power equivalence of the VO_2 max, we first need to determine how much energy is produced per liter of O_2. We have done this for both aerobic processes: the aerobic conversion of glycogen and the aerobic conversion of fatty acids. Consequently, we have divided the numbers from the above table by the stoichiometric number of moles of O_2 in the equation (6 for glycogen and 23 for fatty acids) and then by the molar volume of O_2 (24.3 l/mole at 25°C). The result is given in the table.

Energy Production Per Liter of O_2	ΔG
	(kJ/l O_2)
Aerobic conversion of glycogen	
$C_6H_{12}O_6 + 6O_2 + 38ADP \rightarrow 6CO_2 + 6H_2O + 38ATP$	19.76
Aerobic conversion of fatty acids	
$CH_3(CH_2)_{14}COOH + 23O_2 + 130ADP \rightarrow 16CO_2 + 16H_2O + 130ATP$	17.64

The table shows that the amount of energy produced per liter of O_2 is less for fatty acids than for glycogen. You might think that this is the explanation for the phenomenon of hitting the wall, but it is not. As we saw in an earlier chapter, the correct explanation for this is the fact that the conversion speed and consequently the power produced is much less for fatty acids than for glycogen.

The Power Output at the VO_2 max

From literature we know that at the VO_2 max level, the fuel mix consists of 90% glycogen and 10% fatty acids. Consequently, we can calculate the energy production at the VO_2 max as $0.9*19.76+0.1*17.64 = 19.55$ kJ/l O_2. Next, in order to calculate the power output at the VO_2 max (in watts/kg), all we have to do is to multiply the VO_2 max (in ml/kg/min) by 19.55 (kJ/l), then divide the result by 60 (conversion of minutes to seconds) and finally multiply the outcome with the metabolic efficiency of 25%. The box gives the formula and an example.

Power Output at VO_2 max

watts/kg = $0.25*VO_2$ max*19.55/60

Example VO_2 max = 55.4 ml/kg/min

watts/kg = 0.082*55.4 = 4.54 watts/kg

The example is again valid for our Fast Eddy, who has a VO_2 max of 55.4 ml/kg/min. We remark that the specific power (4.54 watts/kg) at his VO_2 max is obviously higher than his FTP (4 watts/kg), as the FTP can be maintained for one hour instead of 10 minutes.

The Relationship Between FTP and VO_2 max

As we saw earlier the power output during one hour (the FTP) is equal to 88% of the power output at 10 minutes (the VO_2 max). Consequently, there is a fixed relationship between FTP and VO_2 max, which can be easily calculated, as shown in the box.

Relationship Between FTP and VO_2 max

$FTP = 0.88 * 0.25 * VO_2 max * 19.55/60$

$FTP = 0.072 * VO_2 max$

Example: VO_2 max = 55.4 ml/kg/min

FTP = 0.072*55.2 = 4 watts/kg

The example is again valid for our Fast Eddy, who has a VO_2 max of 55.4 and an FTP of 4 watts/kg.

The figure below finally shows the relationship between FTP and VO_2 max for all relevant values of FTP (between 2.4 and 6.4 watts/kg) and VO_2 max (between 33 and 89 ml/kg/min). As we saw earlier the present ultimate limits of the power of the human engine are 6.4 watts/kg and 88 ml/kg/min. These numbers are valid for men; for women the limits are 5.7 watts/kg and 79 ml/kg/min.

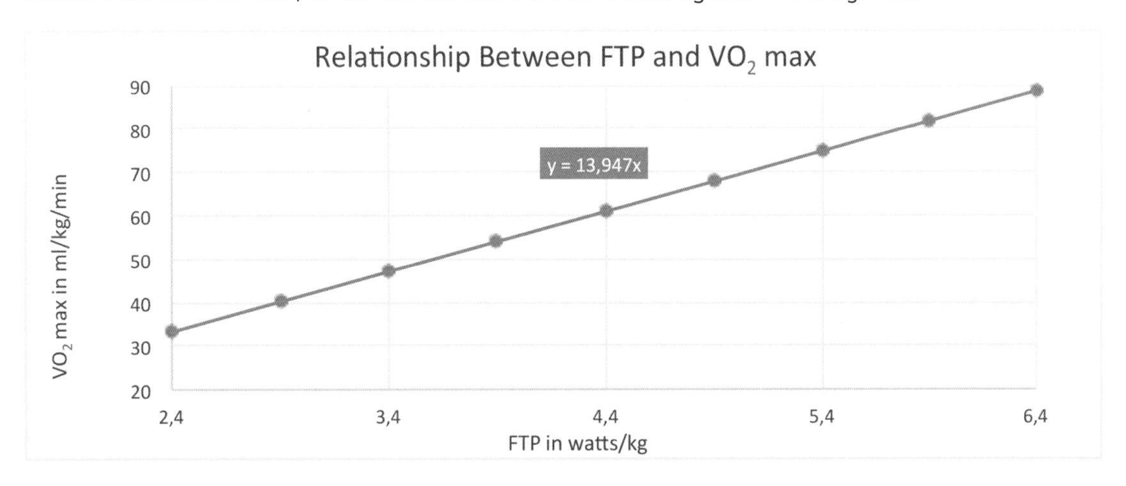

PART IV

HOW FAST CAN YOU BIKE?

18. WORLD-CLASS CYCLISTS AND CYCLING TOURISTS

The race is won by the rider who can suffer the most.
–Eddy Merckx

What better way to compare our own performances than with those of world-class cyclists like Chris Froome, Alberto Contador and Vincenzo Nibali? The unparalleled performances of the great champions of the past, including Eddy Merckx (whom we believe to be the all-time greatest), also provide a source of inspiration to the legion of cycling tourists.

Exactly How Good Are World-Class Cyclists?

In an earlier chapter, we explained that the best parameter to compare cycling performances is the equivalent FTP (in watts or watts/kg) of the cyclist. We also showed that the maximum FTP of male world-class cyclists is 6.4 watts/kg. This value of 6.4 watts/kg is consistent with both the world records in athletics and the theoretical biochemical energy production of the aerobic energy systems of the human engine. For women the maximum FTP is 5.7 watts/kg.

How Fast Can You Cycle With Your FTP?

What does an FTP of 6.4 watts/kg mean? How fast can you cycle with such a human engine, both on the flat and in the mountains? And how much slower are cycling tourists and our hypothetical Fast Eddy?

In this chapter, we present an initial analysis of the differences. We will investigate, now and also in the next chapters, two cases:

1. A time trial of 40 kilometers on a flat course
2. The famous climb to the top of the Alpe d'Huez (14.45 kilometers with an altitude gain of 1,041 meters)

Performance Classes for Men and Women

In this chapter and in the remainder of this book, we will compare performances based on the performance classes as shown in the tables below. These tables are based on a similar system used in athletics and matches well with other systems such as the power profiles.

Performance Classes for Men		**FTP**
Level		**(watts/kg)**
World class	100%	6.4
International	90%	5.8
National	80%	5.1
Regional	70%	4.5
Tourist	60%	3.8
Fair	50%	3.2
Untrained	40%	2.6
Poor	30%	1.9
Very poor	20%	1.4

Performance Classes for Women		**FTP**
Level		**(watts/kg)**
World class	100%	5.7
International	90%	5.1
National	80%	4.6
Regional	70%	4.0
Tourist	60%	3.4
Fair	50%	2.8
Untrained	40%	2.3
Poor	30%	1.7
Very poor	20%	1.1

Race Time at a 40-Kilometer Time Trial

We have calculated the race times of the various performance classes and of Fast Eddy. We did this for the standard conditions, which we specified earlier (c_dA = 0.3 m^2, c_r = 0.004, body weight = 75 kg, bike weight = 8.8 kg, temperature = 20°C). The results are given in the figure and table below. We see that the world-class cyclists can maintain a speed of 47.84 km/h, so their race time at the 40 kilometer is 50.2 minutes. Cycling tourists can maintain a speed of 39.81 km/h, so their race time is 60.3 minutes. Consequently, they cycle some 17% slower than the world-class cyclists. However, their FTP is some 40% less! This corroborates that on flat terrain the FTP is related to the third exponent of the speed.

Fast Eddy performs in the class of cycling tourists with a speed of 40.41 km/h and a race time of 59.4 minutes. In the next chapters we will see how much faster or slower he gets when the conditions change.

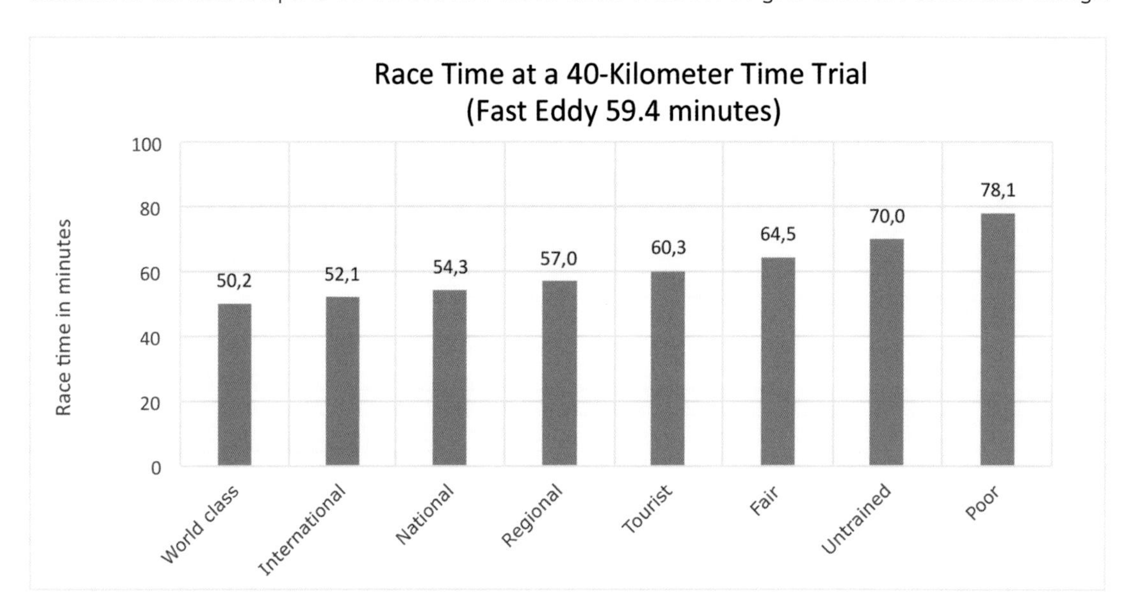

Men's 40-Kilometer Time Trial			
Level	FTP	v	T
	(watts/kg)	(km/h)	(min)
World class	6.4	47.84	50.2
International	5.8	46.08	52.1
National	5.1	44.18	54.3
Regional	4.5	42.10	57.0
Tourist	3.8	39.81	60.3
Fair	3.2	37.23	64.5
Untrained	2.6	34.27	70.0
Poor	1.9	30.72	78.1
Very poor	1.4	27.15	88.4

Performance at the Climb to the Top of the Alpe d'Huez

Again, we calculated the race times of the various performance classes and for the standard conditions. In this case this included a gradient of 7.41% (1,041-meter altitude gain over a distance of 14.45 kilometers). In these calculations, we did not yet take into account the impact of the thin mountain air. The thin air has two effects. The advantage is that the air resistance is lower as a result of the lower density of the air. The disadvantage is that the oxygen uptake capacity of the body is reduced and consequently so is the FTP. The net impact of both effects is negative, so your climbing speed will be lower as we will show in a later chapter.

As the figure and table below show, the world-class cyclists can climb to the top of the Alpe d'Huez in some 37.0 minutes. Marco Pantani's current record time is slightly higher with 37.35. The difference can be explained by the negative impact of the thin mountain air. In a later chapter, we will analyse the climbing times to the Alpe d'Huez in more detail. There we will also answer the question whether Marco achieved his record within the maximum, clean limit of an FTP of 6.4 watts/kg.

Cycling tourists can climb the Alpe d'Huez in 57.8 minutes. Consequently, they are 36% slower than the world-class cyclists. We see that the difference is much bigger than in the 40-kilometer time trial. In the mountains, the time difference is almost the same as the FTP difference. This makes sense as the climbing speed is linearly proportional to the FTP.

Finally, we mention that Fast Eddy reaches the top in 55.7 minutes. In later chapters, we will show how much faster he can climb if he manages to reduce his body weight or the weight of his bike.

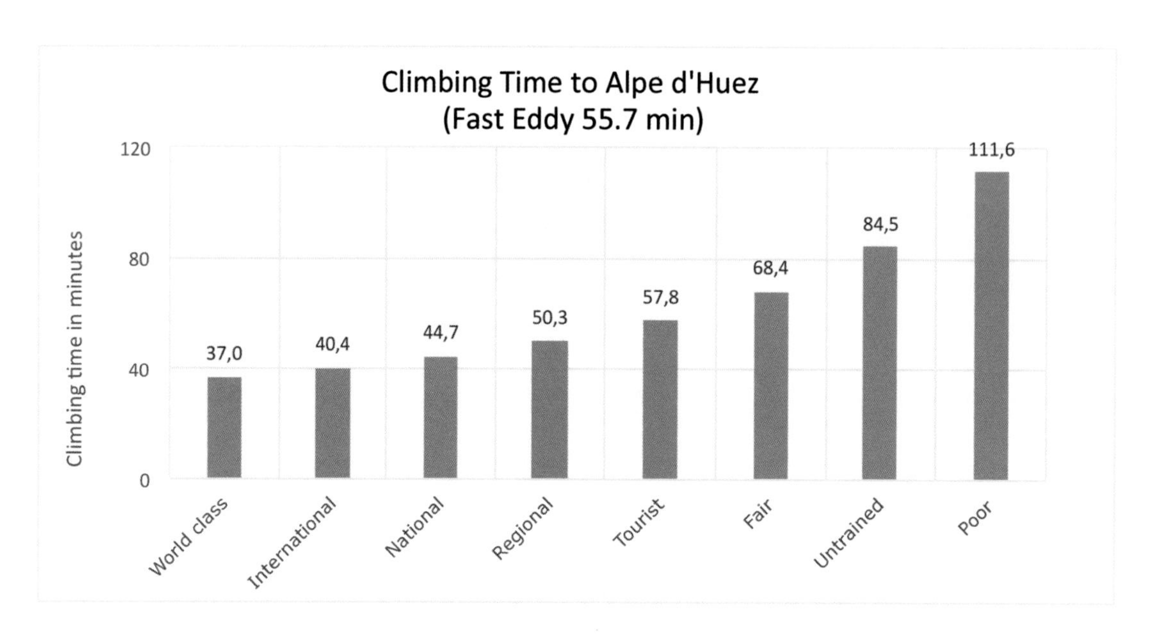

Men's Climb to Alpe d'Huez			
Level	FTP	v	T
	(watts/kg)	(km/h)	(min)
World class	6.4	23.44	37.0
International	5.8	21.47	40.4
National	5.1	19.41	44.7
Regional	4.5	17.25	50.3
Tourist	3.8	15.01	57.8
Fair	3.2	12.68	68.4
Untrained	2.6	10.26	84.5
Poor	1.9	7.77	111.6
Very poor	1.4	5.70	152.1

Cycling tourists can climb the Alpe d'Huez in 57.8 minutes. Consequently, they are 36% slower than world-class cyclists like Chris Froome.

19. THE PERFORMANCE OF THE LADIES

You can't buy happiness, but you can buy a bicycle and that's pretty close.

In the past, only the performances of the male cyclists received attention from the media. Recently, however, the interest in the performance of the ladies has grown, partly as a result of the dominance and impressive string of victories of Dutch cyclist Marianne Vos. In this chapter, we will look more closely at the performances of the female cyclists. We will investigate whether Marianne Vos is such a unique talent that we need to reconsider our views on the limits of human power. Also we will look into the differences between the performance of men and women and discuss the impact of the higher body fat percentage (BFP) of women.

The Maximum FTP of Women

In an earlier chapter, we learned that the present ultimate limit of the power of women is equivalent to an FTP of 5.7 watts/kg. This is some 11% lower than the ultimate limit of the FTP of men, which is 6.4 watts/kg. We believe that this difference is mostly caused by the higher BFP of women. The BFP of elite female athletes is typically some 8-10% higher than that of male elites. Additionally, the muscle mass and the power of the muscles are thought to be somewhat lower for women.

The difference of 11% and the maximum FTP of 5.7 watts/kg is very reproducible. In our calculations on the world records in athletics, we found similar results for all word records between 3,000 meter and the marathon. Paula Radcliffe's exceptional marathon record is equivalent to an FTP of 5.76 watts/kg. We consider this a unique performance which is not likely to be equaled in the near future. Although we do not have specific data on the FTP of Marianne Vos, we do not think it will exceed Paula's as many of Marianne's victories resulted from sprint finishes with other competitors. So, in this chapter we will adopt 5.7 watts/kg as the maximum FTP for women.

The Dutch world-class lady cyclist Marianne Vos in the San Francesco Al Campo time trial of the 2011 Giro d'Italia Internationale Femminile.

Performance Classes of Women

Similar to the men, we have defined performance classes for women in the table below. Again, we will analyze the performances of the various classes at the 40-kilometer time trial and at the climb to the Alpe d'Huez.

Performance Classes for Women		FTP
Level		(watts/kg)
World class	100%	5.7
International	90%	5.1
National	80%	4.6
Regional	70%	4.0
Tourist	60%	3.4
Fair	50%	2.8
Untrained	40%	2.3
Poor	30%	1.7
Very poor	20%	1.1

Race Time at 40-Kilometer Time Trial

We have calculated the race times of the various performance classes. We did this for the standard conditions that we specified earlier (c_dA = 0.3 m^2, c_r = 0.004, bike weight 8.8 kg, temperature 20°C). For the ladies, we used a standard body weight of 65 kg. The results are given in the figure and table below. We see that the elite ladies can maintain a speed of 43.81 km/h, so their race time at the 40 kilometer is 54.8 minutes. Consequently, the ladies cycle 8% slower than the men. We should realize that their total FTP is 23% lower as their body weight is 13% lower than that of the men and their specific FTP is 11% lower. Once more, we see that the speed difference is much less than the power difference. Obviously, this is caused by the fact that the power is related to the cube of the speed.

Lady tourists can maintain a speed of 36.43 km/h, so their race time is 65.9 minutes. Consequently, they cycle some 17% slower than the elite ladies. Fast Eddy can cycle at the level of national class ladies with his speed of 40.41 km/h and race time of 59.4 minutes.

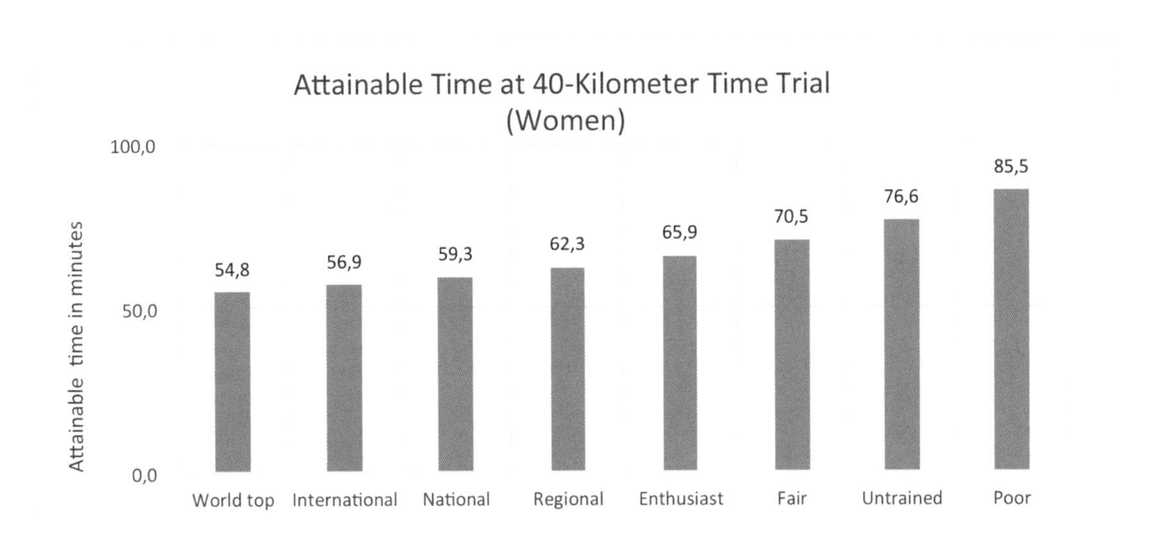

Women at Flat Course			
Level	**FTP**	**v**	**T 40 km**
	(watts/kg)	**(km/h)**	**(min)**
World class	5.7	43.81	54.8
International	5.1	42.19	56.9
National	4.6	40.44	59.3
Regional	4.0	38.54	62.3
Tourist	3.4	36.43	65.9
Fair	2.8	34.06	70.5
Untrained	2.3	31.33	76.6
Poor	1.7	28.07	85.5
Very poor	1.1	23.57	101.8

Race Time to the Top of the Alpe d'Huez

Again, we calculated the race times of the various performance classes and the standard conditions. In this case we included a gradient of 7.41% (a 1,041-meter altitude gain over a distance of 14.45 kilometers). In these calculations, we did not yet take into account the impact of the thin mountain air. The thin air has two effects. The advantage is that the air resistance is lower as a result of the lower density of the air. The disadvantage is that the oxygen uptake capacity of the body is reduced and conseqeuntely so is the FTP. The net impact of both effects is negative, thus your climbing speed is lower as we will show in a later chapter.

As the figure and table below show, the world-class ladies can climb to the top of the Alpe d'Huez in some 41.7 minutwes with a speed of 20.77 km/h. This is only 11% slower than the elite men cyclists. The difference is the same as the difference in FTP (in watts/kg), so this confirms that the lower body weight of the women does not affect their performance in the mountains. Uphill your performance is determined by your FTP in watts/kg!

Lady cycling tourists can climb to the top of the Alpe d'Huez in 65.9 minutes. Consequently, they are 37% slower than the world-class lady cyclists. We see that the difference is much bigger than in the 40-kilometer time trial and almost equal to the 40% difference in FTP. In the mountains, the time difference is almost the same as the FTP difference. This makes sense as the climbing speed is linearly proportional to the FTP.

Contrary to the flat time trial, our Fast Eddy cannot keep up with the national level ladies. At the flat, Fast Eddy compensates for his lower FTP with his higher body weight. In the mountains, only the FTP determines his performance, so he loses to the ladies with a higher FTP.

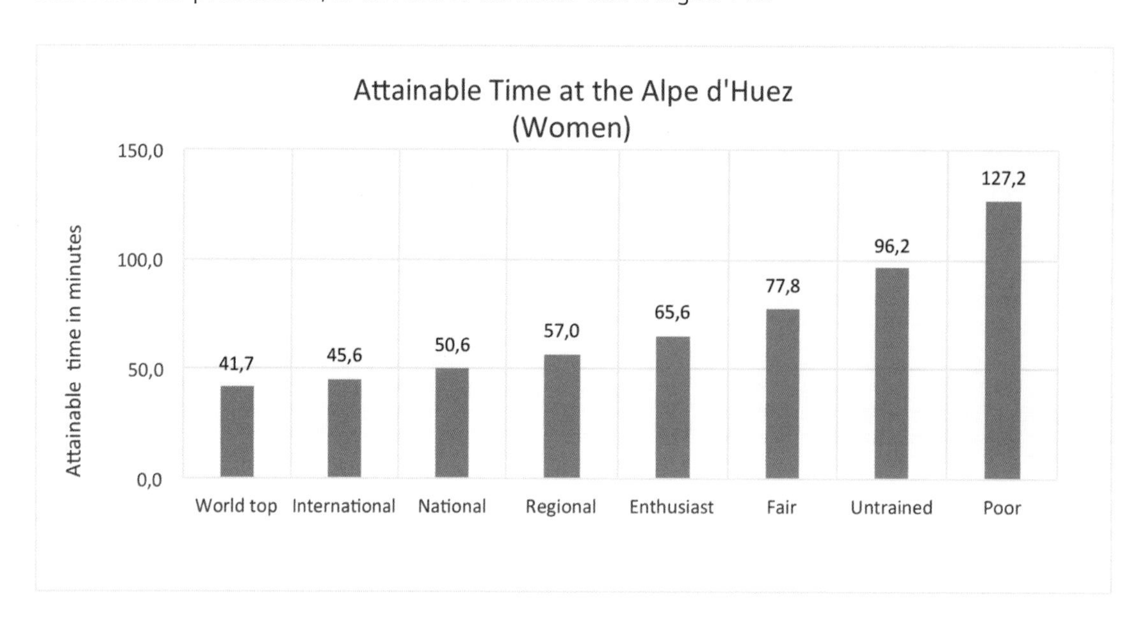

Times at the Alpe d'Huez (Women)			
Level	FTP	v	T Alpe
	(watts/kg)	(km/h)	(min)
World class	5.7	20.77	41.7
International	5.1	18.99	45.6
National	4.6	17.14	50.6
Regional	4.0	15.22	57.0
Tourist	3.4	13.22	65.6
Fair	2.8	11.15	77.8
Untrained	2.3	9.01	96.2
Poor	1.7	6.82	127.2
Very poor	1.1	4.42	196.3

Marianne Vos and Lizzie Armitstead in the 2014 World Championships (Women Elite) road race in Ponferrada, Spain.

20. THE IMPACT OF YOUR FTP

When it's hurting you, that's when you make a difference.
–Eddy Merckx

Your race time is determined by the power of your human engine and the sum of the rolling resistance, the air resistance, the climbing resistance and the mechanical resistance. In the following chapters, we will calculate how fast you can cycle with your human engine in different conditions.

As we saw earlier, the power of your human engine can best be characterized by your FTP. You can determine your FTP with a power meter, both on the road and in the laboratory. Fortunately, you do not have to cycle all-out for one hour; you can limit the test to 10 or 20 minutes. After the test, you can then calculate your FTP by multiplying your power output (in watts/kg) by 0.93 (in case of a 20-minute test) or by 0.88 (for a 10-minute test).

The Relationship Between FTP and VO_2 max

In an earlier chapter, we derived the following relationship between the FTP (in watts/kg) and the VO_2 max (in ml/kg/min):

ADV = 0.072*VO_2 max

This means that if you know your VO_2 max (e.g., from a laboratory test), you can calculate your FTP. The maximum value of the FTP of 6.4 watts/kg is equivalent to a VO_2 max of some 88 ml/kg/min.

How Fast Can You Race With Your FTP?

Of course, large differences exist in the FTP values and consequently the race times of world-class cyclists and cycling tourists. The FTP of world-class cyclists is around 6.4 watts/kg, whereas normal values for young men are only 3.1-4.2 watts/kg. Obviously, these differences will have a big impact on the race times.

Once again, we will look at ideal conditions and the two cases:

1. A time trial of 40 kilometers on a flat course.
2. The famous climb to the top of the Alpe d'Huez (an altitude gain of 1,041 meters over 14.45 kilometers).

Race Time at the 40-Kilometer Time Trial

We have calculated the race times as a function of the FTP. We did this for the standard conditions that we specified earlier (c_dA = 0.3 m^2, c_r = 0.004, body weight = 75 kg, bike weight = 8.8 kg, temperature = 20°C). The results are given in the figures for FTP values between 1.4 and 6.4 watts/kg. As expected, we see that the speed increases much less than proportionally with the FTP (actually only to an exponent of 0.371). This exponent matches well with the theoretical formula of the air resistance (exponent of 0.333). This confirms that in a flat race the impact of the rolling resistance, the climbing resistance and the mechanical resistance is small.

The figures also show the potential benefit that you could obtain by training (possible increase of FTP by 10-30%) or losing body weight (possible increase of FTP by 5-15%). The reader is welcome to use our calculator at www.thesecretofcycling.com to calculate the results for himself.

The figures also show that our Fast Eddy with his FTP of 4 watts/kg will never be able to reach the FTP and the race times of world-class cyclists, not even with the most fanatical training.

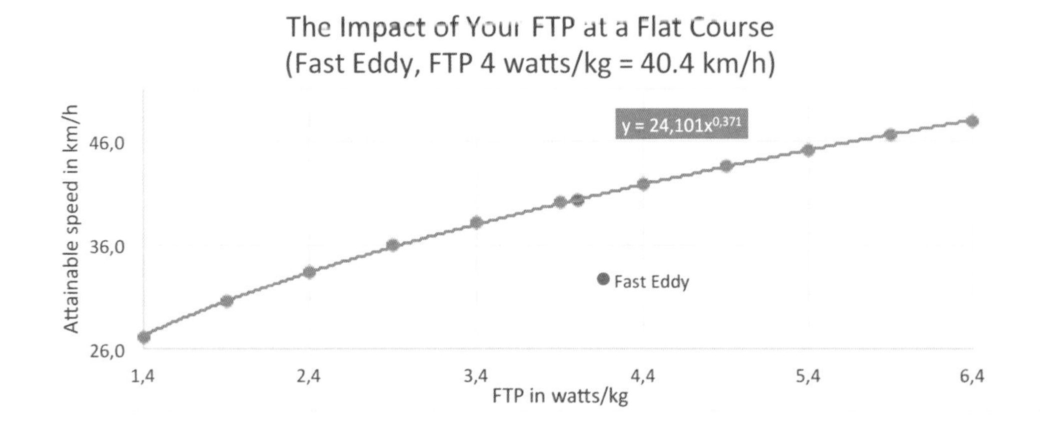

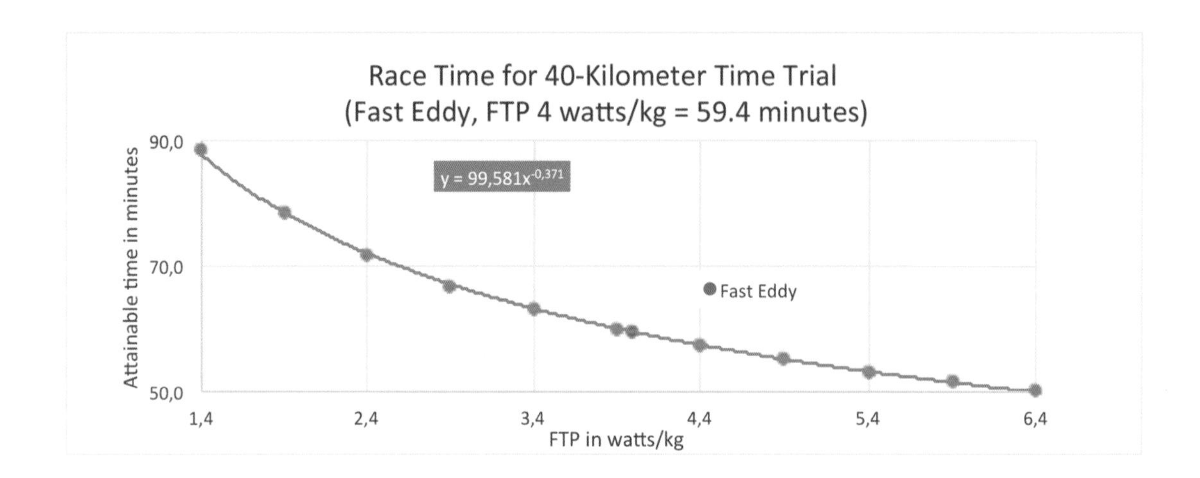

Performance at the Climb to the Top of the Alpe d'Huez

We calculated the race times as a function of the FTP and in the standard conditions. In this case this included a gradient of 7.41% (a 1,04-meter altitude gain over a distance of 14.45 kilometers). In these calculations, we did not yet take into account the impact of the thin mountain air. This will be done in a later chapter.

The results are shown in the figures below for FTP values between 1.4 watts/kg and 6.4 watts/kg. As could be expected, the climbing speed is linearly proportional to the FTP (i.e., the exponent is exactly 1.0). This is in accordance with the formula for the climbing resistance, so we can conclude that the other resistances play a negligable role.

The figures also show the benefit that you could obtain by training (possible increase of FTP by 10-30%) or by losing body weight (possible increase of FTP by 5-15%). The reader is welcome to use our calculator at www.thesecretofcycling.com to calculate the results for himself.

We indicated the performance of Fast Eddy with red dots. In later chapters, we will see how much faster or slower Eddy will get when he manages to shed body fat or when he faces a head wind.

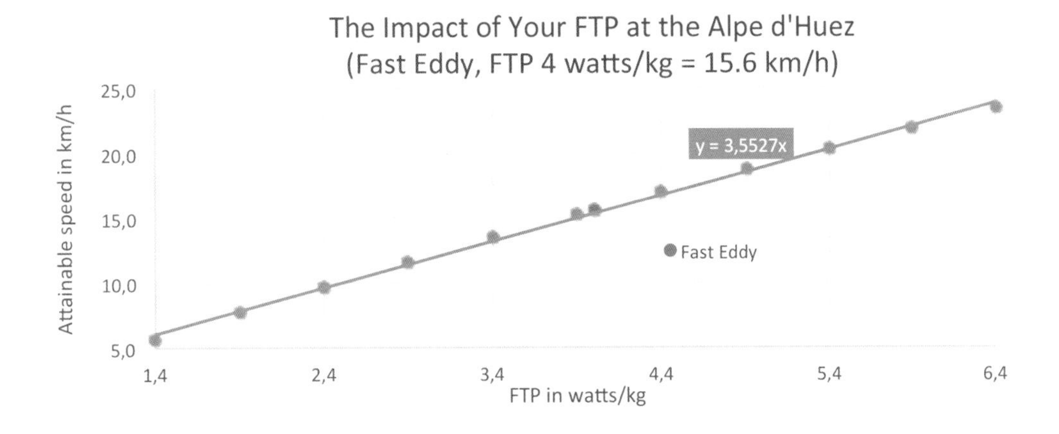

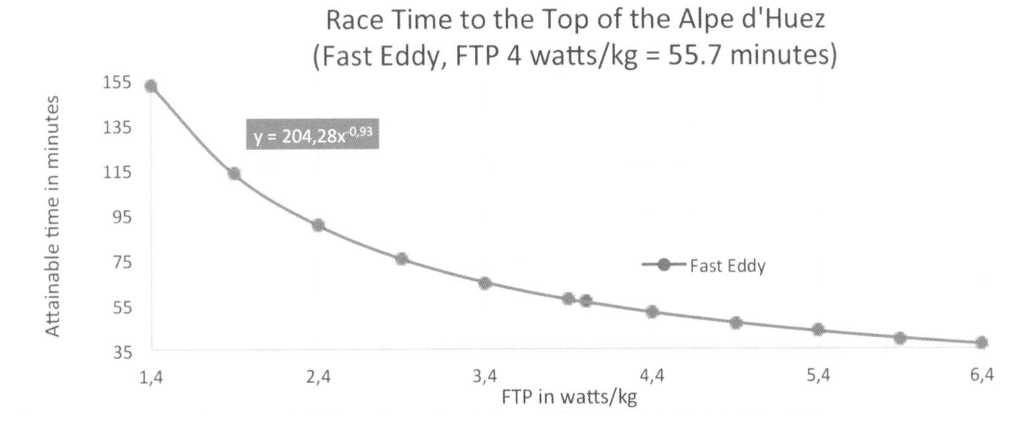

Britain's gold medalist Bradley Wiggins (center), Germany's silver medalist Tony Martin (left) and Britain's bronze medalist Christopher Froome (right) at the podium of the Men's Individual Time Trial during the London 2012 Olympic Games.

21. THE IMPACT OF TIME AND DISTANCE

It never gets easier, you just go faster. —Greg LeMond

We all know that our speed reduces when we have to cycle a larger distance, forcing us to maintain our effort during a longer time. In an earlier chapter, we already discussed this power–time relationship. There we also introduced Pete Riegel's famous running formula:

$$v_2/v_1 = (t_2/t_1)^{-0,07}$$

In his formula t represents the time and v is the speed. So the formula says quite simply that when we have to maintain our effort twice as long, the speed (in running) decreases by 5% ($2^{-0.07} = 0.95$).

Riegel's formula describes the impact of time (and thus distance) accurately for periods of ten minutes and longer. As power is directly proportional to speed, we concluded that the power–time relationship can also be expressed accurately by Riegel's formula.

The decline in power with time as expressed by Riegel's formula can be explained by the change of the fuel mix of the human engine. At longer distances, the speed is slower, so the muscles automatically switch to a fuel mix with more fatty acids.

For time periods shorter than ten minutes, the power output is higher than described by Riegel's formula. This is caused by the increasing share of the anaerobic systems in the fuel mix. Consequently, we were able to derive the table below, which describes the power–time relationship.

We note that this power–time relationship is valid for normal cyclists with a normal fatigue resistance. In practice, some deviations can occur, in particular for:

- Sprinters with a limited fatigue resistance
- Endurance cyclists with exceptional fatigue resistance

In a later chapter, we will discuss the impact of fatigue resistance in more detail.

Time (minutes)	Power (% of FTP)
0.08	385
1	201
5	125
10	113
20	108
40	103
60	100
120	95
240	91

The Impact of Time on the Power Output of Fast Eddy

Fast Eddy has an FTP of 4 watts/kg. Consequently, during ten minutes his power output can be 1.13*4 = 4.52 watts/kg. The figure gives the power–time relationship of Fast Eddy.

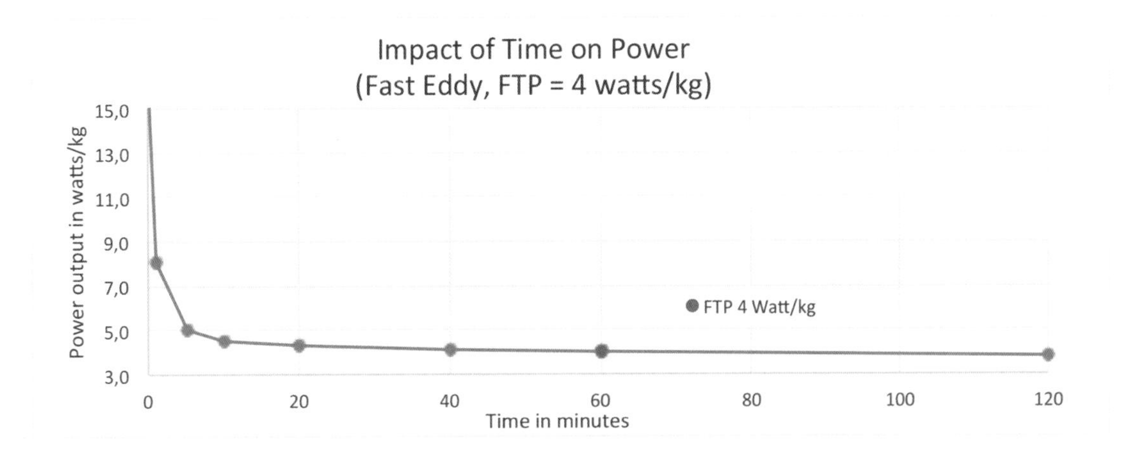

The Impact of Time on the Speed at a Flat Course

In an earlier chapter, we calculated that Fast Eddy can cycle 40.41 kilometers in one hour. Obviously, during shorter times, he can mobilize more power and cycle faster. The speed–time relationship as calculated with our program is given in the figure below.

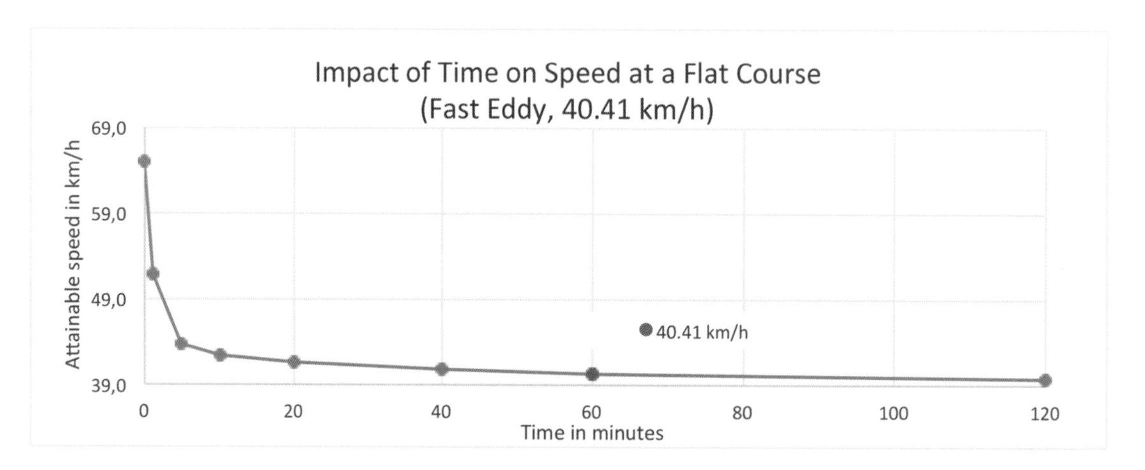

The Impact of Time on the Climbing Speed at the Alpe d'Huez

In an earlier chapter, we calculated that Fast Eddy can maintain a speed of 15.58 km/h at the climb to the Alpe d'Huez during one hour. Obviously, during shorter times, he can mobilize more power and cycle faster. The speed–time relationship as calculated with our program is given in the figure below. We see that in the mountains the relative increase of his speed is higher than on a flat course. This is caused by the fact that uphill the speed, and thus the air resistance, is lower.

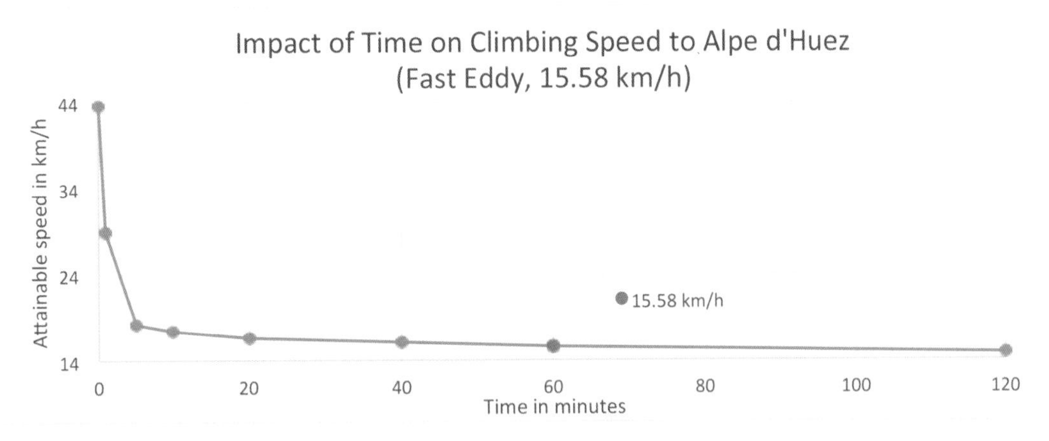

At longer distances the cycling speed is slower.

22. THE IMPACT OF YOUR AGE

You don't give up cycling because you get old; you get old because you give up cycling.

Unfortunately, we all have to face the fact that our performance declines as we grow older. Long-distance runners peak at an age between 25 and 35 years. Above the age of 35, the performances inevitably decline slowly. Consequently, the World Master Athletics (WMA) uses age-grading tables[38] to compare performances of year classes. These tables show in general an annual decline in performance of some 0.8%.

The Statistical Analysis of Elmer Sterken

Professor Elmer Sterken is the rector of the University of Groningen, the Netherlands. His field of expertise is monetary economics, but he is also a committed long-distance runner and an expert on sports statistics. In 2003, he published a paper on age grading[39], which included a detailed statistical analysis of the performance as a function of age. He studied the extensive statistical database of the US Long Distance Running Association that contains many tens of thousands of race times. Using this database, he found a clear relationship between age and performance for both men and women. The figure shows the resulting age-grading factors at the 5K for men between the ages of 5 and 95.

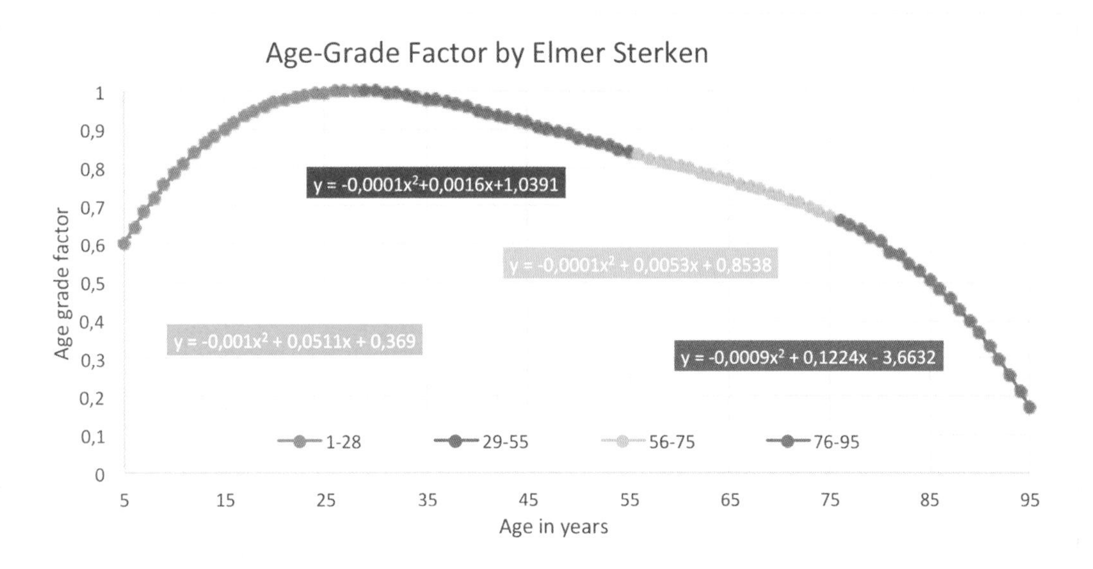

What Does This Mean for the Performance at Different Ages?

We have devided the tables from Sterken's paper into four segments and determined the regression equations as shown in the figure. Some interesting conclusions are:

1. The peak performance is found around the age of 30 years (age-grading factor 1.0).
2. The performance decreases gradually above the age of 35 years. Initially, the annual decline is 0.8%. At an age of 45, the resulting age-grade factor is 0.9. At 60 years, the age grade factor is 0.80.
3. Above the age of 75 years, the annual decline increases more rapidly, even beyond 5% at 85 years and more.
4. In general the performance decline at higher ages is somewhat higher than in accordance with the WMA tables. Apparently, the WMA is too optimistic on the attainable performance by the elder masters.

Obviously, the impact of age is substantial and irreversible. This is the reason for the age-grading system in the masters athletics. Internationally, masters are classified in 5-year age classes (35-39, 40-44, 45-49 and so on). Even with these age classes, the younger master has a significant advantage over his elder peers. Within a 5-year class, this advantage is $(1.008)^5$, which is equivalent to 4%.

Of course, these statistical relationships do not hold for everybody. The annual decline of 0.8% is an average for masters who train and race seriously. Less serious runners may face an annual decline of 1.0% or more. On the other hand, exceptional talents like the famous Canadian multiple world record holder Ed Whitlock managed to limit the annual decline to levels of 0.6% or even less up to a high age.

What Is the Impact of Age on the Race Time at the 40-Kilometer Time Trial?

We have used Sterken's equations to calculate the impact of age on the FTP. As the FTP of our Fast Eddy is 4 watts/kg at the age of 40, we could calculate his theoretical FTP at other ages. Next we calculated the speed and the race time at the 40-kilometer time trial. The results are shown in the figure and table below. In an earlier chapter, we calculated already that Fast Eddy can maintain a speed of 40.41 km/h during one hour, so his race time at the time trial is 59.4 minutes. The table and figure below show that his time is equivalent to a time of 58.2 minutes for someone at the age of 30. As he gets older Fast Eddy will have to accept the fact that his race time will increase up to 62.7 minutes as he reaches the age of 60. We believe this is a proper and interesting way to compare performances at different ages.

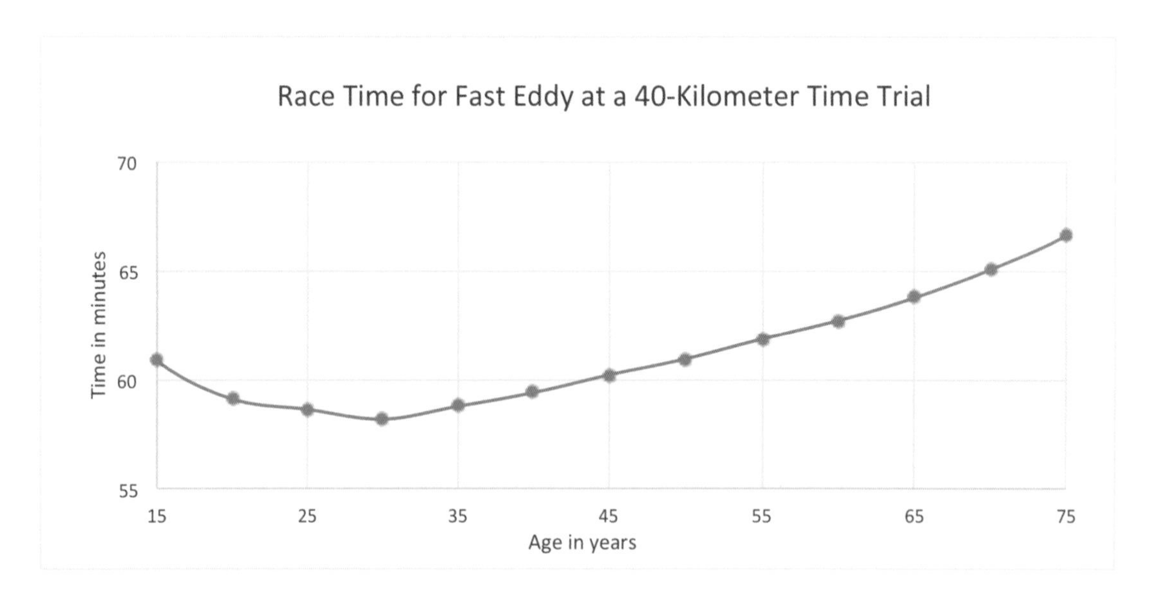

Impact of Age on 40-Kilometer Time Trial			
Age	FTP	T	Difference
(year)	(km/h)	(min)	(sec)
15	39.44	60.9	88
20	40.60	59.1	-17
25	40.93	58.6	-46
30	41.25	58.2	-72
35	40.84	58.8	-37
40	40.41	59.4	0
45	39.86	60.2	49
50	39.38	60.9	93
55	38.79	61.9	148
60	38.26	62.7	200
65	37.63	63.8	263
70	36.88	65.1	340
75	36.01	66.6	435

Of course these calculations are somewhat hypothetical. Nevertheless, they show a very clear picture. Good race times are possible in a broad age range, roughly between 15-55 years. Beyond the age of 60, the decline becomes more progressive.

The Impact of Age on the Climbing Time to the Alpe d'Huez

Of course, we also calculated the climbing times of Fast Eddy to the top of Alpe d'Huez (see the figure and table). We see that the climbing time of Eddy at the age of 40 (55.7 minutes) is equivalent to a climbing time of 52.9 minutes at the age of 30 and a climbing time of 74.5 minutes for a lively senior of 75.

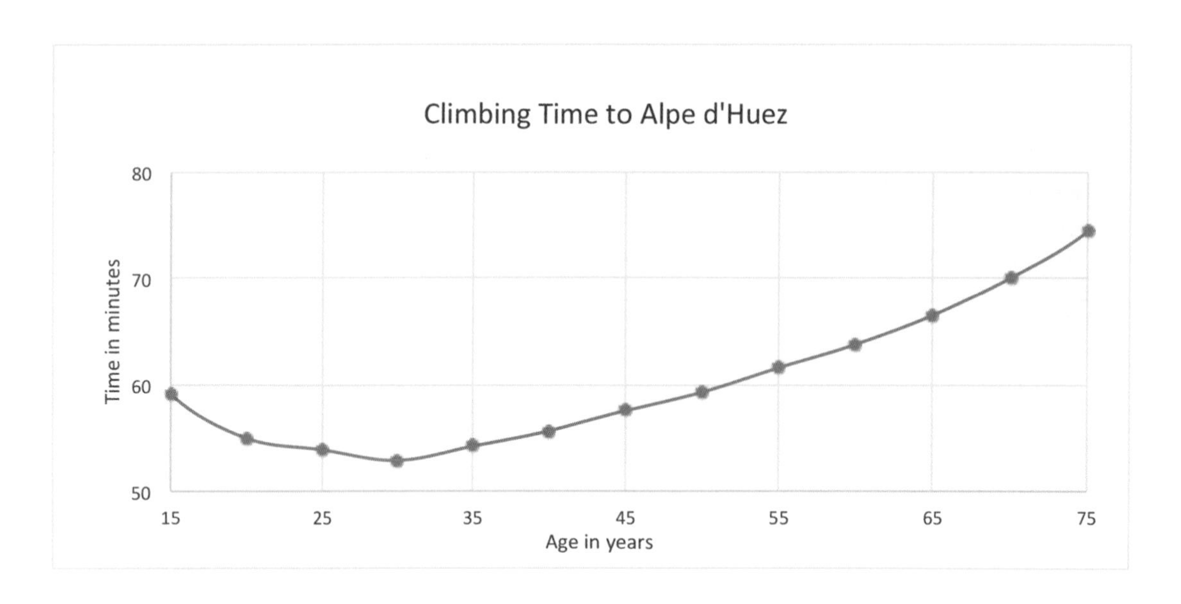

Impact of Age on the Alpe d'Huez			
Age	FTP	T	Difference
(year)	(km/h)	(min)	(sec)
15	14.66	59.1	210
20	15.77	55.0	-40
25	16.09	53.9	-106
30	16.40	52.9	-166
35	15.99	54.2	-87
40	15.58	55.7	0
45	15.06	57.6	116
50	14.61	59.4	222
55	14.06	61.6	360
60	13.58	63.8	490
65	13.02	66.6	655
70	12.38	70.0	864
75	11.65	74.5	1128

The passion for cycling is everlasting and you can compete with cyclists in your own age category.

23. THE PERFORMANCE INDEX

Nothing compares to the simple pleasure of riding a bike.
–John F. Kennedy

Let's say you have climbed to the top of the Alpe d'Huez in 55.7 minutes, just like our Fast Eddy. How good or how bad is this actually? How should you compare your performance with that of others?

Calculate Your FTP

Obviously, the first thing you should do is correct your performance for the conditions of the race, like the weather (temperature, wind, rain), the distance, your bike and the course (including the gradient). This is where you can use the concept of the FTP. The FTP is an objective parameter that can be used to compare one performance with another, as it is corrected for the conditions of the race. In a previous chapter, we have shown how you can use the cycling formula to calculate your FTP from the race result. You can use our calculator at www.thesecretofcycling.com to do this and calculate your own FTP from the results of your race. Your FTP will tell you how good your performance has been, taking into account the conditions of the race.

Compare Your FTP to World-Class Level

Let's suppose that you have climbed to the top of Alpe d'Huez in ideal conditions. In that case your FTP will be the same as our Fast Eddy, 4.00 watts/kg. When we compare this value to the world-class level of 6.40 watts/kg, the ratio is 4.00/6.40 = 62.5%. What does this number tell us? In a previous chapter, we have shown that cyclists can be classified in accordance with the table below:

Power Levels (Men)		FTP
Class		(watts/kg)
World class	100%	6.4
International	90%	5.8
National	80%	5.1
Regional	70%	4.5
Tourist	60%	3.8
Fair	50%	3.2
Untrained	40%	2.6
Poor	30%	1.9
Very poor	20%	1.4

Consequently, the performance of our Fast Eddy (and you) can be classified as tourist. The performance index is defined as the ratio of your FTP to world-class level, so in this case your performance index would be 62.5%.

Correct for Your Age

As we saw earlier, age has a big impact on the performance. So, when a 60-year-old cyclist climbs the Alpe d'Huez in 55.7 minutes, his performance index should be higher than that of a 30-year-old cyclist with the same time. In order to make a fair comparison, we should correct for the age. We will do this, using Sterken's equations which we saw in an earlier chapter. We have prepared the table and figure below for this purpose. In the table, the first column gives the maximum value of the FTP as a function of age at the world-class level. The other columns give the classes of international, national, regional, tourist and fair level. We can see that when someone climbs the Alpe d'Huez in 55.7 minutes at the age of 60, his performance index would be 4.00/5.20 = 77%. A 75-year-old cyclist with a 55.7 minutes climbing time would have a performance index of 91%, so this cyclist would be at the international level!

Performance Index as a Function of Age and Class						
Age	Max. FTP	FTP 90%	FTP 80%	FTP 70%	FTP 60%	FTP 50%
(years)	(watts/kg)	(watts/kg)	(watts/kg)	(watts/kg)	(watts/kg)	(watts/kg)
10	4.84	4.35	3.87	3.39	2.90	2.42
15	5.64	5.08	4.51	3.95	3.38	2.82
20	6.11	5.50	4.89	4.28	3.67	3.06
25	6.25	5.62	5.00	4.37	3.75	3.12
30	6.40	5.76	5.12	4.48	3.84	3.20
35	6.22	5.60	4.98	4.35	3.73	3.11
40	6.03	5.43	4.82	4.22	3.62	3.02
45	5.81	5.23	4.65	4.07	3.49	2.90
50	5.56	5.00	4.44	3.89	3.33	2.78
55	5.39	4.85	4.32	3.78	3.24	2.70
60	5.20	4.68	4.16	3.64	3.12	2.60
65	4.97	4.47	3.97	3.48	2.98	2.48
70	4.70	4.23	3.76	3.29	2.82	2.35
75	4.41	3.97	3.53	3.09	2.64	2.20
80	4.01	3.61	3.21	2.80	2.40	2.00

Cycling is fun and good for your health, no matter what level or intensity!

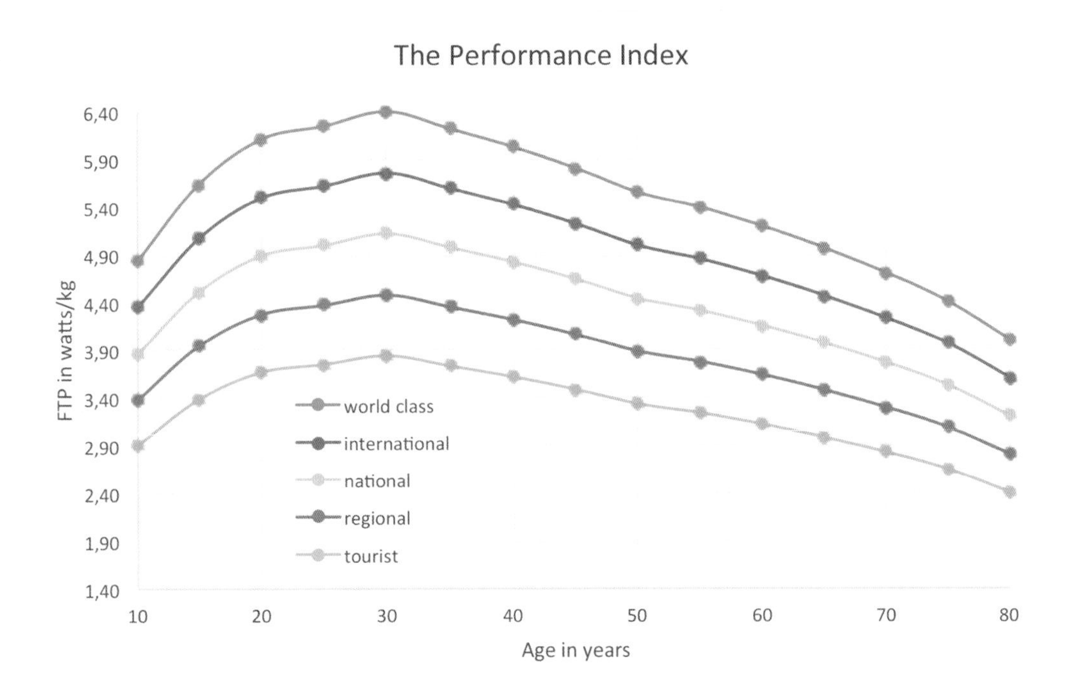

In summary, we can conclude that it is possible to compare cycling performances of different distances, different conditions and different ages. In order to do this, you should first calculate your FTP, taking into account the distance and the conditions of the race. Then, you should determine the ratio of your FTP to the maximum FTP, taking into account your age. This ratio is the performance index, which is the objective measure of your performance as a percentage of the world-class level at your age.

Finally, we note that we think it is fun to calculate your performance index. However, a low performance index should not reduce your enjoyment of cycling or your self-esteem. Cycling is fun and good for your health, no matter what level or intensity!

24. THE IMPACT OF YOUR BODY WEIGHT

Here's where less is more!

Cyclists are usually skinny, which can easily be understood. Once you start cycling, you will lose body fat; once you lose body fat, your cycling will improve. You will become better and faster as a result of the training and as a result of shedding body fat. You will experience a positive flow. More or less automatically, you will get better and leaner once you get started. Cyclists congratulate each other on their racing weight. However, non-cyclists among your family or friends might inquire whether you are quite well.

How Big Is the Impact of Your Body Weight?

The mathematics of the impact of body weight on your cycling performance is quite simple. Normally, your human engine has a fixed power output (P, in watts). When you shed body fat, your body weight will decrease, but your power output (P) remains constant. Consequently, your FTP (in watts/kg) increases when you reduce your body weight. The result is that you can cycle at a higher speed! Particularly uphill, your speed is inversely proportional to your body weight. You can also say that it will be easier to cycle at a certain speed when you lose body fat. This makes sense as you have to spend less energy as a result of your reduced body weight, whereas the power of your human engine has remained the same. Of course, all this is true when you avoid excessive weight loss, so your muscle mass and power are not compromised.

The inverse relationship between your body weight and your cycling performance can be seen immediately from the definition of the FTP in watts/kg body weight. The lower your body weight is, the higher your FTP becomes and thus the better your cycling performance. Next to talent and training, your body weight is actually the main factor determining your race times.

How Big Is the Impact of Body Weight on the Performance of Fast Eddy?

Fast Eddy weighs 75 kg and has an FTP of 4 watts/kg, so his total power output is 4*75 = 300 watts. We have calculated what will happen if he reduces his body weight up to a minimum of 70 kg or gains weight up to 80 kg. Once again, we have looked at ideal conditions and the two cases:

1. A time trial of 40 kilometers on a flat course.
2. The famous climb to the top of the Alpe d'Huez (an altitude gain of 1,041 meters over 14.45 kilometers).

A negative value means that Eddy loses weight and consequently cycles faster. A positive value means he gains weight and consequently cycles slower. The reader can calculate the impact on his own performance with our calculator at www.thesecretofcycling.com.

German cyclist Jan Ullrich stands on a scale during a medical examination for the Tour de France.

Race Time at a 40-Kilometer Time Trial

The results are presented in the table and figure below. We see that the attainable speed is indeed inversely dependent on the body weight of Fast Eddy. However, the impact is not so big. For every kilogram that he loses, his speed increases by 0.02 km/h (0.06%), so he gains only two seconds on the 40-kilometer time trial. The impact is so small because on the flat course the air resistance is the dominant factor and the air resistance is not influenced by the body weight.

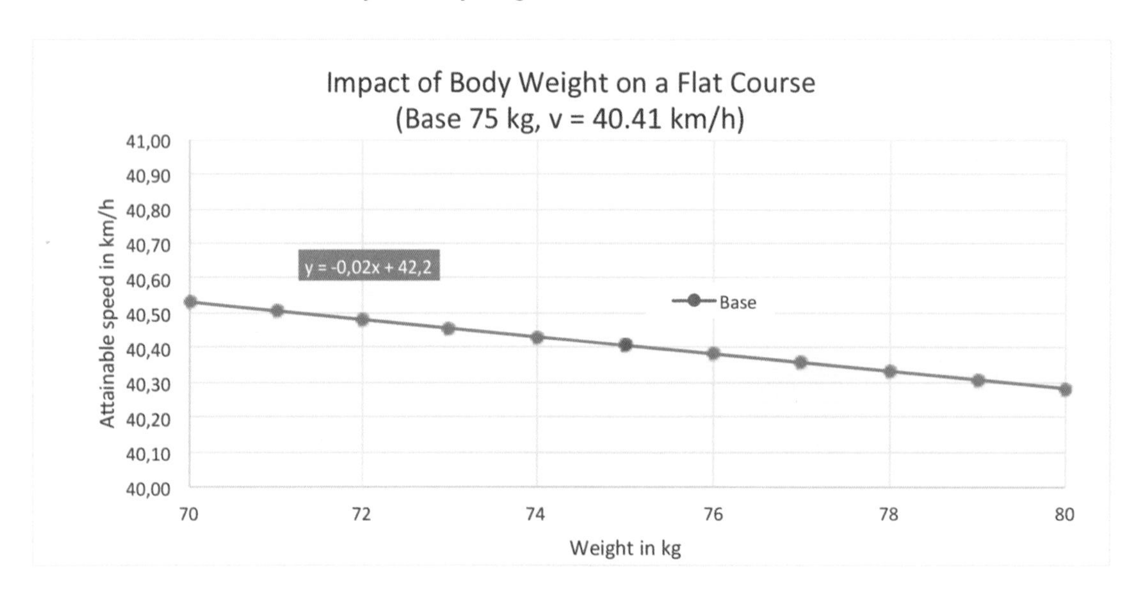

Impact of Body Weight at a 40-Kilometer Time Trial			
Body weight	v	T	Difference
(kg)	(km/h)	(sec)	(sec)
80	40.28	3575	-11
79	40.31	3572	-9
78	40.33	3570	-7
77	40.36	3568	-4
76	40.38	3566	-2
75	40.41	3564	-
74	40.43	3562	2
73	40.46	3559	4
72	40.48	3557	7
71	40.51	3555	9
70	40.53	3553	11

Race Time to the Top of Alpe d'Huez

Again, we have made the calculations and presented the results in a similar table and figure. Again, we see that the attainable speed is inversely proportional to the body weight. However, in this case the impact is much bigger. For every kilogram that he loses, his speed increases by 0.16 km/h (1.03%), so Fast Eddy gains 35 seconds on the climb. The advantage of losing weight is so big because uphill the attainable time is determined primarily by the climbing resistance, which of course is directly proportional to the weight. So you should try to be as lightweight as possible in the mountains. In a later chapter, we will show that the same applies to the weight of your bicycle.

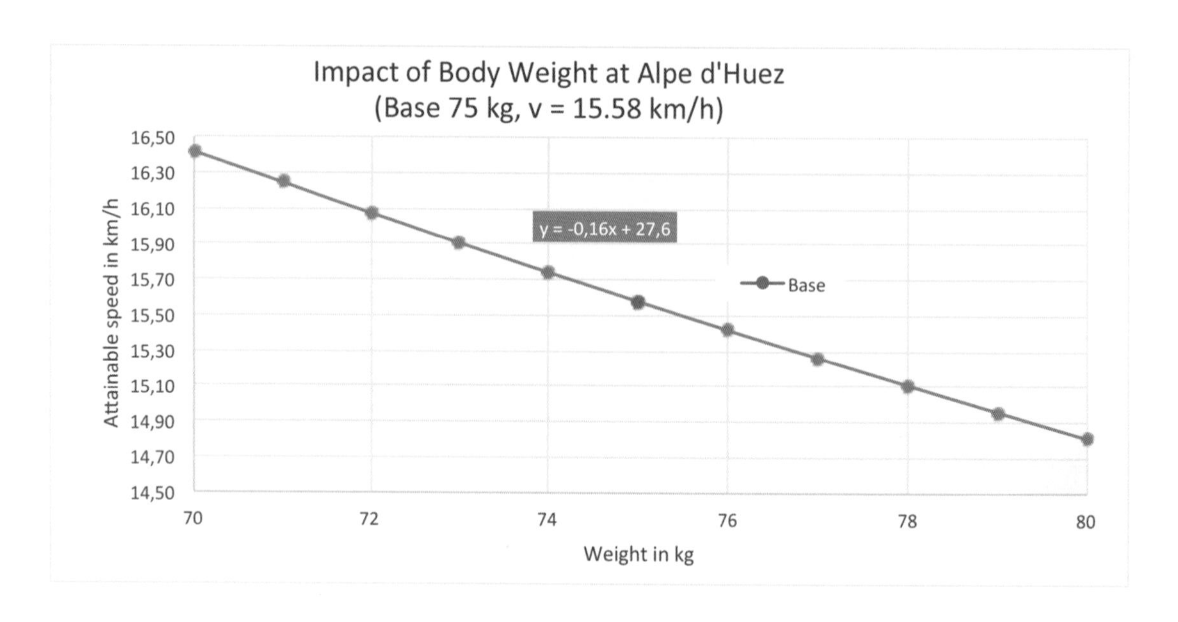

Impact of Body Weight at Alpe d'Huez			
Body weight	v	T	Difference
(kg)	(km/h)	(sec)	(sec)
80	14.81	3512	-173
79	14.96	3477	-138
78	15.11	3443	-104
77	15.26	3408	-69
76	15.42	3374	-34
75	15.58	3339	-
74	15.74	3305	34
73	15.91	3270	69
72	16.07	3236	103
71	16.24	3202	137
70	16.42	3168	171

In short, we conclude that losing weight is a promising strategy if you want to improve your performance, particularly uphill. How much weight you can lose depends mainly on your body fat percentage. This will be discusses in another chapter. Of course, it may not be easy to eat and drink less. Also, you will have to pay attention to the composition of your diet to prevent deficiencies and optimize your health. This will also be dealt with in another chapter.

On the other hand, your speed will drop if you gain weight. This is actually one of the reasons performance declines with age; most people gain weight as they get older.

Elite cyclists waiting on the road to Alpe d'Huez.

25. BMI, BFP AND RACING WEIGHT

With self-discipline all things are possible.
–Theodore Roosevelt

In the previous chapter, we saw that your body weight is one of the main factors determining your performance. We cannot change our talent and we have to face the fact that we grow older. But we can manage our diet and prevent gaining weight! For most of us, it will even be possible to shed some body fat. This requires only willpower, as we will have to eat and drink less and train more! Earlier we saw that our FTP is inversely proportional to our body weight, so our performance will definitely benefit from losing body fat. But how far can we go? What is the optimal racing weight?

Body Mass Index (BMI)

Most people will be familiar with the concept of the body mass index (BMI) as an indicator of weight. The BMI is defined as:

$BMI = m/L^2$

In this formula, the body weight (m) is expressed in kg and the length (L) in meters. So, if you are 1.75 meters tall and weigh 65 kg, your BMI is $65/(1.75)^2 = 21.2$. This is considered a normal weight, according to the table and figure below.

Body Mass Index Classification	
	BMI
Underweight	< 18.5
Normal (healthy weight)	18.5 - 25
Overweight	25 - 30
Obese	30 - 40
Very severely obese	> 40

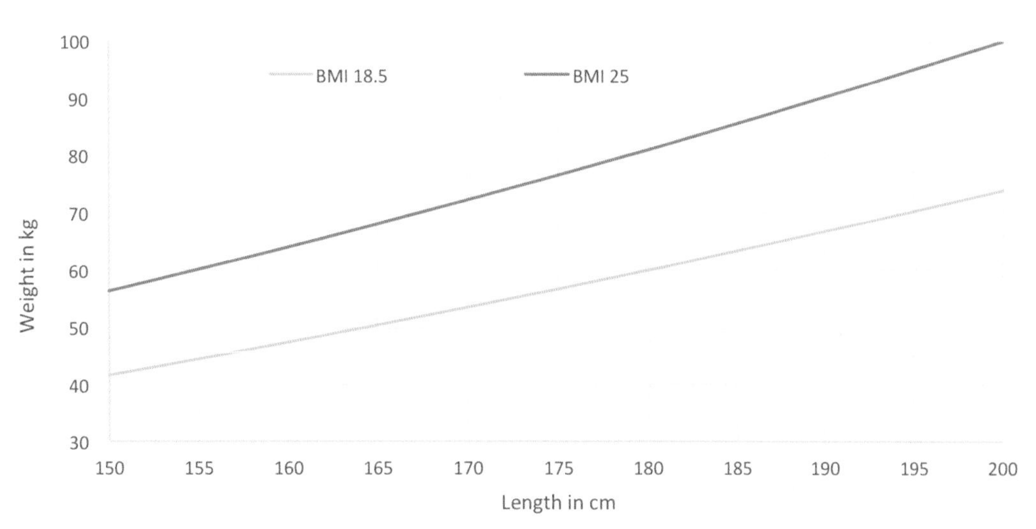

We note that the classification of the BMI is valid for normal people. Runners and cyclists are usually skinny and may have a BMI of less than 18.5. For runners and cyclists the BMI is actually a less meaningful index as compared to the body fat percentage (BFP). We will explain this below.

Lean Body Mass

Our body is composed of fat and fat-free body mass. The latter includes the bones and muscles and is usually denoted as lean body mass (LBM). In the literature, a number of formulas[33,34] have been presented to approximate the LBM as a function of weight and length:

For men: **LBM = 0.32810*m+33.929*L-29.5336**

For women: **LBM = 0.29569*m+41.813*L-43.2933**

As an example we use a man of 65 kg and 1.75 meters; according to the formula his LBM is 51.2 kg.

Body Fat Percentage (BFP)

The body fat percentage (BFP) is defined as:

BFP = (m-LBM)/m

This means our man of 65 kg and 1.75 meters has a BFP of (65-51.2)/65 = 21.1%.

There are several ways to have your BFP determined. These include skin fold measurements, bioelectric impedance scales, hydrostatic weighing and a DEXA full-body scan. All of these measurements should be preferred over the abovementioned formulas, as large individual differences do exist between people. Nevertheless, we used the formulas to prepare the figure below. These figures should be used as a first indication only, so don't be alarmed if your data deviate from the lines! To be sure, you should have your BFP determined in a sports medical center.

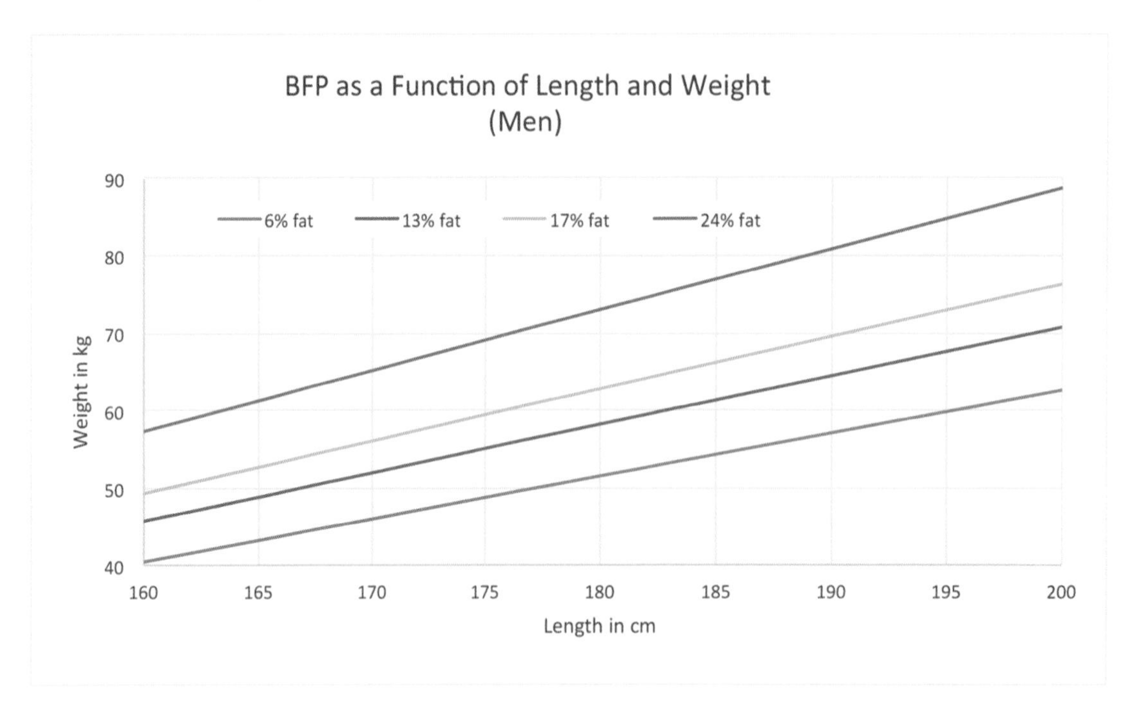

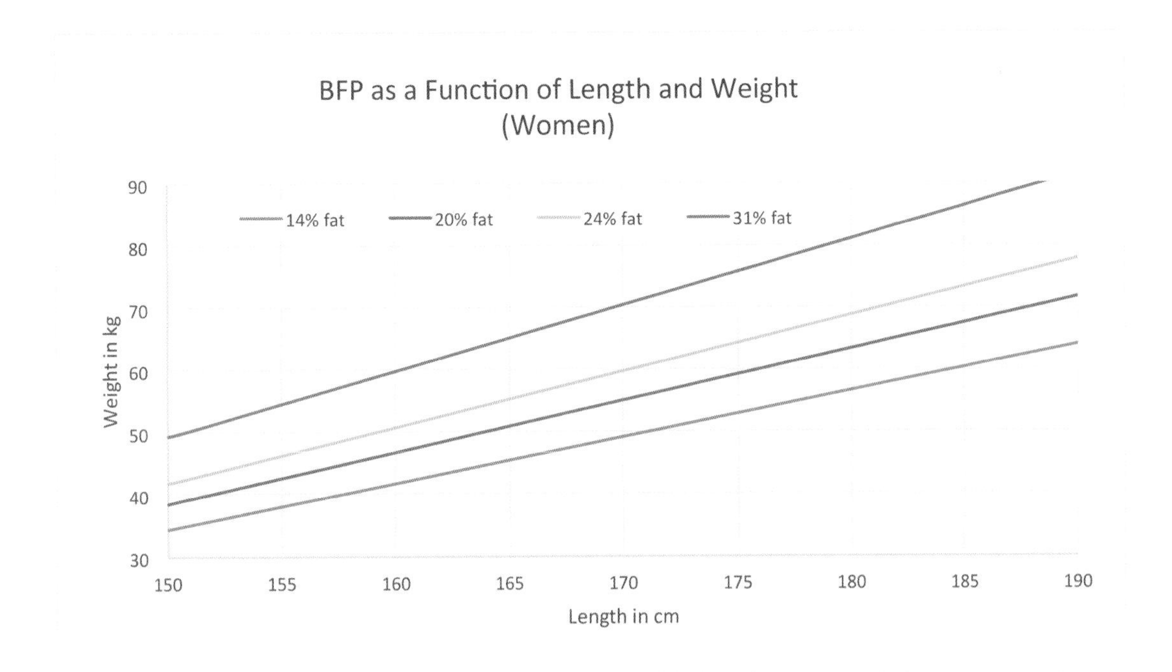

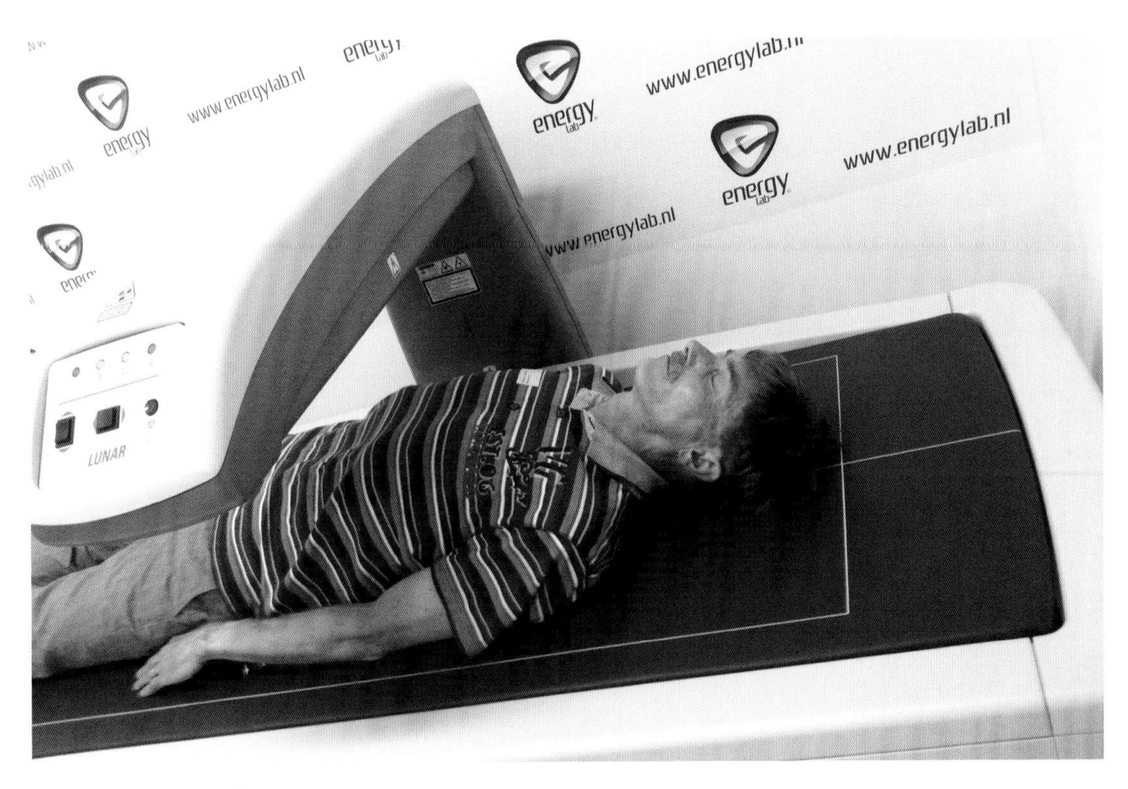

Author Ron experiences a full-body scan.

Optimal Racing Weight

So what is your optimal racing weight? In theory, for an optimal performance in running and cycling, your body weight should be as low as possible, though you should not go so far as to compromise the power and mass of your leg muscles. Also it is generally believed that some essential fat is required in our organs and other parts of the body. We have summarized the literature recommendations regarding BFP in the table below.

Recommendations for Fat Percentage (%)		
	Women	**Men**
Essential fat	10-15	2-5
Athletes	14-20	6-13
Fitness	21-24	14-17
Average	25-31	18-24
Overweight	> 32	> 25

The table shows that women generally have about 8% more fat than men. We believe that this is the main reason for the 10% lower FTP (and performance) of women as compared to men.

We note that we should consider our BFP as a kind of reserve that our body has stocked up for emergencies. In the past this function was essential to cope with times of food shortages. However, nowadays we live in a time of abundance with the result that most of us stock up too much body fat, so we gain body weight. If you want to perform as well as possible, you should make sure that you get rid of the surplus body fat and lower your BFP as much as possible. Of course, it may not be easy to eat and drink less and avoid those snacks and sodas. You will also have to pay attention to eating healthy and varied food as explained in other chapters (with lots of vegetables and fruits). Finally you should take ample time to reduce your BFP and body weight, and avoid extreme weight loss and unhealthy effects, such as *Anorexia Atletica.*

Cycling is fun. Losing some body fat improves your performance, health and the quality of your life.

26. HOW TO LOSE BODY FAT AND GAIN FITNESS

Be the change you want to see in the world.
–Mahatma Gandhi

Your body weight does not only determine your performance in running and cycling, it is also one of the most important factors in your physical and mental well-being. In this chapter, we will discuss the personal experiences of author Hans. We note that Ron had similar experiences. We will describe how they managed to shed body fat. Also we will describe the positive impact this had on their health, performance and quality of life.

The Experiences of Author Hans

Hans first realized the importance of his body weight in 2011, when he cleaned up his attic and found an old running logbook from 1980. In this he read that in 1980 his body weight had been 57.5 kg, whereas by 2011 this had increased (slowly and unnoticed) to 68.5 kg. At that moment he decided to try to shed the additional body fat and get back to his earlier body weight. He started to limit his daily calorie intake, abandoning snacks and sodas. He paid attention to a healthy and varied nutrition: lots of vegetables and fruits, less meat and fat, no sugar in the tea and coffee and drinking lots of water. At first this was tough. He felt hungry all day, but he was motivated and persevered. After some time, it became easier and he actually started to enjoy his new low-fat diet. And with success, as can be seen from the table below! Since the end of 2012 his body weight is back at the 1980 level of 57.5 kg.

Body Weight of Hans van Dijk	
Year	**(kg)**
1980	57.5
1990	63
2003	64.5
2009	67
2011	68.5
2012	57.5

How to Lose Body Fat

The mathematics of losing weight is very simple: you just have to make sure that on a daily basis your energy (calorie) balance is (slightly) negative. So your daily energy use has to exceed the energy intake with your food. In an earlier chapter, we saw that the energy value of body fat is 37.6 kJ/gram. This means that you can calculate your daily weight loss from your daily energy balance as shown in the box.

Weight loss (in g/day) = (Energy use (in kJ/day)-Energy intake (in kJ/day))/37.6

The daily energy use is comprised of the base metabolism and the energy used for running. The daily metabolism of Hans uses around 6,500 kJ and his daily one-hour training around 2,500 kJ. He managed to reduce the energy intake with his food to some 6,700 kJ, so his daily energy balance was negative by 2,300 kJ. This resulted in a daily weight loss of 2,300/37.6 = 60 grams of body fat. This theoretical calculation matched perfectly well with the actual weight loss that Hans experienced in 2012, as can be seen in the figure.

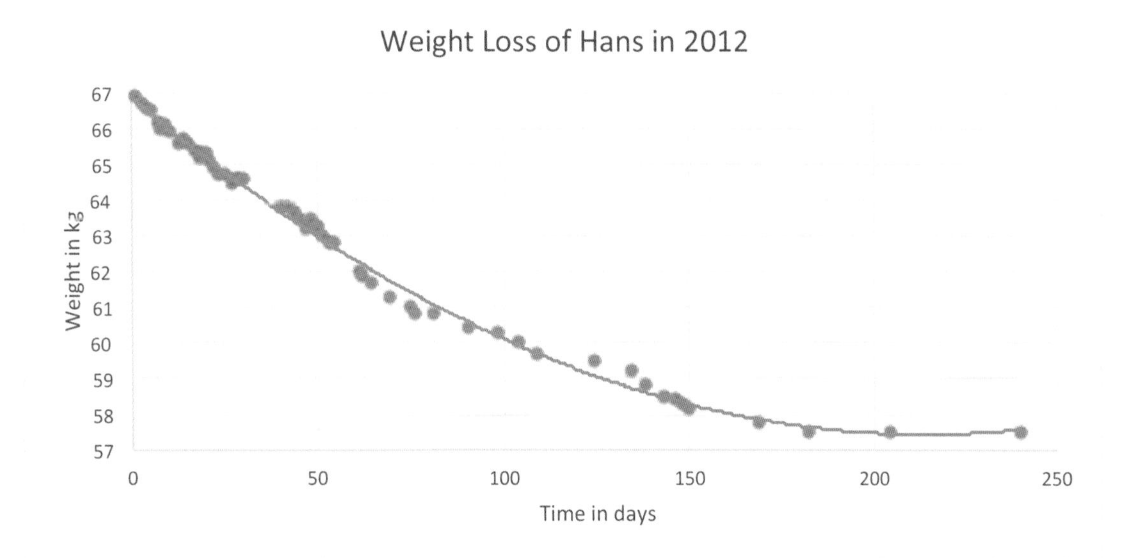

As could be expected, the weight loss gradually decreased. As his weight decreased, both his base metabolism and the energy used for running also decreased. So his energy balance became less negative and his weight automatically approached the equilibrium value of 57.5 kg. This took a period of 6 months for a total weight loss of 11 kg. In this period his waist size decreased from 82 to 69 cm. His clothing did not fit anymore and even his calf size reduced from 36 to 33 cm!

Impact on Body Fat Percentage (BFP)

Hans had his BFP determined by means of skin fold measurements at the end of 2011, when his body weight was still 68 kg. His BFP turned out to be 22%, which means that he had a total of 0.22*68 = 15 kg of body fat. As we saw in an earlier chapter, we can calculate that his lean body mass (LBM) was 68-15 = 53 kg. Hans realized that he could lose the majority of the 15 kg of body fat, thus improving his fitness. When we presume that his LBM remained constant at 53 kg, we can calculate his BFP as a function of his body weight, as shown in the table below.

BFP Hans van Dijk	
Weight	BFP
(kg)	%
68	22
66	20
64	17
60	12
58	9
56	5

The table shows that theoretically Hans could go as far as 56 kg, before reaching the critical level of 5% BFP. In literature this is the lower limit for athletes and thought to be the amount of essential body fat necessary to support body and organ functions. In practice the weight of Hans stabilized at 57.5 kg, so he could not reach the 56 kg (without severely restricting his diet). At the end of 2012, Hans had his BFP determined once more, this time with an EDAX full-body scan. The result was that his BFP was 6.5%, so this was close to the calculations. Also it was so low that Hans concluded that he had done enough and he should not strive for additional weight loss. The advantage of losing another kg would be small and would not outweigh the possible risk of compromising his body functions.

Impact on Cholesterol Levels

One important side effect of his weight loss in 2012 was that Hans experienced a dramatic improvement in his cholesterol levels, as shown in the table below.

Cholesterol Data for Hans van Dijk					
Date	**Total**	**Triglycerides**	**HDL**	**LDL**	**Ratio Total/HDL**
Normal ranges	**< 5 ***	**2.1**	**> 0.9**	**2.5-3.5**	**< 5**
23-1-1990	5.7				
6-10-2003	6.8	2.2	1.4	4.4	4.9
2-2-2005	6.6				
11-4-2007	6.1	2.0	1.4	3.9	4.5
11-8-2010	7.2	1.9	1.6	4.8	4.6
6-1-2011	7.7	3.1	1.5	4.8	5.0
17-5-2011	6.8	1.6	1.5	4.7	4.5
30-11-2011	7.3		1.4		5.2
24-7-2012	**5.5**	**0.9**	**1.9**	**3.1**	**2.9**
6-11-2012	**4.6**		**2.2**		**2.1**

An elevated level of cholesterol (in particular the LDL and the ratio total/HDL) is considered to be an important risk factor for cardiovascular diseases. Before 2012, the levels of Hans were higher than recommended. In 2012 they dropped by some 30% or more and at the end of 2012 all data complied to all recommended levels!

Impact on Fitness

The fitness level of Hans increased spectacularly during 2012. His resting heart rate dropped from 45 to 40, he felt reborn and had lots of energy. Before and after his weight loss, he took a physical fitness test (including a running test on a treadmill with breathing gas analysis and ECG) at the Dutch Olympic Sports Center Papendal. The results are shown in the table.

Fitness Tests for Hans at Papendal 2011-2012			
			Improvement
	2011	2012	(%)
Body weight in kg	68.5	58	18
VO_2 max in ml/kg/min	51	60	18
Speed at FTP in km/h	13.5	16	19
HR at FTP in bpm	153	157	3
Maximal speed in km/h	17.5	19	9
Vital capacity in ml	4500	4860	8
BFP in %	14	6.9	51
Waist size in cm	82	69	19
Total cholesterol in mmol/l	7.3	4.6	37
HDL in mmol/l	1.4	2.2	36
Cholesterol ratio	5.2	2.1	60

As can be seen from the table, all parameters showed a very significant improvement. His VO_2 max increased from 51 to 60 ml/kg/min, so by 18%. This means that his FTP increased from 3.7 to 4.3 watts/kg.

Impact on Running Performance

The details on the spectacular improvement of his race times were already given in our earlier book[1]. In 2012, his performance at all distances improved by some 15%, more or less equivalent to his weight loss.

Impact on Quality of Life

Both Hans and Ron feel that this is probably the most rewarding advantage of losing body fat. They both feel reborn and more fit and healthy. They are cheerful, feel young and enjoy life. They sleep well, have lots of energy all day and enjoy their less-fat meals. They run as light as a feather and have delight in their daily runs in the great outdoors!

Hans van Dijk between the Russians Alexandr Kaplenko (207) and winner Leonid Tikhonov (1120) at the 5,000-meter M55 final of the World Master Games 2013 in Turin (Italy). Hans benefitted from his weight loss and won the silver medal.

27. THE IMPACT OF THE WEIGHT OF YOUR BIKE

I want to ride my bicycle. –Queen

Look at all those sparkling bikes in the shop; so many options and choices. Which bike is the one for you? Next to your personal preference and your budget, there are also some aspects that will have an impact on your performance. These include the aerodynamics and the weight. In this chapter, we will investigate the impact of the weight of your bike on your performance.

The Math of the Impact of the Weight of Your Bike

The mathematics of the impact of the weight of your bike on your cycling performance is quite simple. In principle, your human engine has a more or less fixed power output (P, in watts). That means that your specific power (P/m) is inversely proportional to your total weight (i.e., the sum of your body weight and the weight of your bike). So, with a lower bike weight your specific power is higher and you can cycle faster. This makes sense as the rolling resistance, the climbing resistance and the mechanical resistance will be lower when your bike weighs less. Consequently, the weight of your bike is an important factor determining your performance.

How Big Is the Impact of the Weight of the Bike of Fast Eddy?

In the standard conditions, the bike of Fast Eddy weighs 8.8 kg. We have calculated what will happen if the weight of the bike is reduced to the UCI minimum of 6.8 kg or increased to 10.8 kg. Once again, we will look at ideal conditions and the two cases:

1. A time trial of 40 kilometers on a flat course.
2. The famous climb to the top of the Alpe d'Huez (an altitude gain of 1,041 meters over 14.45 kilometers).

A negative value means that Eddy loses weight and consequently cycles faster. A positive value means he gains weight and consequently cycles slower. The reader can calculate the impact on his own performance with our calculator at www.thesecretofcycling.com.

Race Time at a 40-Kilometer Time Trial

The results are presented in the table and figure. We see that the attainable speed is indeed inversely dependent on the weight of the bike. However, the impact is not so big. For every kilogram lower in weight, his speed increases by 0.02 km/h (0.06%), so he gains only two seconds on the 40-kilometer time trial. The impact is so small because in this case the air resistance is the dominant factor and the air resistance is not influenced by the weight.

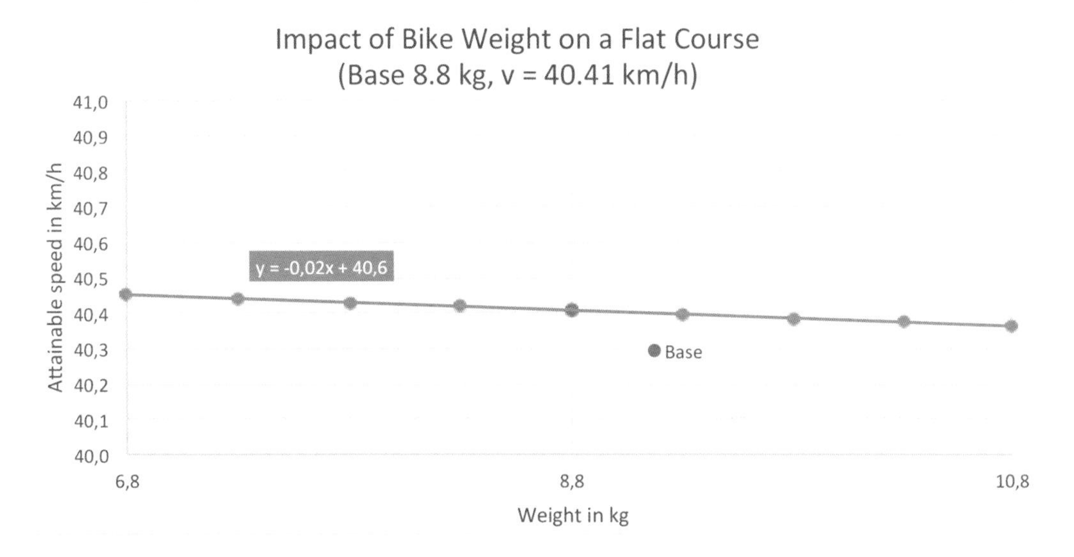

Your bike should weigh as little as possible in the mountains. On a flat course the impact is not so big.

Impact of Bike Weight on a Flat Course			
Weight	v	T	Difference
(kg)	(km/h)	(min)	(sec)
6.8	40.45	59.33	4
7.3	40.44	59.35	3
7.8	40.43	59.36	2
8.3	40.42	59.38	1
8.8	40.41	59.40	-
9.3	40.40	59.41	-1
9.8	40.38	59.43	-2
10.3	40.37	59.44	-3
10.8	40.36	59.46	-4

Race Time to the Top of Alpe d'Huez

Again, we have made the calculations and presented the results in a similar table and figure, and we see that the attainable speed is inversely proportional to the weight. However, in this case the impact is much bigger. For every kilogram lower in weight, his speed increases by 0.16 km/h (1.03%), so Fast Eddy gains 35 seconds on the climb. The advantage of a lower weight is so big because uphill the attainable time is determined primarily by the climbing resistance, which of course is directly proportional to the weight. So your bike should weigh as little as possible in the mountains. This even applies to the weight of your water bottle!

In summary, we conclude that you can cycle faster when your total weight is lower. The impact is much bigger in the mountains as compared to on a flat course. It does not matter whether you reduce the weight of your bike or your body weight: the impact of one kilogram of weight reduction is exactly the same in both cases! It is up to you which option you prefer.

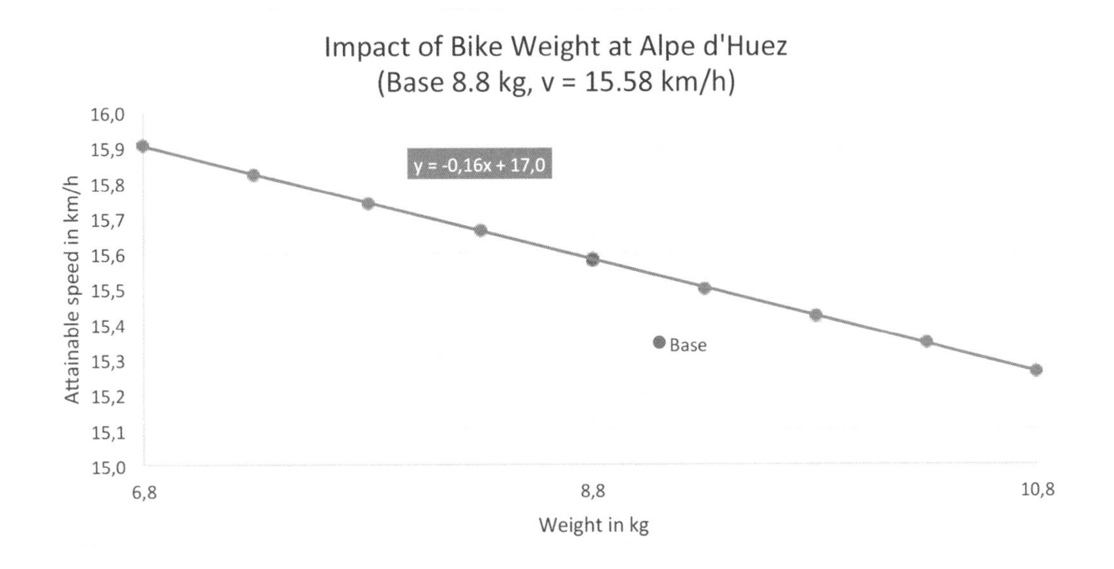

Impact of Bike Weight at Alpe d'Huez			
Weight	v	T	Difference
(kg)	(km/h)	(min)	(sec)
6.8	15.91	54.51	69
7.3	15.82	54.79	51
7.8	15.74	55.08	34
8.3	15.66	55.36	17
8.8	15.58	55.65	-
9.3	15.50	55.94	-17
9.8	15.42	56.23	-34
10.3	15.34	56.51	-52
10.8	15.26	56.80	-69

28. THE IMPACT OF TRAINING

The single greatest cause of improvement is staying injury-free.

For most people, training will lead to an increase of the FTP. This means that the attainable speed at most distances will also increase. However, at short distances the impact on speed will usually not be so big. Sprinters are born, although they should train as well.

Possible Effects of Training

From most textbooks and papers on training[36,41], the following conclusions on the impact of training can be drawn:

1. The FTP (and attainable speed for longer distances) can be improved by some 10-20% (maximum 30%). The time to exhaustion can even be improved by a factor of 10!
2. The effect of training can be reached rather quickly, in some weeks or months. The training effect is also lost quickly when the athlete stops training.
3. The intensity of the training is the most important factor determining the effect. In order to get the biggest improvement, it is vital to train at a high intensity. This means close to the maximum heart rate (MHR) and close to or above the FTP. Consequently, interval training is the most effective method.

In an earlier chapter, we have already discussed the different training methods, including interval training.

Limitations of Research

We note that in practice it is quite difficult to optimize your training and get the best results. Consequently, the impact of training is less predictable than other factors, such as the impact of distance, body weight or age. The variability of the impact of training is caused by the following factors:

1. Most research into the impact of training is limited to a period of some weeks or months only. Consequently, it is not possible to predict the long-term impact (in which many cyclists are interested).

2. Most research is done on a limited group of athletes, both in numbers and in level. Consequently, it is difficult or even impossible to draw statistically sound conclusions.
3. In practice, many factors change simultaneously, such as the body weight, the training program, the physical fitness, the conditions of training and racing and so on.

This means we should be more humble in predicting the impact of training on the attainable race times. In this chapter, we will just illustrate the potential impact by assuming that our Fast Eddy can increase his FTP by 10, 20 or 30% as a result of training. The 30% should be regarded as the maximum value for raw beginners while for experienced cyclists an increase by 10% is more likely.

Race Time at the 40-Kilometer Time Trial

Once again, we calculated the attainable speed and race time for Fast Eddy in the standard conditions, both for his regular FTP of 4 watts/kg and for increases by 10, 20 and 30%. The figure and table below show the results. The attainable speed increases from 40.41 km/h for the base case to 44.43 km/h for the case when his FTP has increased by 30%. We see that an increase of the FTP by 30% results only in a 10% increase in speed. This makes sense as the air resistance is the determining factor, so theoretically the speed depends on the FTP to an exponent of 0.33. We also see that Fast Eddy might gain 322 seconds on the time trial, a fine result! Of course many cyclists may not reach such an improvement. As we said before, an increase of the FTP by 10% should be more realistic for experienced cyclists. This would lead to a gain in race time of 121 seconds. Of course, these calculations give the impact of training on the FTP only. Other improvements are also possible, like better aerodynamics. This will be discussed in another chapter.

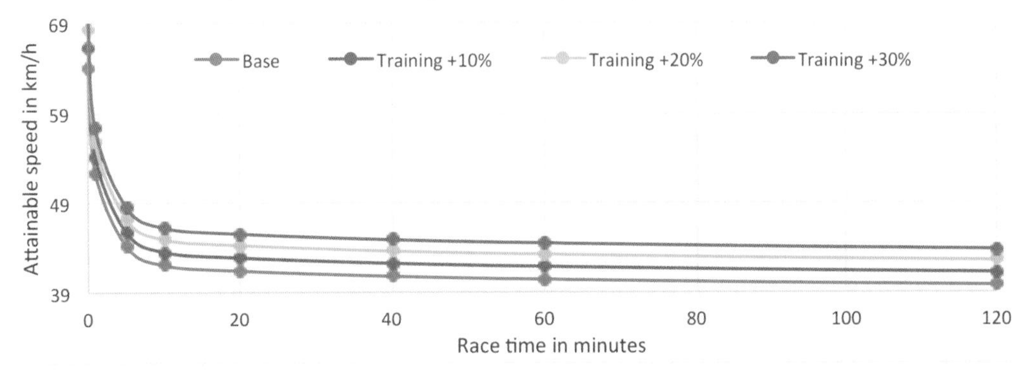

Impact of Training at a Flat Course				
	FTP	v	T 40 km	Difference
	(watts/kg)	(km/h)	(min)	(sec)
Base	4.0	40.41	59.4	-
Training +10%	4.4	41.83	57.4	-121
Training +20%	4.8	43.16	55.6	-228
Training +30%	5.2	44.43	54.0	-322

Race Time to the Top of the Alpe d'Huez

The results of our calculations are given in the table and figure below. The attainable speed increases from 15.58 km/h for the base FTP to 19.67 km/h for the case with a 30% higher FTP. This is an increase in speed of 26%, almost equal to the increase in FTP. Again we see that in the mountains, the FTP is the decisive parameter. Of course, this is caused by the fact that the climbing resistance determines the race time. With a 30% increase in FTP, Fast Eddy could gain 694 seconds on his race time! Even with a more realistic increase in FTP of 10%, the gain in race time is still big (275 seconds).

Consequently, we conclude that—next to losing weight and improving aerodynamics—training is the best option to get faster.

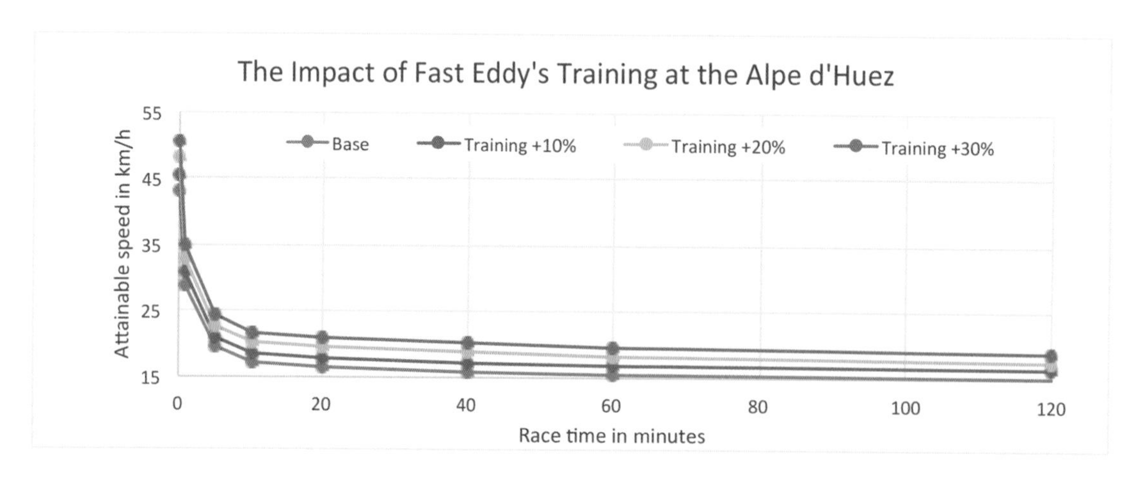

Impact of Training at the Alpe d'Huez				
	FTP	v	T Alpe	Difference
	(watts/kg)	(km/h)	(min)	(sec)
Base	4.0	15.58	55.6	-
Training +10%	4.4	16.98	51.1	-275
Training +20%	4.8	18.34	47.3	-503
Training +30%	5.2	19.67	44.1	-694

In order to get the biggest improvement, it is vital to train at a high intensity.

29. THE IMPACT OF YOUR HEART RATE

Cycling gives us the evidence we are well.

We can envisage the human heart as a pump. When we want to increase the flow of a pump, we need to increase the number of revolutions per minute. Similarly, the heart rate (HR, in number of beats per minute) needs to increase in order to provide a higher blood flow (and consequently more oxygen) to the muscles. The capacity of a pump is usually defined in l/h. Similarly, the capacity of the cardiovascular system is defined by the oxygen transport capacity, the VO_2 max (in l O_2/min, or more usually in ml O_2/min/kg body weight).

MHR and RHR

As stated above, the HR will increase with exercise in order to provide the muscles with more blood and more oxygen. The relationship is more or less linear between two limits:

1. **The upper limit is the maximum heart rate (MHR).**
   The human heart has a natural upper limit, which protects the heart from overloading. For most people, the MHR is in the order of 150-200 bpm, although this declines with age. The following formulas can be found in literature[42]:

   - MHR = 220-age (in years)
   - MHR = 205.8-0.685*age (men)
   - MHR = 206-0.88*age (women)

   The first formula is said to be more appropriate for sedentary people, whereas the other formulas are thought to better describe the HR of athletes, who stay active and fit. The figure gives the relationship according to the formulas.

2. **The lower limit is the resting heart rate (RHR).**
   The resting heart rate is the most distinctive difference between trained athletes and inactive persons. The RHR of trained athletes is always low, certainly below 50 and sometimes below 40 bpm. Five-time Tour de France winner Eddy Merckx had a RHR of just 33 bpm! The RHR of sedentary people is significantly higher, over 60 and sometimes over 70 bpm. Although individual differences and exceptions to the rule may occur, the RHR is a very useful indicator of your fitness.

The reason for the low RHR in trained athletes is that the sports heart has a higher stroke volume. Consequently, in order to provide the same blood flow, the RHR can be lower. This means that the heart has an easy job providing the blood flow required during rest and for the base metabolism. This also explains why trained athletes feel fit and energetic all day.

The Capacity of the Heart as a Function of the Difference Between MHR and RHR

Obviously, the difference between MHR and RHR is an important factor determining the capacity of the heart. As we age, the MHR declines and consequently so does the VO_2 max and our performance. In an earlier chapter, we learned that the decline in performance of master athletes is around 0.8% per year. A large part of this decline can be explained by the annual decline in MHR (0.685 bpm for men, see the above formula). As an example, we use a person with an MHR of 160 and an RHR of 45. The decline of

MHR by 0.685 bpm corresponds to a decline in VO_2 of (160-45)/(159.315-45) = 1.006 or 0.6% per year. The above figure also shows that on average the MHR of women is around 10% lower than the MHR of men. This corresponds more or less to the difference in performance between men and women. As an example, we use the data for the age of 55. At this age the average MHR for men is 168 bpm, for women it is 158 bpm. Assuming the RHR is 45 in both cases, the difference in heart capacity becomes (168-45)/(158-45) = 1.088 or 8.8%.

How to Estimate Your VO_2 max and FTP From Your MHR and RHR

In an earlier chapter, we learned that we can use the following formula to get a rough estimate of the VO_2 max:

VO_2 max = 15*MHR/RHR

Also, we know that there is a fixed relationship between the VO_2 max and the FTP:

FTP = 0.072*VO_2 max

These formulas are almost too good to be true, because they enable us to estimate the FTP, based solely on the MHR (and thus on the age) and the RHR. The figures below give this relationship both for men and for women.

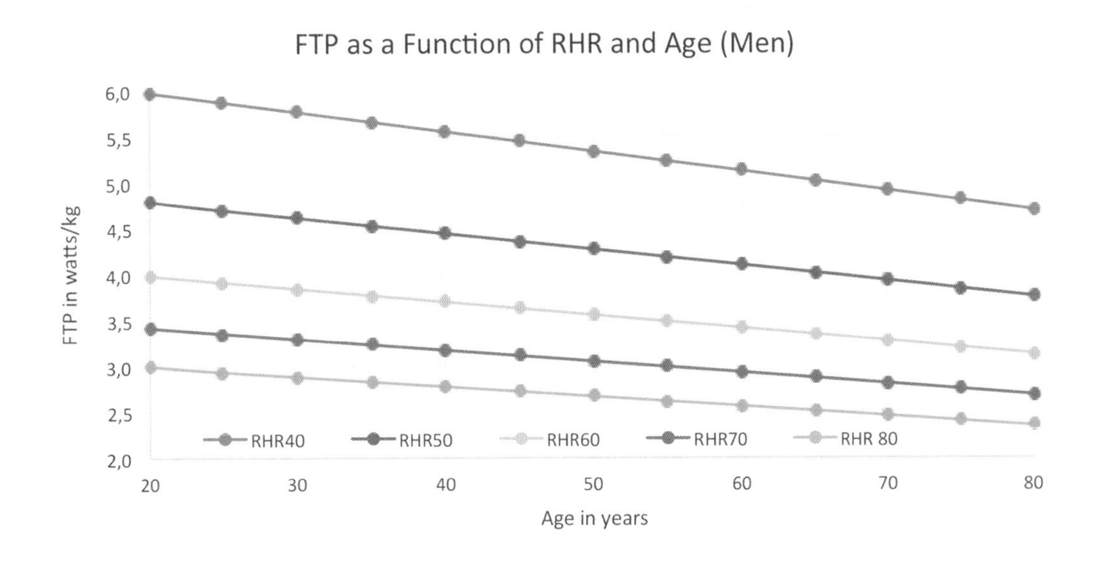

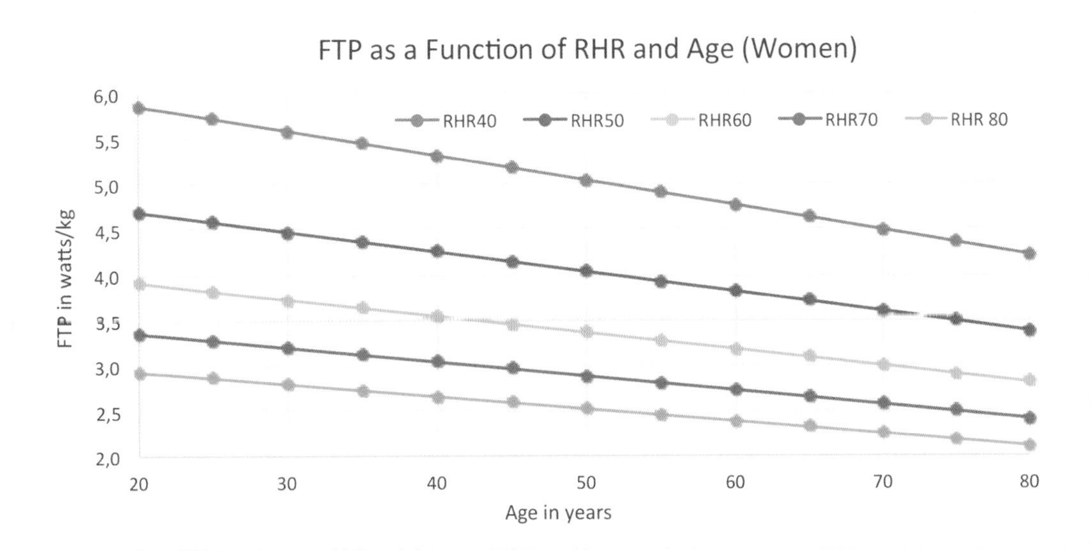

It gets even better when we realize that the FTP enables us to calculate the attainable speed on the flat 40-kilometer time trial and on the climb to the Alpe d'Huez, just like we have done in the other chapters. So, with these formulas it is possible to make a rough estimate of your performance based solely on your age and RHR.

The figures below clearly show the decline in performance as a function of age. They also show the distinct impact of the RHR.

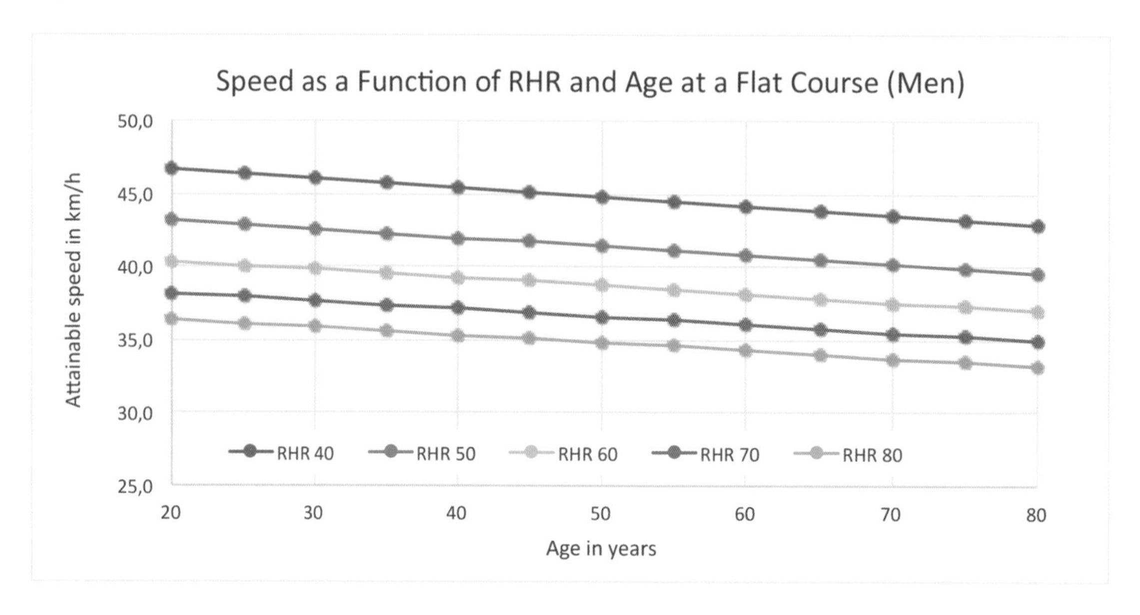

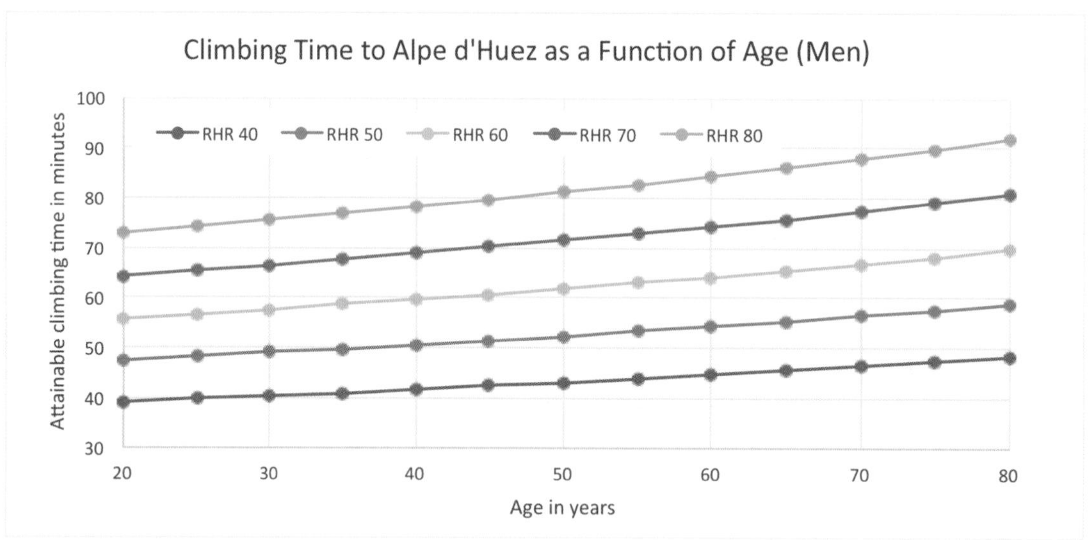

We end this chapter with some cautionary notes. Obviously, the formulas should only be used as a first indication of your FTP and cycling performance. They should be seen as statistically average values. It is quite possible that your results will differ from the estimates. Furthermore, we feel that the predicted performances are rather optimistic, in particular for low values of the RHR. Finally, it should be noted that the results are only attainable if you have trained well to fully mobilize your potential.

For the climb to the Alpe d'Huez it is possible to make a rough estimate of your performance based solely on your age and RHR.

30. WHY SHOULD YOU TRAIN WITH POWER METERS?

The best rides are the ones where you bite off much more than you can chew, and live through it. –Doug Bradbury

Recent years show a clear upward trend in the sales of power meters. The interest in training with power meters has increased significantly. Training with a power meter has many advantages. In this chapter we present an overview of these benefits, and we illustrate this with some images of the many power meters and accessories from the personal collection of author Guido.

1. **Training with a power meter gives you a complete overview of your effort.**
   It records your effort from a circulation point of view (heart rate), and from a muscular standpoint (power in watts). The data of your power meter show exactly how much time you have spent in your target zones. Mark your areas of interest on the basis of data from your ride (uphill, sprints, breakaways), and analyze these data by yourself or together with your coach.

SRM Shimano Dura Ace 11-speed.

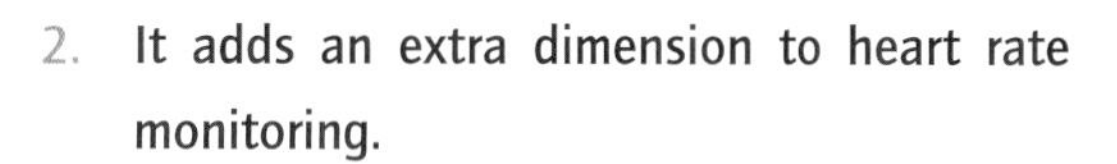

2. **It adds an extra dimension to heart rate monitoring.**
   Heart rate alone does not tell you how to improve your actual performance. It only tells you how often your heart beats. A power meter measures the amount of work per second, and analyzes your efficiency by relating your heart rate to your power, your cadence and your speed.

Rotor Power.

3. **You can see how your fitness evolves.**
   Know with certainty that your fitness improves, and know when you have reached a peak. Avoid overreaching (and thereby overtraining) by keeping track of your training stress score (TSS) and intensity factor (IF) levels.

4. **You can analyze your races better.**
   A power meter can help you analyze your ride better. You can easily see if and where you have used too much energy. Have you made a tactical error in a race, but did not realize that at the time? Did you use too much power and get into the red zone? By looking back at the data, you can virtually repeat the race and know afterwards exactly what the right decision would have been at the time.

5. **Know your strengths and weaknesses.**
   Do you drop from the group when your cadence drops below 80 rpm? Are you strong for five minutes but have less power over 20 minutes? Do you struggle after three minutes when you cycle at 105% of your FTP? By analyzing your power data you can determine your strengths and weaknesses and cycle a better race.

6. **It improves the interactions with your coach!**
   It brings you and your trainer or coach closer together. Your trainer or coach can use better information to improve your training plan. He can instantly see what you are doing in races and training rides, and give informed suggestions for further improvements.

Quarq SRAM red.

Powertap G3 hub.

Polar Power Pedals.

7. **It helps to maximize your physical abilities!**
When you train with a power meter, you can concentrate better on the workload. This gives you extra motivation to improve your efforts. For example, if you cycle a five-minute interval on a certain level and you see that your power decreases at the end of the five minutes, you can start the next interval at a slightly lower level so you can continue the intervals at constant power and thereby achieve a better training effect.

Pioneer left and right crank.

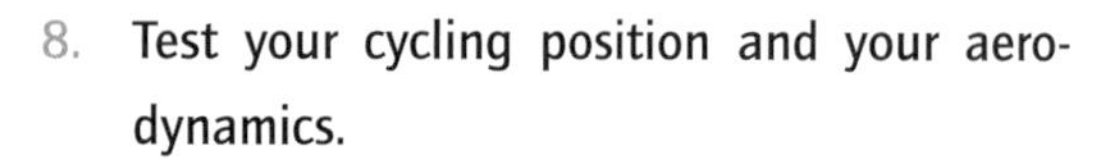

8. **Test your cycling position and your aero-dynamics.**
Your bike position is the most important factor in determining your speed when you cycle at a flat course, so you can determine your optimal aero position and improve your speed.

Garmin Vector.

9. **Record the variation of pace during races and training.**
This helps you to improve your estimate of the optimal pace in interval training, hill climbs and time trials. When you know your FTP, you can choose and maintain the corresponding power during a time trial and climb very well, so you know you have performed at your maximum level.

Infocrank.

10. **You have access to a mobile test lab.**
With a power meter you can test yourself regularly so you can identify (on a quantitative basis) areas where you are improving and where you still need to work on. Training is testing, testing is training!

11. **It registers training data every second.**
    It provides a good log of each ride! You know exactly what you've done every second of the ride. By storing all the data in your database, you get a complete overview of your performance and how your training was structured towards the race season. There are various useful applications such as TrainingPeaks, Strava, Garmin Connect and Polar. These provide all relevant performance information. Some offer very useful trend analysis and correlation of data.

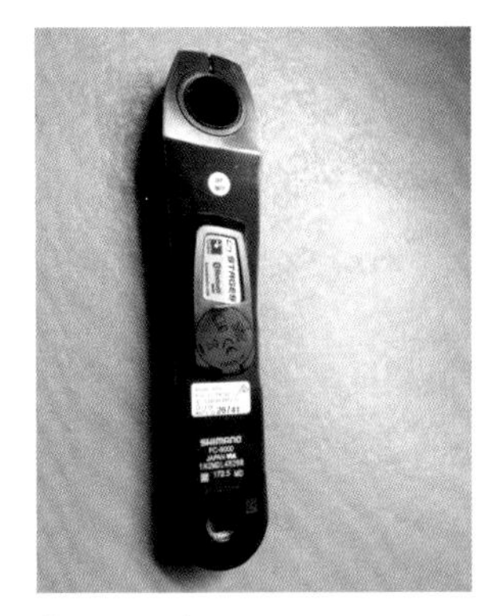

Stages crank.

12. **Improve your indoor training.**
    Use your indoor training in the most efficient manner. Focus on your intervals with exact wattages for optimal improvement.

Quarq Elsa.

13. **Know the quantity of energy consumed for optimizing your diet.**
    Knowing how much energy (in kJ) you used in training or a race, gives the opportunity to have a well-balanced recovery meal in terms of calories. You will recover faster and better and will be able to race more effectively the next day.

14. **Plan, check, do and act in your training like the pros do.**
    You can train efficiently towards the target race. In professional cycling, every peak performance is supported by power meters (classics, time trials, mountain stages, hour record).

Powertap C1 chainring power meter.

31. OPTIMIZING YOUR TRAINING WITH POWER METERS

Success is measured in racing times, not training mileage.

The theory and practice of cycling indicate that you have to train hard to ride fast. This seems logical, but what is hard? What is optimal? Remember that you need to ensure that your training stimulates all four energy systems of your human engine and the training must be of a level that is comparable to your efforts in the race. This includes the following:

1. Training of endurance (slow pace, long duration).
2. Training of aerobic–anaerobic transition (pace at 85-95% of FTP).
3. Training of anaerobic capacity (pace above FTP, very short duration).

Cycle computers and power meters are a great asset for optimizing your training.

Training Your Endurance

Endurance can be trained quite well. Untrained cyclists are already tired after an hour, while trained cyclists can easily train for 4-6 hours. However, the training of too many cyclists consists only of endurance training at a leisurely pace. Although this is an enjoyable form of exercise and it is very pleasant to cycle at a slow pace alone or with a group, it is not advisable to limit your training to this type. In this way your body gets used to cycling slow and not to cycling fast, which is what you need to do in races. Cycling is a sport with many pace changes. The entire spectrum of easy endurance paces to maximal sprints can be found in races. The impact of endurance training on your aerobic capacity is limited and the impact on your anaerobic capacity is zero. Although endurance training is an essential part of the training plan, you have to complement it with impulses for the training of the anaerobic systems.

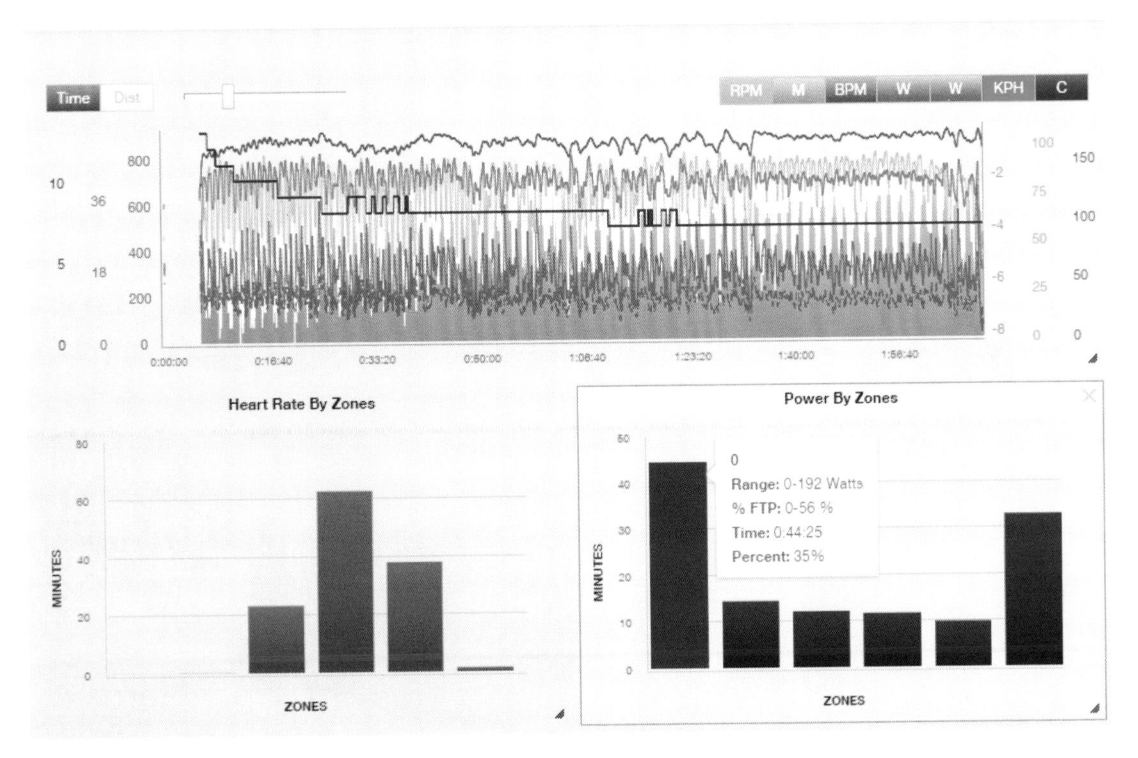

TrainingPeaks presentation of a criterium, illustrating a race with pace changes.

Training Your Aerobic and Anaerobic Capacity

In the training it is important to approach the power, the HR and the pace that you achieve in the races. Because this is very hard, you can maintain this effort for a short time only. Therefore interval training is essential. During the intervals you can achieve high levels of power, HR and pace, whereas your body can recover between the intervals. As this recovery is fast (HR decreases exponentially within 10-20 seconds), you can do the next interval quickly and you can still train a relatively long time at a high intensity. In interval training it is very important to find a good balance between intensity and recovery. As interval training is hard, you need at least two days of recovery time so any muscle damage can be restored and lactic acid can be removed and broken down. In practice, this means that your training plan contains no more than 2-3 interval training sessions per week. Interval days are usually sandwiched between days with lower intensity training.

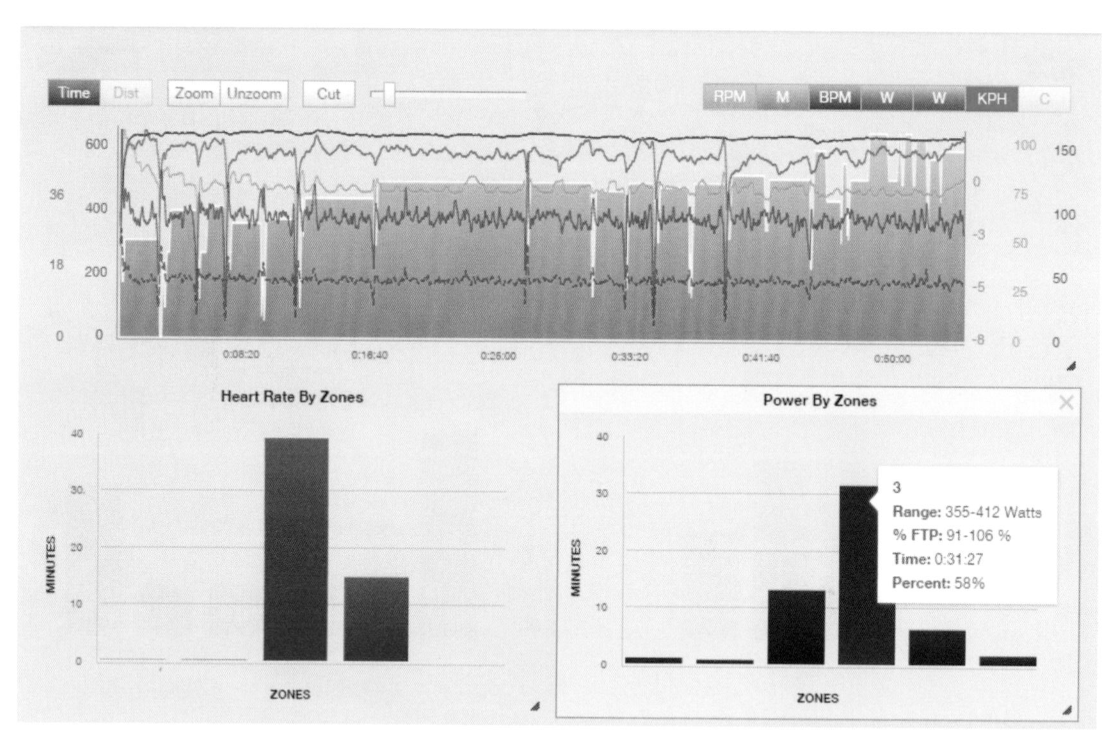

TrainingPeaks presentation of a time trial, illustrating a race at maximum effort.

What Is an Optimal Workout?

It is important to know what your goals are in order to develop a training plan. In addition, you must realize what your options are to train and how much time you have available. If your goal is to cycle criterions, then you have to train differently than when you want to specialize in time trials.

The characteristics of a criterion are totally different from a time trial, even when they both take one hour. Obviously in a criterion your power will frequently be in a very low zone (zone 0) or in a very high zone (zone 5). Your cycling speed can be very fast or a rate at which your legs are almost stationary. In a time trial you will have to push power in the zone just below and above the transition point (zones 2, 3 and 4). This distinction is important to know in order to create an optimal training plan.

For every cyclist it is important to have a good aerobic base, but for the cyclist who rides up to one-hour races it is not as important as for a cyclist who wants to ride 200-kilometer classics.

To train the aerobic capacity, you can use various workouts:

1. Extensive endurance training: training in zone 1. Gradually build up the duration and later the number of workouts. The duration varies from 1-2 hours up to 6 hours in the build-up phase. As the season approaches the duration will decline again. In season, you can choose to continue once per week to maintain this aspect. As an example you can ride three hours in zone 1.
2. Intensive endurance or speed endurance training: training in zone 2. The duration of this form of training is about 20-90 minutes, which can be divided into blocks. This form of training can also be mixed with extensive endurance training by alternating intensive with extensive blocks. The intensity remains below the FTP. An example is riding for two hours alternating three 10-minute intervals in zone 2, with a break of 10 minutes in zone 1.
3. Extensive interval training: Here you do 3-6 blocks of five minutes with an intensity just below the FTP. The breaks between the blocks are short (about 1 to 5 minutes). An example of this kind of training is two hours with four blocks of 8 minutes in zone 3, with a break of 2 minutes in zone 1.

To improve the anaerobic capacity, you can use:

1. Intense interval training: This includes short but intensive blocks where the intensity is above the FTP (105-120% of FTP) and the interval blocks have a length of 30 seconds up to 1-6 minutes. Breaks are often longer than the intervals, about 3-4 times as long. An example is a training of 90 minutes with six blocks of 2 minutes in zone 4, with a break of 3 minutes in zone 1. Or for VO_2 max training 4 x 4 minutes in zone 4 with a 4minute break in between.

2. Maximum sprint training: This is comprised of multiple short sprints in succession to a certain wattage until the moment your energy gets exhausted. An example is 10 x 20 seconds sprints with a three-minute break. When the average power over the 20 seconds drops by more than 10% this energy system is exhausted and the training is finished.

To create an optimal training plan you will have to analyze what is needed in the races. All aspects of the race should come back into your training plan.

Rest = Training

Along with the above, it is crucial that sufficient rest and recovery is included in the program. An example of a week training schedule could be:

» **Monday:**
Recovery training: 60-90 minutes in zones 0 and 1, easy active recovery cycling
» **Tuesday:**
Interval training: short intensive intervals in zone 4
» **Wednesday:**
Long endurance training: training of 3-4 hours in zones 1 and 2
» **Thursday:**
Rest or recovery training: 60 minutes in zones 0 and 1
» **Friday:**
Extensive interval training: intervals at 90-95% of your FTP (i.e., in zone 3)
» **Saturday:**
Race preparation, warm-up with some short accelerations
» **Sunday:**
Race day

Races are actually the best training. In a race you ride at an even higher level than in training, often almost at maximum for a long period of time. It is also wise to keep a training logbook and regularly do a standard training round. You can then graphically track the relationship between your power, HR and speed. In this way you can adjust your progress and monitor your training.

All aspects of the race should be included in your training plan.

32. HOW TO DETERMINE YOUR FTP WITH POWER METERS

If you want to be the best cyclist you can be, start now. Don't spend the rest of your life wondering if you can do it.

Once you have purchased a power meter, the next question is how to get the most benefit from it? What are the important values to determine? How do you do that? In this chapter we will explain how you can make a good start by determining your FTP with a power meter.

Determine Your FTP

In an earlier chapter we learned the concept of the functional threshold power (FTP). The FTP is the amount of power that you can maintain for one hour. When you push more than the FTP, your legs will quickly get tired. If you push less than your FTP, cycling is easier and you can maintain it much longer than one hour.

You can determine your FTP in different ways. One way is to do a laboratory test under controlled conditions. This will be discussed in one of the next chapters. It is also possible to determine the FTP yourself in a field test. A field test could consist of one hour of cycling at the highest possible power. This highest possible power is your FTP. Since one hour of cycling at your FTP level is very hard and not easily incorporated in a training week, a shorter test was developed by Hunter Allen and Andrew Coggan[7]. Their test is based on 20 minutes of riding at your highest possible intensity. By correcting the average power for the shorter duration, you can then calculate your FTP. Allen and Coggan take a percentage of 95% of the average power measured for 20 minutes. However, from the power–time relationship, we use a ratio of $(60/20)^{-0.07} = 0.93$ or 93%.

$$FTP = 0.93 * SP_{20\ minutes}$$

A field test like this can be performed regularly and be easily integrated into training plans. Do this test once every 6-8 weeks to assess your performance and check whether your progress is developing as desired.

Hunter Allen during a workshop on training and racing with a power meter at the Sports Medical and Performance Centre (SMA Midden Nederland) in Amersfoort, the Netherlands.

What Does the Field Test Look Like?

1. Twenty-minute warm-up of cycling at an easy pace (zone 1, 65% MHR).
2. Accelerations, three one-minute intervals at a high cadence (> 100-120/min), alternating with a one-minute break.
3. Three minutes of easy cycling in zone 1.
4. Three to five minutes of cycling at 110-120% of the estimated FTP. This is sufficient to recruit muscle fibers so that you are well prepared for the 20-minute time trial.
5. Ten minutes of easy cycling in zone 1.
6. Twenty-minute time trial. Try to ride the time trial as evenly as possible at a level that you can maintain for 20 minutes. Try to avoid staring too fast and prevent a complete break down at the end. Do not start too slow because you should not have too much energy left at the end.
7. Twenty-to-thirty-minute cool-down of easy cycling.

By repeating this test regularly you will get a better picture of the level you have to cycle at for a good test result.

We take Fast Eddy as an example. In the 20-minute time trial Eddy realizes an average power of 322 watts. Consequently, his FTP equals 0.93*322 = 300 watts.

Calculate Your Training Zones

Now that you know your FTP, you can calculate your training zones. Hunter Allen and Andrew Coggan have defined seven different zones (0-6) for the training of the four energy systems of the human engine:

Zone 0: Active Recovery
Power < 55% of FTP
Training in this area is aimed at active recovery with a duration of 30-90 minutes.

Zone 1: Endurance
Power between 55-75% of FTP
In this zone, easy endurance training is carried out, ranging from 1-8 hours.

Zone 2: Tempo
Power between 75-90% of FTP
In this zone, speed and endurance training is conducted in combination with enhanced duration blocks. The duration of the training in this zone varies between 45 minutes and 3 hours.

Zone 3: FTP Training
Power between 90-105% of FTP
In this zone, extended interval training can be done with the aim of improving the FTP. The interval blocks vary from 3-30 minutes. Total duration of interval blocks in this zone is generally 10-60 minutes.

Zone 4: VO_2 max Training
Power between 105-120% of FTP
In this zone, shorter interval blocks are cycled for the purpose of improving the anaerobic power and to improve the VO_2 max. The length of the interval blocks is 1-6 minutes. The total duration of the interval blocks in this zone is 5-30 minutes.

Zone 5: Anaerobic Capacity Training
Power between 120-150% of FTP
This form of training consists of short, very intense intervals lasting from 30 seconds to 3 minutes. The total duration of the interval blocks in this zone is 3-15 minutes.

Zone 6: Neuromuscular Power

Power much higher than 150% of FTP

These are maximal, very short, intense sprints of 5-30 seconds which can be performed with a standing start or a flying start. These training sessions put more stress on the musculoskeletal system and less on the metabolic system. You can only evaluate your power after the workout as the sprints are so short and intense.

Zone	Training goal	Training form
0	Circulation in muscles	Warming up, cooling down, technical exercise, recovery from a race or heavy training
1	Improve aerobic capacity and aerobic efficiency	Endurance training
2	Improve transition from aerobic to anaerobic system	Endurance training with long tempo blocks
3	Improve lactate threshold power and anaerobic efficiency	Interval training with blocks of 3-30 minutes with relatively short breaks
4	Improve lactate tolerance and VO_2 max	Interval training with short blocks of high speed and high intensity (1-6 minutes)
5	Improve anaerobic capacity	Accelerations and controlled sprints, short intensive intervals (between 30 seconds and 3 minutes)
6	Improve explosive power	Full sprint (5-30 seconds)

Example: Fast Eddy, FTP 300 Watts			
Training zones:	**%FTP**	**Lower limit (watts)**	**Upper limit (watts)**
Zone 0: Active Recovery	< 55%	-	165
Zone 1: Endurance	55-75%	165	225
Zone 2: Tempo	75-90%	225	270
Zone 3: FTP Training	90-105%	270	315
Zone 4: VO_2 max Training	105-120%	315	360
Zone 5: Anaerobic Capacity Training	120-150%	360	450
Zone 6: Neuromuscular Power	Maximal (>> 150%)	>> 450	

33. HOW TO ANALYZE THE DATA OF YOUR POWER METER

When my legs hurt, I say: "Shut up legs! Do what I tell you to." –Jens Voigt

When you race and train with a power meter, it makes sense that you spend some time analyzing the power data from your workout or race. These data are a source of information on your performance which you can use to get better!

For cyclists who are just starting to train with a power meter it is often difficult to find any structure in the data and charts available. In this chapter we will help you to read and understand the information. In other chapters of this book, we give more details on the background and significance of the various aspects.

The first time you cycle with a power meter, you'll notice quickly that the power data may fluctuate severely. When you accelerate it may vary from 0 to 400-500 watts. This is not surprising. It is difficult to push constant power during cycling. The power varies because you have to cope with the influence of wind, slopes, curves and the ever-changing forces on the pedals. Fortunately in practice you will quickly get used to this. A useful trick is to set the cycling computer in such a way that it shows an average value of the collected data over 3-10 seconds instead of every second. As a result the extremes are reduced and the information is better visualized.

After a training or race you can have a look at the data and analyze these. There are several apps on the market to assist you, such as TrainingPeaks. You can synchronize your data with these apps. This is possible with an Internet connection via Bluetooth, mobile network, WiFi and other options for data transfer. After you've uploaded the data, you can start analyzing it. For this book we used the app TrainingPeaks. This app has great potential and calculates many different parameters, which we will explain below.

After a training or race you can analyze the power meter data.

Which Parameters Are Relevant and What Do They Mean?

Average power (watts)

This speaks for itself. These are all measured power data divided by the total number of readings. If you do not pedal, the measured value is 0. The average power is determined including those zeros. If you do not take the zero values into account the average value would obviously get too high and would not accurately reflect your effort.

Watts per kilogram (watts/kg)

If you want to compare your values with other cyclists it is important to divide the power by your body weight in kilograms. Then you get a more objective comparison than just absolute power. Power per kilogram (or specific power) is an important value if you want to say something about how fast you can cycle. The higher this value is, the better you are. Previously we have shown that the limit of the human power over one hour (FTP) for women and men is 5.7 watts/kg and 6.4 watts/kg respectively.

Normalized power (P_n or NP, watts)

The normalized power is a calculation of the power that you would have pushed if you had cycled at a constant speed. Variations in speed cost more effort and therefore power. The figure shows an average power of 230 watts and a normalized power of 243 watts. The difference is thus a factor (VI) of 243/230 = 1.06.

Variability index (VI)

This is calculated by dividing the normalized power by the average power. This says something about the variability of the power. If you've cycled very consistently with few ups and downs than the VI will be 1.0. When you cycle with more variation the normalized power (P_n or NP) will increase and therefore the VI will too. Typical values for a flat time trial are between 1.0 and 1.02. A criterion, however, has a VI of 1.2 or even more.

Training stress score (TSS)

This is a parameter which represents both the intensity and duration of the training or race. This parameter can also be used to compare the load of a particular training. When you have cycled for one hour at your FTP, it corresponds to 100 TSS points. When you cycle for two hours with an intensity of 80% of your FTP you get $(0.8)^2*2*100 = 128$ points. A TSS between 100 and 200 means that you will have no adverse effects on your training the next day. Above 300 means that it has been a hard workout or race and several days of recovery are required. The recovery time depends on your aerobic capacity and your performance index.

Intensity factor (IF)

This parameter says something about how intense your workout or race has been compared to your FTP. The IF is calculated by dividing the normalized power by your FTP. Typical IF values for endurance training are between 0.75 and 0.85. In a 4-kilometer cycling pursuit on the track you will easily exceed an IF of 1.15.

Work or energy (in kJ)

By using a power meter, it is easy to calculate the energy you have pushed during your workout or race. As the metabolic efficiency is 25%, you know that you will have used about four times as much metabolic energy. Since 1 kcal equals 4.18 kJ, the metabolic energy consumption of your body in kcal roughly equals the value in kJ indicated by your power meter.

Peak power

The table shows what your best values were for various time intervals. By collecting all the power meter data for each time interval the best value can be determined, as well as the all-time values. You can quickly see whether you have got a new personal best. It also helps you gather the data required for a power profile test that we have described in another chapter.

Efficiency factor (EF)

This is calculated by dividing the normalized power by the average heart rate of the training or interval in the training. By comparing this value with a similar training or interval, you can see if you improved your aerobic efficiency over a given period. The value in itself does not say much, but an increase or a decrease in this ratio is relevant. If the ratio increases, this means that you have more power at the same heart rate, or the same power at a lower heart rate. In short, you have become more efficient and better!

Power–heart rate ratio (Power:HR)

If the heart rate increases during aerobic endurance training while the intensity (power) remains the same, the aerobic base is insufficient and should be better developed. The same applies when the heart rate remains the same but the power output decreases. To assess the ratio between power and heart rate, you can divide an endurance training with constant load into two equal parts. Compare the power and HR rate of the first half with the second half. With a decrease of more than 5%, an improvement of the aerobic base is possible and necessary.

The cycle computer of elite cyclist Robert Gesink displays all relevant data of the ride in real time.

The Example Shown in the Figure

The next figure shows an example of an analysis in TrainingPeaks. The example is a two-hour endurance training, which was cycled with a relatively constant power between 230 and 250 watts. From this you can conclude the following:

- The average power is 230 watts.
- The specific power or power per kg is 3,11 watts/kg (body weight 74 kg).
- The normalized power (NP) is 243 watts.
- The variability index (V) is 1.06, so the training was not at a constant speed because the VI should be between 1.0 and 1.05.
- The training stress score (TSS) is 122.8, a fairly easy workout for this cyclist.
- The intensity factor (IF) is 0.79, within the range of 0.75 and 0.85 which stands for a regular endurance training.
- The work is 1655 kJ, meaning the cyclist burned around 1655 kcal.
- The peak power values are right at the bottom, but because this was an endurance training the values are not very useful.
- The efficiency factor (EF) is the normalized power (243 watts) divided by the average heart rate (HRavg, 134/min). So the EF is 243/134 = 1.81.
- The power to HR ratio is -1.29%. This shows that an improvement occurred in the second half of the training. Since it is a long endurance training, you can conclude that the aerobic base is fine!

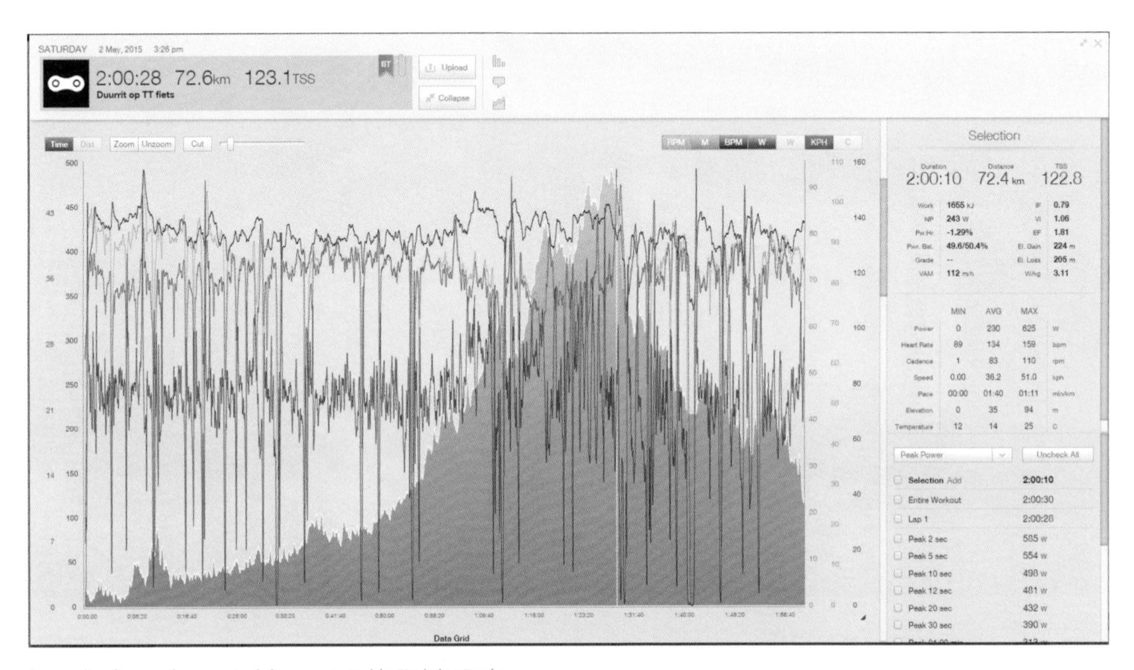

Example of an endurance training presented in TrainingPeaks.

Ergonomic and aerodynamic positioned bike computer for power meter readings.

34. POWER PROFILE TESTING

The only source of knowledge is experience.
–Albert Einstein

The power profile test was originally designed by Hunter Allen and Andrew Coggan[7] to compare cyclists. Using their power profile chart you can visualize the relative strengths and weaknesses of a cyclist. A power profile test makes it possible to accurately determine the level of a cyclist. With this information a training plan can be individually targeted.

What Is a Power Profile Test?

A power profile summarizes the power a cyclist can push during different periods of time. The periods range from very short maximal sprints to a length similar to a time trial. Together, the power data divided by the body weight of the cyclist form a power profile which can be seen as a fingerprint image of the cyclist. The app TrainingPeaks can be used to generate power profiles.

With the permission of the authors and publisher you find a table on the last page of this chapter. With this table you can create your own power profile and compare your profile with others. The time periods that have been defined by Allen and Coggan are 5 seconds, 1 minute, 5 minutes and 20 minutes. The underlying idea for these time periods are that they correspond best with the neuromuscular power (5 seconds), the anaerobic capacity (1 minute), the VO_2 max (5 minutes) and the anaerobic threshold (FTP). The FTP can generally be calculated as 93% of the 20-minute power value found with TrainingPeaks. The table has been designed by using lots of data from various categories of cyclists, ranging from the absolute world top to untrained cyclists.

What Can You Learn From a Power Profile?

A power profile test provides lots of useful information about the cyclist. Are you a climber or a sprinter? Are you a time-trial specialist, or are you an all-rounder? With this information you can optimize your training on the basis of power-related training zones to focus the training on your objectives. By doing the test again halfway through or after a training period, you can check whether improvement has occurred and make timely adjustments to your training plan.

How Does the Test Work?

The test consists of two parts in which various interval periods are cycled. In each interval you try to get the highest possible average power over the specified period of time. In between the intervals are recovery periods. Between parts 1 and 2 of the test you rest a few days. Optionally you can also first cycle part 2, and then do part 1 after that.

Test Protocol: Part 1 (Short, Anaerobic)

1. Warm up for about 45 minutes, including three intervals of one minute at high cadence (> 110 rpm) and high intensity (80-90% of FTP) with one minute of easy cycling in between.
2. Cycle for five minutes at FTP level.
3. Recover with 3-5 minutes of easy cycling.
4. Test: Cycle all out for one minute followed by ten minutes of easy cycling.
5. Test: Starting at a speed of 30-32 km/h, cycle for five minutes while increasing speed until all out. Push as hard as you can in the last 45 seconds.
6. Recover with 10 minutes of easy cycling.
7. Test: Starting from the saddle with a speed of 30-32 km/h, cycle all out for one minute and end by sitting on the saddle again to finish.
8. Recover with 3-5 minutes of easy cycling.
9. Test: Starting from the saddle with a speed of 30-32 km/h, cycle all out for one minute and end by sitting on the saddle again to finish.
10. Recover with 3-5 minutes of easy cycling.
11. Test: Starting from the saddle with a speed of 24-25 km/h, sprint for 15 seconds.
12. Recover with 2-3 minutes of easy cycling.
13. Test: Starting from the saddle with a speed of 24-25 km/h, sprint for 15 seconds.
14. Cool down for 20-30 minutes.

Test Protocol: Part 2 (20 Minutes)

1. Warm up for about 30-45 minutes, including three one-minute intervals at high cadence cycle (> 110 rpm) and high intensity (80-90% of FTP) with one minute of easy cycling in between.

2. Cycle at a steady pace of maximum effort for five minutes to encourage recruitment of muscle fibers and blood flow.

3. Recover for 10 minutes of easy cycling.

4. Test: Cycle for 20 minutes at a steady pace of maximum effort. Check your pace after 5 minutes.

5. Cool down for 20-30 minutes.

By highlighting your own results in TrainingPeaks (5 seconds, 1 minute, 5 minutes and FTP) you can find yourselves in one of the different categories. Thus, it is possible to determine a unique pattern for each cyclist, to identify individual weaknesses and strengths, and to develop a well-targeted training plan and adjust the training plan as necessary based on the findings.

In this way cyclists can be easily categorized:
All-rounders score solid values at 5 seconds, 1 minute and 5 minutes as well as for FTP. These cyclists do not peak in any of the intervals very well, but are generally not really bad at all. This profile you often see for novice and young riders who have not yet specialized in a specific discipline. Also, many cyclists and especially cycle tour lovers will fit this profile.

Sprinters score very well on the 1-, 2- and 5-second all-out values. They can push very high power on the pedals during a short period of time. However, you will see a clear decline from 1-5 minutes. FTP is often less well developed.

Time-trial specialists and climbers have very high FTP values. On the other hand, they are significantly weaker in neuromuscular power and anaerobic capacity. The 1-, 2- and 5-second all-out values—and often the 1-minute value—are relatively less developed.

Test Results for Fast Eddy		
	Watts	Watts/kg
5 seconds	1122	14.96
1 minute	565	7.53
5 minutes	357	4.76
60 minutes	300	4

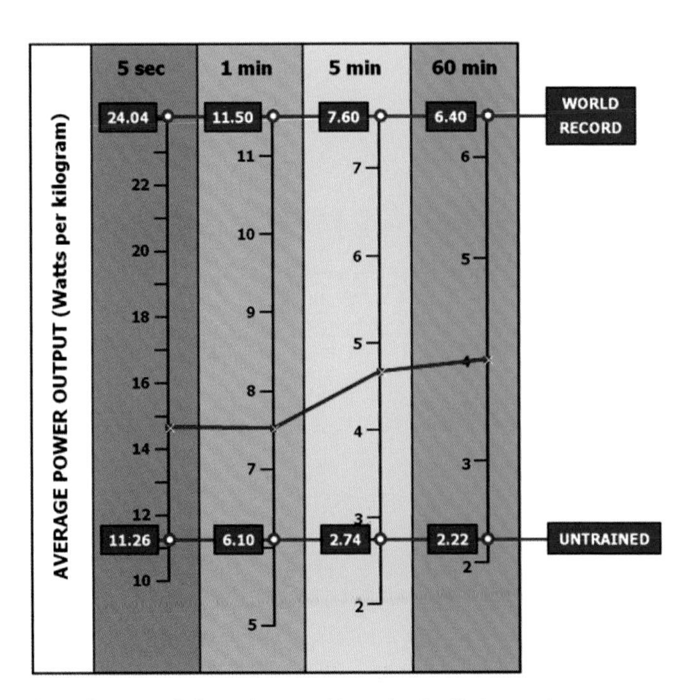

The performance of all-rounder Fast Eddy can be classified as tourist.

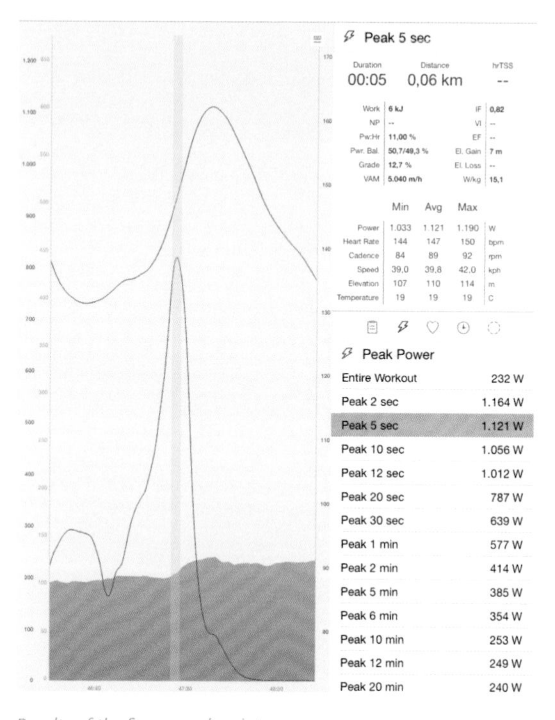

Results of the five-second sprint.

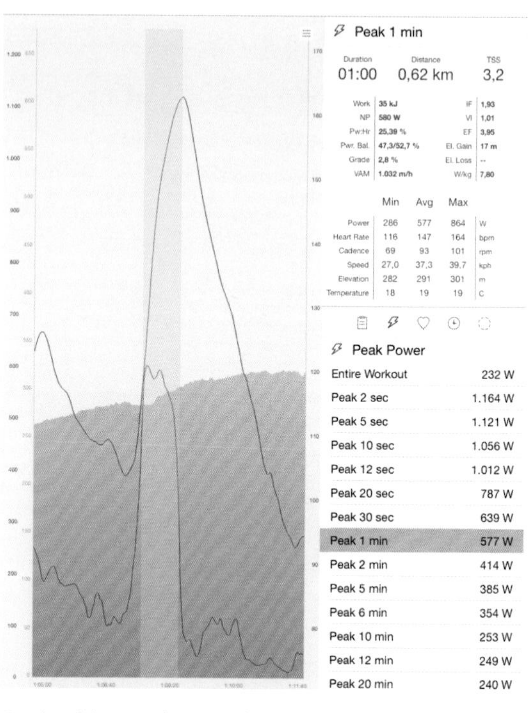

Results of the one-minute maximal.

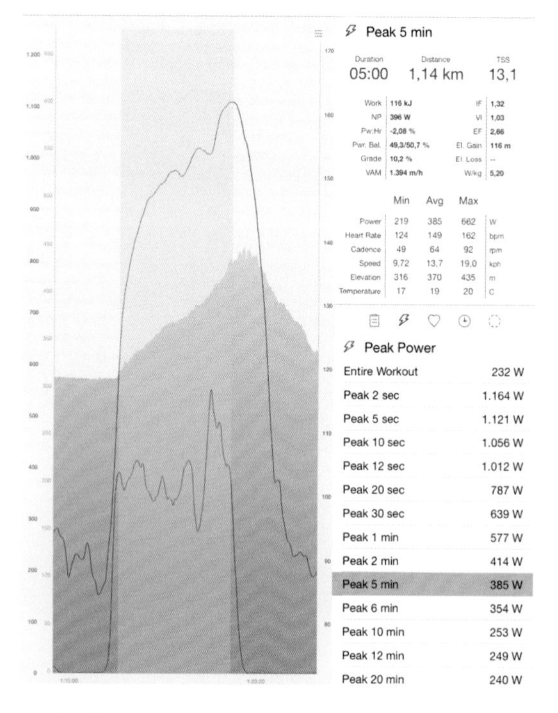

Results of the five-minute maximal.

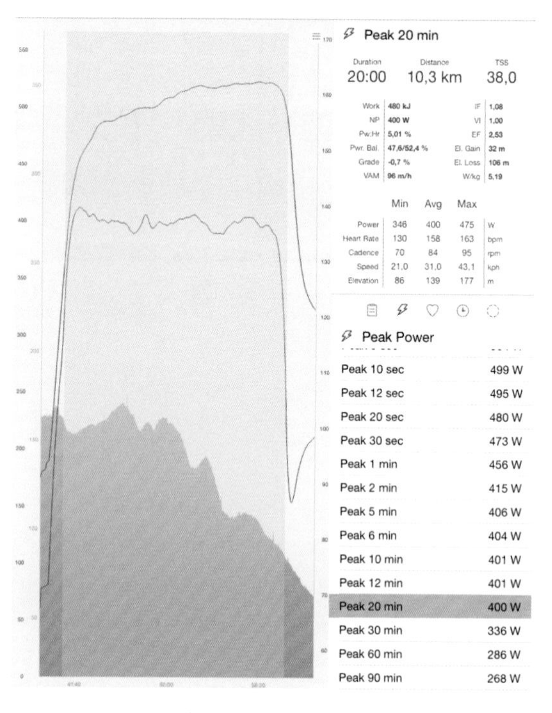

Results of the 20-minute test.

TABLE 4.1 Power Profile Chart

	MAXIMAL POWER OUTPUT (W/kg)							
	Men				Women			
	5 sec.	1 min.	5 min.	FTP	5 sec.	1 min.	5 min.	FTP
	25.18	11.50	7.60	6.40	19.42	9.29	6.74	5.69
	24.88	11.39	7.50	6.31	19.20	9.20	6.64	5.61
	24.59	11.27	7.39	6.22	18.99	9.11	6.55	5.53
	24.29	11.16	7.29	6.13	18.77	9.02	6.45	5.44
World class (e.g., international pro)	24.00	11.04	7.19	6.04	18.56	8.93	6.36	5.36
	23.70	10.93	7.08	5.96	18.34	8.84	6.26	5.28
	23.40	10.81	6.98	5.87	18.13	8.75	6.17	5.20
	23.11	10.70	6.88	5.78	17.91	8.66	6.07	5.12
	22.81	10.58	6.77	5.69	17.70	8.56	5.98	5.03
	22.51	10.47	6.67	5.60	17.48	8.47	5.88	4.95
Exceptional (e.g., domestic pro)	22.22	10.35	6.57	5.51	17.26	8.38	5.79	4.87
	21.92	10.24	6.46	5.42	17.05	8.29	5.69	4.79
	21.63	10.12	6.36	5.33	16.83	8.20	5.60	4.70
	21.33	10.01	6.26	5.24	16.62	8.11	5.50	4.62
	21.03	9.89	6.15	5.15	16.40	8.02	5.41	4.54
	20.74	9.78	6.05	5.07	16.19	7.93	5.31	4.46
Excellent (e.g., Cat. I)	20.44	9.66	5.95	4.98	15.97	7.84	5.21	4.38
	20.15	9.55	5.84	4.89	15.76	7.75	5.12	4.29
	19.85	9.43	5.74	4.80	15.54	7.66	5.02	4.21
	19.55	9.32	5.64	4.71	15.32	7.57	4.93	4.13
	19.26	9.20	5.53	4.62	15.11	7.48	4.83	4.05
	18.96	9.09	5.43	4.53	14.89	7.39	4.74	3.97
Very good (e.g., Cat. II)	18.66	8.97	5.33	4.44	14.68	7.30	4.64	3.88
	18.37	8.86	5.22	4.35	14.46	7.21	4.55	3.80
	18.07	8.74	5.12	4.27	14.25	7.11	4.45	3.72
	17.78	8.63	5.01	4.18	14.03	7.02	4.36	3.64
	17.48	8.51	4.91	4.09	13.82	6.93	4.26	3.55
	17.18	8.40	4.81	4.00	13.60	6.84	4.17	3.47
	16.89	8.28	4.70	3.91	13.39	6.75	4.07	3.39
Good (e.g., Cat. III)	16.59	8.17	4.60	3.82	13.17	6.66	3.98	3.31
	16.29	8.05	4.50	3.73	12.95	6.57	3.88	3.23
	16.00	7.94	4.39	3.64	12.74	6.48	3.79	3.14
	15.70	7.82	4.29	3.55	12.52	6.39	3.69	3.06
	15.41	7.71	4.19	3.47	12.31	6.30	3.59	2.98
	15.11	7.59	4.08	3.38	12.09	6.21	3.50	2.90
Moderate (e.g., Cat. IV)	14.81	7.48	3.98	3.29	11.88	6.12	3.40	2.82
	14.52	7.36	3.88	3.20	11.66	6.03	3.31	2.73
	14.22	7.25	3.77	3.11	11.45	5.94	3.21	2.65
	13.93	7.13	3.67	3.02	11.23	5.85	3.12	2.57
	13.63	7.02	3.57	2.93	11.01	5.76	3.02	2.49
	13.33	6.90	3.46	2.84	10.80	5.66	2.93	2.40
Fair (e.g., Cat. V)	13.04	6.79	3.36	2.75	10.58	5.57	2.83	2.32
	12.74	6.67	3.26	2.66	10.37	5.48	2.74	2.24
	12.44	6.56	3.15	2.58	10.15	5.39	2.64	2.16
	12.15	6.44	3.05	2.49	9.94	5.30	2.55	2.08
	11.85	6.33	2.95	2.40	9.72	5.21	2.45	1.99
	11.56	6.21	2.84	2.31	9.51	5.12	2.36	1.91
Untrained (nonracer)	11.26	6.10	2.74	2.22	9.29	5.03	2.26	1.83
	10.96	5.99	2.64	2.13	9.07	4.94	2.16	1.75
	10.67	5.87	2.53	2.04	8.86	4.85	2.07	1.67
	10.37	5.76	2.43	1.95	8.64	4.76	1.97	1.58
	10.08	5.64	2.33	1.86	8.43	4.67	1.88	1.50

Courtesy: Training & Racing with a Power Meter, 2nd ed., by Hunter Allen & Andrew Coggan (Velopress 2010)[7].

35. LABORATORY TESTING

Fitness is the new wealth. –Erben Wennemars

The laboratory of a sports medical advice centre (SMA) offers various tests. In this chapter we elaborate on the testing of the aerobic and anaerobic systems of a cyclist.

To test the aerobic system the load is increased step by step. Such a test goes beyond your anaerobic threshold until your maximum effort level is reached. This is called the anaerobic threshold test. This test provides an accurate assessment of your FTP.

The Wingate test is used to determine the anaerobic capacity. The anaerobic system is tested by an all-out sprint for 30 seconds.

Anaerobic Threshold Test

For the anaerobic threshold test, ergospirometry, or breath analysis, is used for an accurate determination of the FTP. In addition to the heart activity (HR) and blood pressure, the composition of the exhaled air at each breath is measured, including the concentrations of oxygen (O_2) and carbon dioxide (CO_2). The software generates various graphs that show the energy consumption in the body. During this test various parameters are determined which provide information about your fitness. With this information, specific individual limitations can be diagnosed, and training schedules and advice can be optimized.

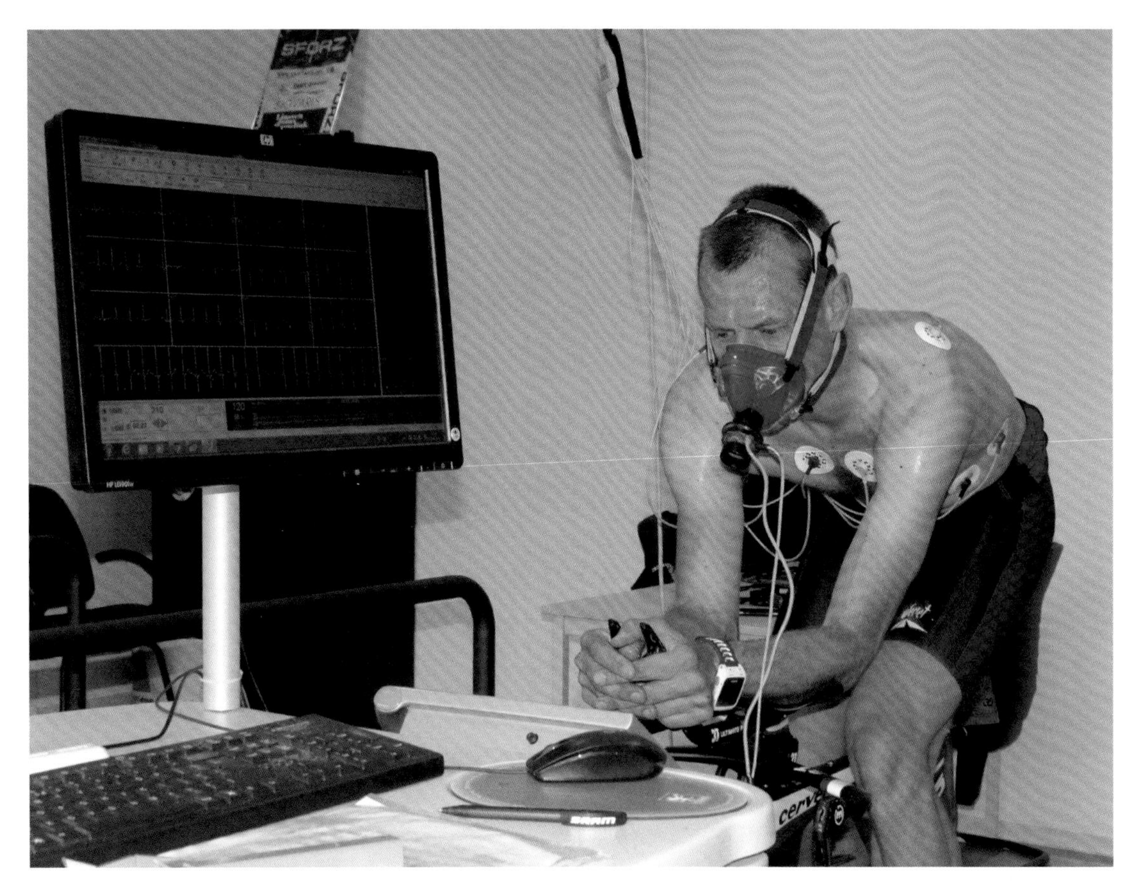

Author Guido Vroemen during an anaerobic threshold test.

Protocol Anaerobic Threshold Test

For this test it is important to choose the correct values for the starting resistance (watts) and the increase of the wattage per step. In order to ensure that the body gets the opportunity to reach a new equilibrium in each step, the length of a step should be sufficiently long. A three-minute step length is suitable. Longer lengths are allowed, but certainly not less. The starting wattage is determined on the basis of the body weight of the cyclist and is between 1.5 and 2 watts/kg. At each step 20-30 watts per three minutes are added. Once the anaerobic threshold has been passed, the interval length is reduced from three minutes to one minute until the maximum power is reached.

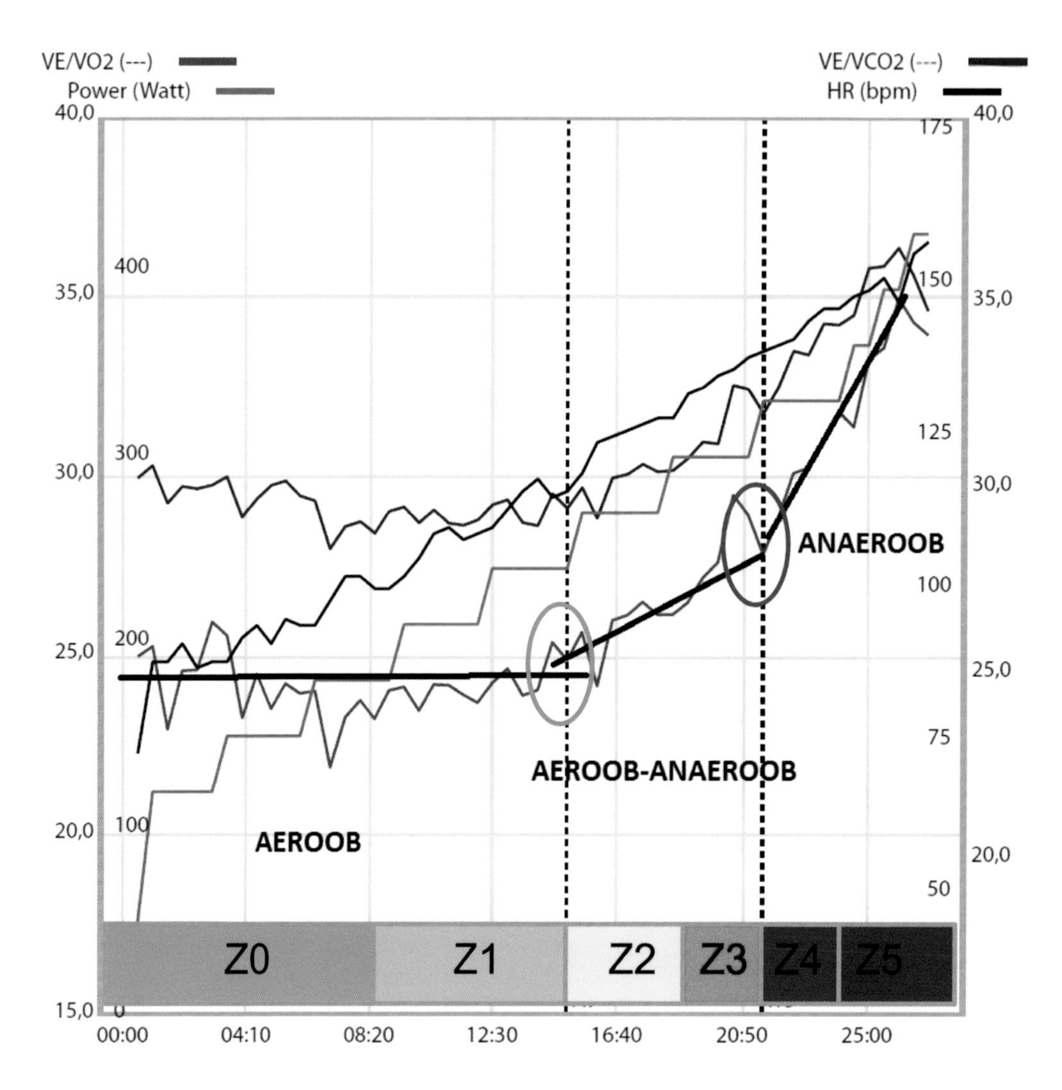

Output of an aerobic and anaerobic threshold test.

Which Parameters Are Measured During the Ergospirometry Test?

Ventilation

The ventilation is the volume of exhaled air (VE) in one minute. The VE is calculated from the number of breaths per minute, the respiratory rate (RR) and the breath volume (BV).

$$VE = RR * BV$$

At rest the RR is about 10-12 times per minute with a BV of about 500-1000 ml. Thus, the VE at rest is about 5-10 l/min. During maximal effort the respiratory rate (RR) may increase to 60-70/min and the breath volume (BV, depending on total lung volume) up to 3-4 liters. So the VE during maximum effort can be up to 200 l/min.

Circulation

The circulation, also known as cardiac output (CO) is calculated from the heart rate (HR) and the volume of blood circulated per stroke (SV).

$$CO = HR*SV$$

At rest, the RHR is about 50-60 beats/minute (this is lower for well-trained cyclists) and the SV is about 60-80 ml. The CO at rest is 4-5 l/min.

During maximum effort HR may increase up to 200 and the SV of well-trained cyclists to 150-200 ml. Consequently the CO during maximum effort can increase to 30-40 l/min.

The stroke volume (SV) cannot yet be measured simply during a test. The heartbeat (HR) is determined from the electrocardiogram (ECG).

Oxygen concentration

During the test the oxygen (O_2) content of every breath is measured. By determining the difference with the outside air (20.93% oxygen) it can be calculated how much oxygen is absorbed into the body. At maximum effort the maximum oxygen uptake (VO_2 max) can be determined.

Carbon dioxide concentration

The amount of carbon dioxide is determined in the exhaled air and compared with the outside air (0.03% CO_2). Consequently, the amount of CO_2 produced by the body can be calculated.

Respiratory quotient (RQ)

This parameter indicates the sources of energy that your body uses to push the pedals. The RQ is the amount of CO_2 in l/min produced divided by the amount of O_2 in l/min inhaled.

$$RQ = VCO_2/VO_2$$

If only fatty acids are used, RQ is 0.7. If glycogen (carbohydrates) are used exclusively, RQ is 1.0. At an RQ of 0.85, the carbohydrate and fatty acids ratio is 50-50%.

This parameter can be used to indicate the amount of fat oxidation during various efforts.

Equivalents (VE/VO_2 and VE/VCO_2)

These parameters say something about the amount of air required to ventilate one liter of oxygen, or exhale one liter of carbon dioxide.

Aerobic threshold (first ventilatory threshold)

This is the threshold where the formation of lactic acid starts. To this point the amount of lactic acid you produce can be easily removed and broken down by your body. The concentration of lactic acid hardly increases until this point. This threshold is between zones 1 and 2. In the graph this point can be recognized as the point where the VE/VO_2 starts rising.

Anaerobic threshold (second ventilatory threshold)

From this point you produce so much lactic acid that your body can no longer break it down sufficiently, so there is a significant increase in the lactic acid concentration. The further you get above this threshold, the shorter you can maintain the effort. This threshold is between zones 3 and 4. In the graph the point can be recognized as the moment where both VE/VO_2 and VE/VCO_2 no longer remain in a steady state and begin to rise.

The maximum oxygen uptake capacity (VO_2 max)

The maximum oxygen uptake capacity is measured in milliliters per minute (as ml/min). In order to make the parameter comparable with other cyclists it is divided by the body weight in kilograms and expressed as ml/kg/min. For more information about VO_2 max also see one of the earlier chapters.

Wingate Test

The Wingate test is a sprint test on a bicycle ergometer which measures the sprint power during 30 seconds. The sprint assessment is based on the explosive starting force, the acceleration and the time the sprint can be maintained. The test is a widely used and reliable method to determine these capabilities for track cyclists and sprinters. It provides useful information to optimize a specific training program. The starting force is the strong explosive power required for the initial acceleration. The acceleration is the ability to accelerate to the speed limit. The time during which the maximum effort can be maintained is also called resilience in the language of a trainer. This is the resistance of the cyclist against fatigue or acidification.

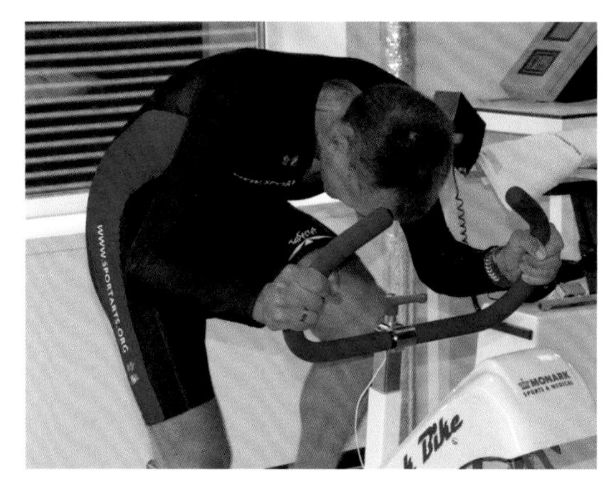

The Wingate test, an all-out sprint of 30 seconds.

Protocol

Make sure that the cyclist has done a good warm-up for about 10-15 minutes with several short accelerations. The test can be started on command or automatically when a certain cadence is exceeded. The resistance used at the ergometer in this test is equivalent to 7.5% of the body weight. After the start the cyclist will do a full, all-out sprint for 30 seconds. The test provides a maximum power during this sprint (peak power), an average power (average power) and the decrease in the maximum power to the minimum during the 30 seconds. This decrease is also called the fatigue index.

After 30 seconds, it is important to make sure that the cyclist does not stop immediately but cycles easily to ensure a good cool-down. If the cyclist stops immediately he can have physical problems because of the massive production of lactic acid and the adverse blood distribution during the test (i.e., a lot of blood in the legs and little in head).

Test Information

Bout Duration [s]: 30

Person Weight [kg]: 76,0

Date and Time:

Supervisor:

Analysis

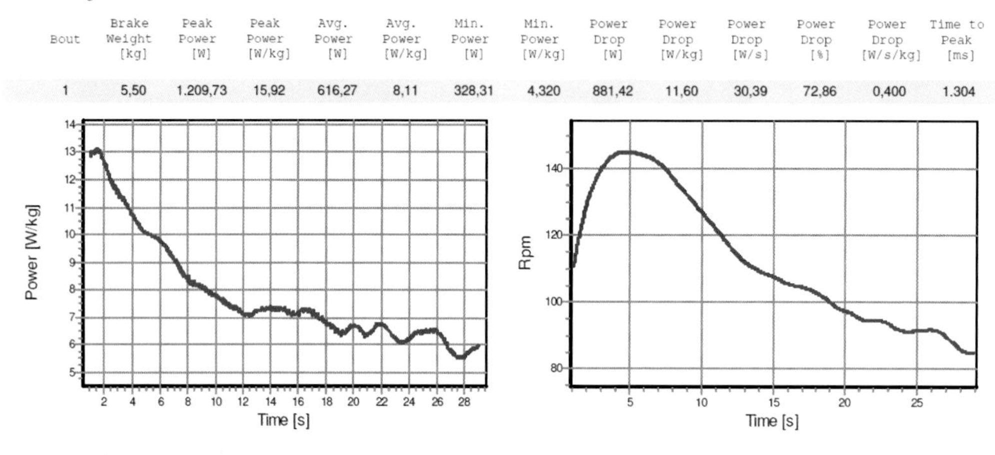

Bout	Brake Weight [kg]	Peak Power [W]	Peak Power [W/kg]	Avg. Power [W]	Avg. Power [W/kg]	Min. Power [W]	Min. Power [W/kg]	Power Drop [W]	Power Drop [W/kg]	Power Drop [W/s]	Power Drop [%]	Power Drop [W/s/kg]	Time to Peak [ms]
1	5,50	1.209,73	15,92	616,27	8,11	328,31	4,320	881,42	11,60	30,39	72,86	0,400	1.304

Wingate test results.

Results

For purposes of illustration, the results of a Wingate test by author Guido are shown in the figure and summarized in the table.

Wingate Test by Guido	
Parameter	**Value**
Peak power	1209 watts
Peak power	15.92 watts/kg
Time to peak	1.3 sec
Average power	616 watts
Average power	8.11 watts/kg
Minimum power	328 watts
Minimum power	4.32 watts/kg
Power drop	881 watts
Power drop	11.60 watts/kg
Fatigue index	30.39 watts/sec
Fatigue index	72.90%

It can be seen that in the first two seconds of the test the peak power is already reached. The pedaling frequency is 4-6 seconds at a maximum of 150 revolutions/minute. The decline in the power amounts to 881 watts. The fatigue index is 881/1209 = 72.9%.

The peak power is very good, but drops back too quickly. For the long sprint there is clearly room for improvement.

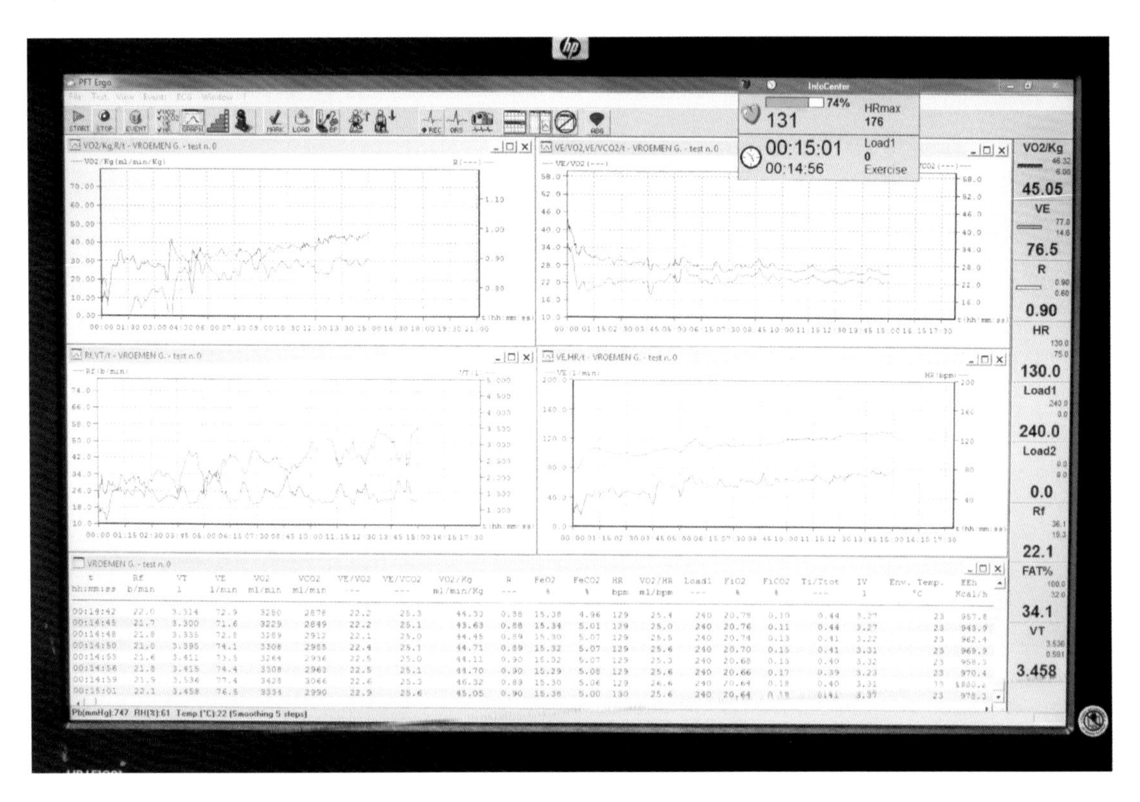

Parameters measured during an ergospirometry test by author Guido Vroemen.

36. PEDALING EFFICIENCY

Ride as much or as little, as long or as short as you feel. But ride! –Eddy Merckx

To optimize cycling performance, it is important to maximize your cycling efficiency. In cycling, the gross efficiency is sometimes defined as the ratio of the external work output to the metabolic energy expenditure:

Gross efficiency =
Energy output (external work) / Energy input (metabolic expenditure)*100 %

So far, we have used the term metabolic efficiency to describe the ratio between energy output and energy input in the muscles of our human engine. In practice, the GE (and thus the ME) can be determined by measuring the external work with a power meter and the metabolic expenditure via indirect calorimetry (respiratory gas exchange or ergospirometry)

Example: Cyclist 70 kg

Power (= external energy output) = 210 watts (= 210 J/s)

VO_2 = 2.8 l/min → (= metabolic expenditure) = 2.8*1000*19.55/60 = 912 J/s

GE = ME = 210/912*100 % = 23 %

In the above example, the energy value of O_2 has been set at 19.55 kJ/l.

In literature, the ME is usually set at 25%. This value is believed to represent the theoretical ratio for the energy production in the muscles themselves. In cycling practice, GE values between 20-25% can be found. Lower values can be caused by a lower cycling efficiency .

Which Biomechanical Factors Influence the Cycling Efficiency?

Saddle height

The saddle height should be optimized for leg length; small changes in saddle height may affect GE and lower limb kinematics. A proper bike fit is a prerequisite for a smooth pedal stroke. In the right position you'll maximize your power output and you will be able to adapt your technique to different terrain, cadences and effort levels.

Cadence

High-cadence cycling (> 90-100 rpm) at low load (< 150 watts) results in a lower GE than low-cadence cycling (< 80 rpm) at the same low load. In general, the GE is lower at a higher cadence.

Crank length

The influence on GE is small; 170, 172.5 and 175 mm cranks will not lead to more than 0.5-1% differences in GE, so cyclists can choose the crank length they prefer.

Foot position

Placing your foot properly over the body of the pedal will help to ensure maximum pedal power and efficiency. Position your foot over your bicycle pedal so that the ball of your foot, also called the metatarsal, is directly over the pivot arm of the pedal. The pedal's pivot arm is the axis, which runs through the body of the pedal. Positioning your metatarsal over this part of the pedal maximizes stability.

A factor that may contribute to the GE is the pedaling technique (i.e., the way that the forces produced by the cyclist's muscles are transferred to the crank). Forces, torques or power delivered by the cyclist to the pedals can be measured using force pedals or instrumented cranks. Nowadays power meters can also measure these. In this way it is possible to measure the pedaling efficiency. This is calculated by measuring the forces that have a positive contribution to the rotation of the cranks divided by the theoretical maximum. Obviously, in the upstroke it is very difficult to achieve a positive force. Riders with a good pedaling efficiency may reach a zero force in the upstroke; in this case there is no negative contribution in the upstroke.

Pedaling Phases

You can divide the pedal stroke in to four different zones:

Zone 1: from 12 o'clock to 5 o'clock
This is the power phase zone. In this zone you can produce the most power; it is also called the push down phase.

Zone 2: from 5 o'clock to 7 o'clock
This is the transition to the upstroke phase. The ankle will be extended a little to about 10-20 degrees by the calf muscles. In this phase you can transfer some energy in the crank. It is also called the pullback phase.

Zone 3: from 7 o'clock to 9 o'clock
In the upstroke phase you should not focus on pulling up the leg as hard as you can, but just try to lift the leg as it doesn't put any weight on the pedal. The pedal is actually pushing your leg up, so the goal is to lose as little power as possible.

Zone 4: from 9 o'clock to 12 o'clock
This is the second part of the upstroke and you have to set up for the down stroke starting from 12 o'clock.

Muscles Active in Cycling[43]

For a cyclist in the saddle, most of the power is pushed between the 12 o'clock and 5 o'clock positions (the power phase). This is where the majority of the muscles are activated. Hip and knee extension are the primary movements of the pedal stroke. The muscles involved are mainly the gluteus maximus and the quadriceps, and the antagonists biceps femoris, the semimembranosus and the gastrocnemius. The power phase involves extending the hip and the knee, pressing downward on the pedal. This action starts with a combination of the gluteus maximus and quadriceps muscles, but then is joined by the hamstrings and calf muscles at about the 3 o'clock position. This shows the need for equally strong hamstrings, hips and quadriceps. These groups of muscles make up the largest volume of muscles used in a pedal revolution.

Between the 6 o'clock and 12 o'clock positions, there is some knee flexion to assist in bringing the pedal back to the top. However this flexion is assisted by the greater downward force being placed on the opposite pedal by the opposite leg. Any extra assistance bringing the returning pedal back to the top is a benefit. The muscles that help return the foot to the top range are the hamstrings (biceps femoris and semimembranosus) and calves (gastrocnemius and soleus). These muscles act at the bottom of the stroke, pulling the foot backwards (pullback phase) to the quadriceps at the top, lifting the knee back to the 12 o'clock position.

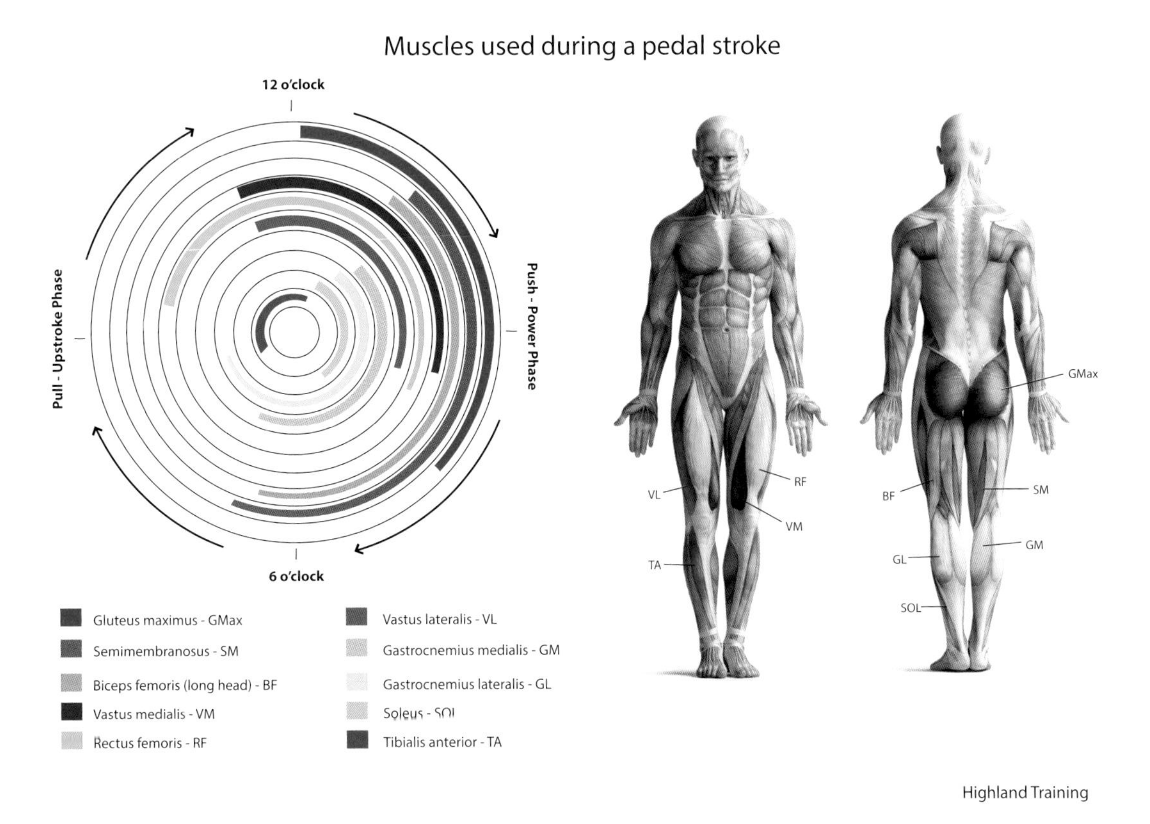

Pedal phasing and muscles active in cycling (courtesy Mike Schultz/Highland training & TrainingPeaks).

Which Forces Act on the Pedal?

The first is the tangential force that is actually turning the cranks. It runs perpendicular to the crank throughout the 360° of rotation. The second is the radial force, which acts parallel to the crank and directly down along the length of the cranks, outwards from the bottom bracket. These two forces are the result of the pedal force. Ideally, 100% of the pedal force should act tangential and 0% radial. Obviously, this cannot be achieved in reality.

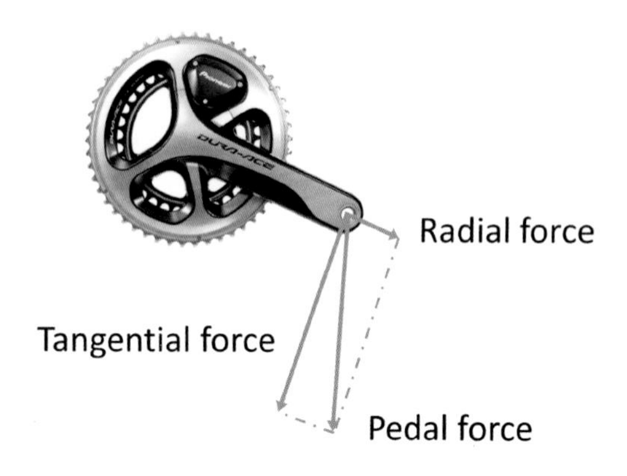

Forces acting on a pedal.

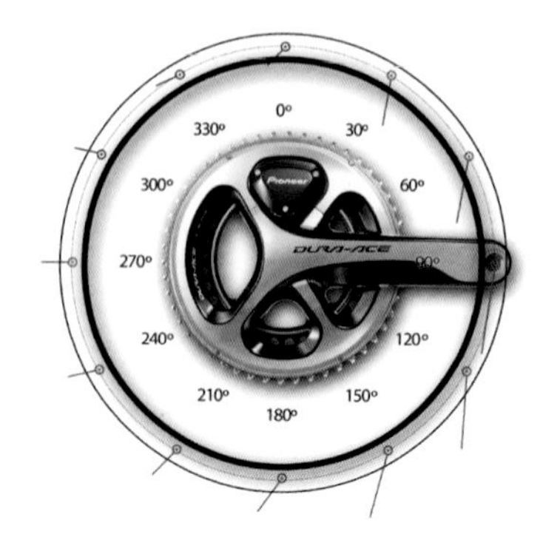

The pedaling forces can be calculated and visualized by a Pioneer power meter.

An example of a power meter that can calculate and visualize this pedal force is the Pioneer power meter. This enables you to measure and see not only cadence and individual left and right power, but also power output and power direction at thirty-degree intervals. The measured power output and power direction are displayed as force vectors, so you can discover your own pedaling characteristics. The force vector is a directional visualization that allows you to check your pedaling status at 30-degree intervals throughout rotation.

Quantify Your Pedaling Efficiency

From the total force to the crank over one rotation of 360 degrees, the proportion of force contributing to the rotation is quantified as pedaling efficiency. Your pedaling efficiency is visualized numerically to provide an easy-to-understand guide for efficient pedaling training.

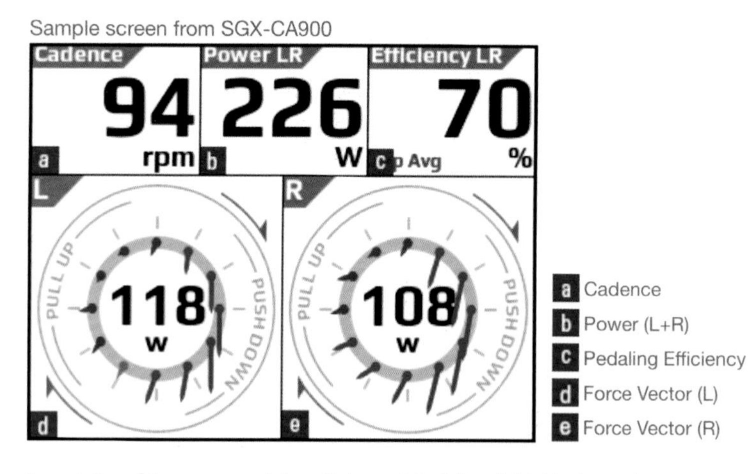

Presentation of the average pedaling efficiency of the left and right leg in one lap.

Cycling Dynamics

This chart shows the power applied to a pedal in a typical rotation of the crank. It starts off positively on the downward movement, but there is a negative component in the second half of the rotation if the pedal isn't completely unloaded or lifted up. P^+ is the power pushing the pedal forward, while P^- is the power pushing the pedal in the opposite direction. P_{max} is the maximum power, while P_{avg} is the average power.

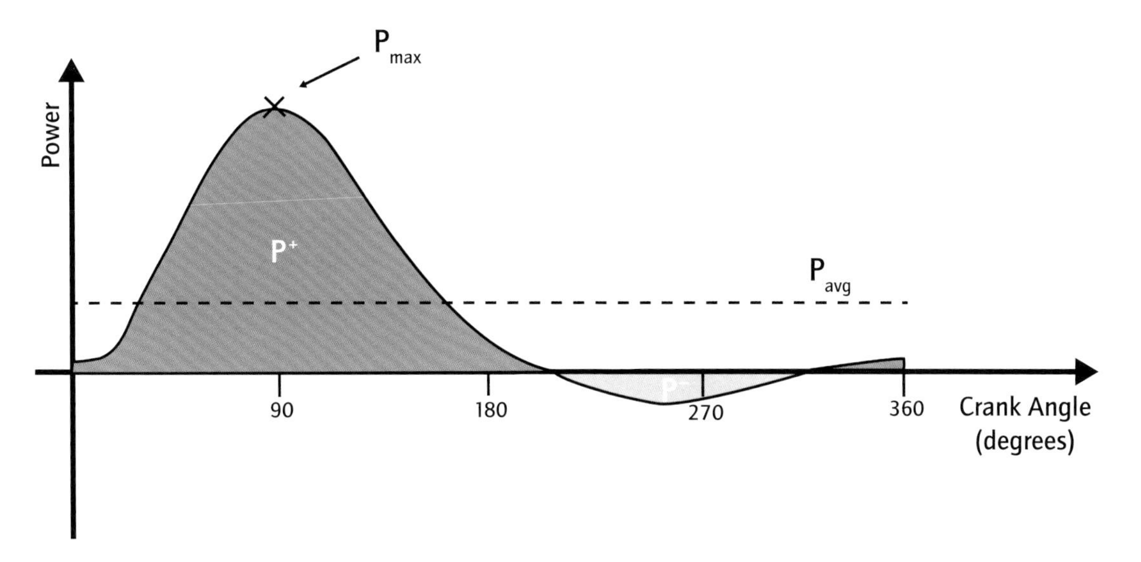

Power applied to a pedal in a rotation of the crank.

Torque effectiveness (TE) measures how much of the power is pushing the pedal forward. It is calculated as $(P^+ + P^-)/P^+$ and is normally displayed as a percentage (P^- will be a negative value or zero). A value of 100% means that all of the power was pushing the pedal in a positive direction. Values of 60-100% are common.

Pedal smoothness (PS) measures how smoothly power is delivered. It is calculated as P_{avg}/P_{max} and is normally displayed as a percentage. A value of 100% means that the power is constant throughout the revolution. Values of 10-40% are common.

Torque effectiveness and pedal smoothness are measured independently for each leg, and these data are calculated by the power meter. However, the question remains whether the maximization of force effectiveness across pedaling techniques improves the GE.

37. THE IMPACT OF ALTITUDE TRAINING

If you go (with a break), you can either win or not win. If you don't go for it, you definitely won't win. –Jens Voigt

This is one of the most debated aspects in the preparation of elite cyclists for the Grand Tours and major races. During a prolonged stay at altitude, the cyclist's body adapts to the lower availability of oxygen in the thin mountain air. In practice, altitudes of between 2,500 and 4,000 meters are recommended for altitude training. Research has shown that at altitude the kidneys produce an increased amount of the hormone erythropoietin or EPO. This hormone stimulates the production of red blood cells. Consequently, the blood hemoglobin level and the oxygen transport capacity (VO_2 max) of the cardiovascular system increase. Upon return to sea level, the cyclist will benefit for some time–about a month–from the increased oxygen transport capacity. His FTP will be slightly increased and accordingly his race times will be somewhat better.

Altitude Training Regimes

The principle of altitude training has been known for many years, but many questions remain on the best regime and the results in practice. The most explicit opinion on the topic was voiced by Sir Roger Bannister (the first man to run a sub 4-minute mile). His answer to the question how one could best be adapted to altitude was: "There are two ways. Get born at altitude.... or train there for 25 years."

Often, the fact that Kenyans and Ethiopians live and train their entire lives at altitude is used to explain their dominance in long-distance running. For generations, their bodies have been adapted to the altitude, giving them an advantage at sea level.

Elite cyclists living at sea level try to obtain a similar competitive edge by training at altitude for some weeks prior to the Grand Tours. However, the results have not always been satisfactory. In part, this can be explained by the fact that it is difficult, if not impossible, to train at the same speed and intensity at altitude. During the first days at altitude, the cyclist may even suffer from altitude disease. Also during the remaining time, the cyclist will be forced to adapt his training program.

In practice, the following training regimes can be distinguished:

1. **Live High, Train High (LHTH)**
   This is the classic regime. Typically it involves a training block of 18 days at an altitude of 2,500 meters. As mentioned before, the results can be mixed and sometimes even not demonstrable. This may be attributed to the fact that the cyclist will struggle to train as well as at sea level.

2. **Live High, Train Low (LHTL)**
   Nowadays, this is considered to be the best regime. Typically, it involves living for about one month at an altitude of 2,500-3,000 meters and training at an altitude of 1,250 meters. This will enable the cyclist to maintain the same high-intensity training program as at sea level. Various studies have shown that an increase in the FTP of around 2.5% can be achieved in this way.

3. **Artificial altitude in an altitude simulation tent or house**
   These systems use equipment to reduce the oxygen level of the air from 21% to 15%, thus simulating the thin mountain air. In theory, this enables the cyclist to carry out the LHTL regime, as he will sleep at artificial altitude and can carry out his training at sea level. In practice, the results are somewhat mixed. This may be caused by the fact that it is not easy to spend sufficient time in the altitude simulating tent or house.

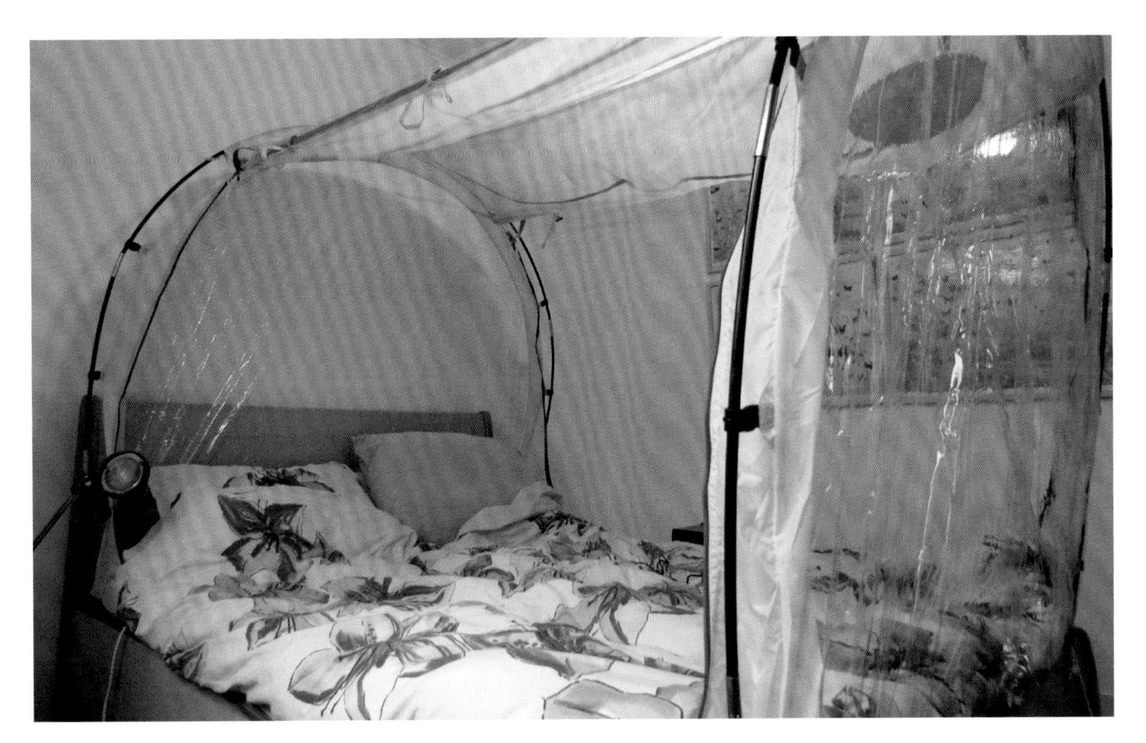

Living high can be simulated with an oxygen tent. Author Hans van Dijk and his wife slept for a month at artificial altitude in their bedroom.

How Big is the Impact on the 40-Kilometer Time Trial?

As an example, we have calculated the impact of an increase of the FTP by 2.5%, which seems to be the most realistic number for an LHTL training regime. The results are shown in the table and figure below. We see that Fast Eddy could increase his speed by 0.7% from 40.41 km/h to 40.70 km/h. Again, we find that the gain in speed is much less than the gain in power. This makes sense, as the air resistance increases to the cube of the speed. The total race time at the 40-kilometer time trial improves by 26 seconds!

Impact of Altitude Training on a Flat Course		
Time	v base	v altitude training
(min)	(km/h)	(km/h)
0.08	64.02	64.46
1	52.32	52.68
5	44.18	44.50
10	42.01	42.32
20	41.39	41.68
40	40.77	41.06
60	40.41	40.70
120	39.80	40.09
240	39.20	39.48

Impact of Altitude training on a Flat Time Trial			
Fast Eddy	v	T 40 km	Difference
	(km/h)	(sec)	(sec)
Base	40.41	3564	-
Altitude training +2.5%	40.70	3538	-26

How Big Is the Impact on the Climb to the Alpe d'Huez?

Again, we made the calculations for the standard conditions and an increase of the FTP by 2.5%. The results are shown in the table and figure below. We see that the speed of Fast Eddy increases by 2.2% from 15.58 km/h to 15.93 km/h. This is only slightly less than the 2.5% increase of his FTP, as could be expected. The climbing resistance is the major factor in this case and this is linearly proportional to the speed. Fast Eddy reaches the top after 54.4 minutes, so he gains 74 seconds on the climb. Certainly, an interesting improvement!

Impact of Altitude Training on Alpe d'Huez		
Time	**v base**	**v altitude training**
(min)	**(km/h)**	**(km/h)**
0.08	43.00	43.54
1	28.67	29.10
5	19.41	19.75
10	17.16	17.47
20	16.54	16.83
40	15.93	16.21
60	15.58	15.86
120	15.00	15.27
240	14.44	14.70

Impact of Altitude Training on Alpe d'Huez			
Fast Eddy	**v**	**T Alpe**	**Difference**
	(km/h)	**(min)**	**(sec)**
Base	15.58	55.6	-
Altitude training +2.5%	15.93	54.4	-74

In summary, we conclude that altitude training may provide an interesting competitive edge. Finally, we note that these results are not guaranteed. As discussed, the impact can be variable, depending on the training regime and the individual response of the cyclist's body.

38. THE IMPACT OF YOUR FATIGUE RESISTANCE

Pain is temporary, pride lasts forever!

You may have experienced being beaten by a cyclist after 200 kilometers, whereas you have easily beaten him in a shorter race. How can we explain this? Are you less resistant to fatigue than other cyclists?

Fatigue resistance is a complicated phenomenon. It is influenced by factors such as body posture (small and skinny cyclists have an advantage), physiology (using the fatty acid energy system is favorable), training (in particular the amount of long rides) and psychology (mental power to dig deep for a long time). In this chapter, we will analyze the impact of fatigue resistance on your race times. In other chapters, we will see what you can do to improve it.

Riegel's Formula

Mathematically, we can simulate the fatigue resistance by the exponent in Riegel's formula:

$$v_2/v_1 = (d_2/d_1)^{-0,07}$$

As we saw earlier, for most people -0.07 is the correct exponent to be used in the formula. This is also valid for the speed–distance relationship of the world records of men, women and masters in athletics. Nevertheless, the exponent is not necessarily the same for everybody and in all conditions. Some variations have been observed in practice. The results of sprinters and prologue specialists with a limited fatigue resistance can best be described by an exponent of -0.09. On the other hand, the results of ultra-cyclists with exceptional fatigue resistance can best be described by an exponent of -0.05.

Power Profiles for Sprinters, All-Round Cyclists and Ultra-Cyclists

In an earlier chapter, we calculated the power profiles for three different types of cyclists: sprinters, all-round cyclists and ultra-cyclists. These are given in the table below.

Power Profile Relative to FTP			
Time	Sprinter	All-round	Ultra
(minutes)	(-)	(-)	(-)
0	4.23	3.74	3.28
1	2.35	2.10	1.86
5	1.47	1.19	1.15
10	1.17	1.13	1.09
20	1.10	1.08	1.06
40	1.04	1.03	1.02
60	1.00	1.00	1.00
120	0.94	0.95	0.97
240	0.88	0.91	0.93

The table shows clearly that the differences can be substantial. Ultra-cyclists can maintain a higher percentage of their FTP for a longer time. On the other hand, they can mobilize less power during a short time, so their sprinting capacity is less. For sprinters, obviously the reverse is the case. The table was made relative to the FTP, so all powers are 1.00 at the one-hour mark.

What Is the Impact of the Fatigue Resistance on the Power and Performance of Fast Eddy?

We have calculated the impact of the fatigue resistance, both on the power and on the performance at the flat course and on the climb to the Alpe d'Huez. The results are given in the figure below. They show that sprinters can mobilize more power during a short time, enabling them to sprint faster. In a flat finish they could reach a speed of 67.2 km/h (for a few seconds), whereas ultra-cyclists can only reach 61.6 km/h. On the other hand, the ultra-cyclists have the upper hand during long races. They can maintain a speed of 39.4 km/h over four hours, whereas sprinters drop back to 38.6 km/h.

Depending on his targets, Fast Eddy could try to improve his fatigue resistance by means of training. As he trains more, he will definitely improve as he will lose body fat (very important as it decreases the energy cost for cycling) and his fatty acid energy system will be stimulated. However, at some point he will also have to face his limitations. Fatigue resistance definitely can be improved by training, but not everyone has the fatigue resistance of an ultra-cyclist!

It will be more difficult for Fast Eddy to improve his sprinting capacities. Losing body weight has little impact, and training and developing sprinting fibers is not so easy. Sprinters are born!

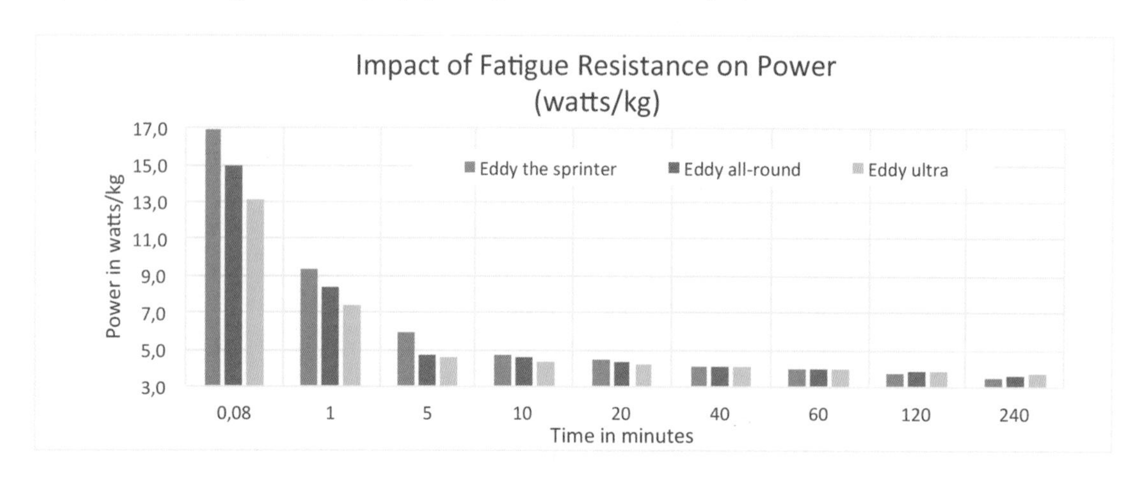

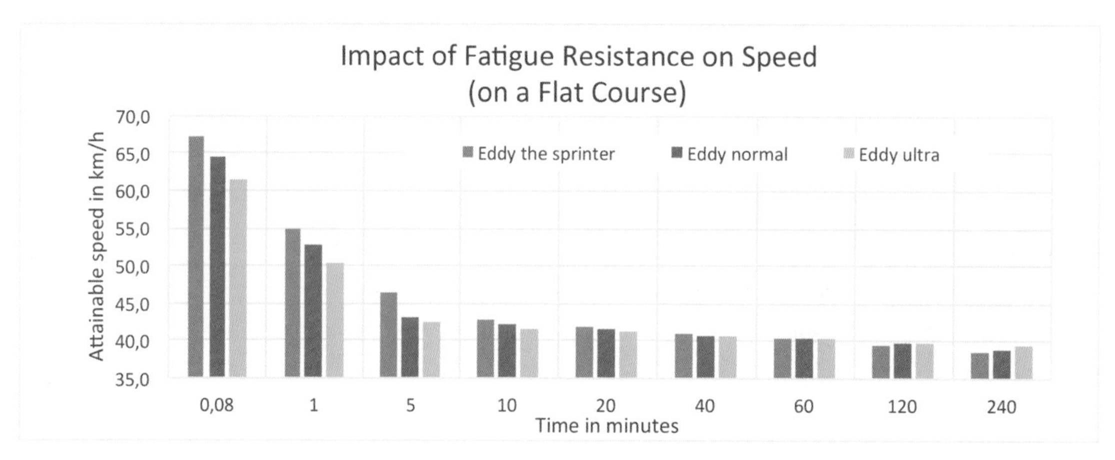

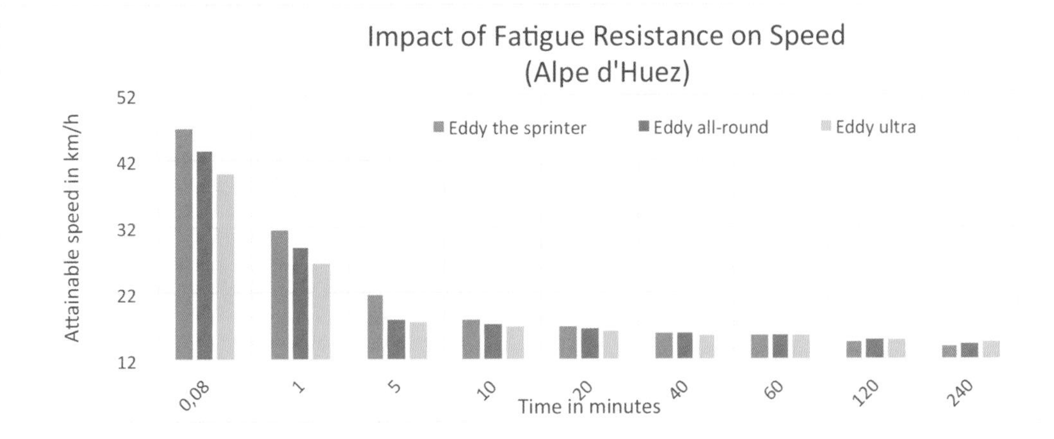

Elite cyclist Tom Dumoulin in La Vuelta 2015. Dumoulin possesses excellent all-round cycling qualities.

39. THE IMPACT OF THE ROLLING RESISTANCE

Learn to ride a bicycle. You will not regret it if you live.
–Mark Twain

In the chapter on the cycling formula, we learned that we can calculate the rolling resistance with the formula:

$$P_r = c_r mgv$$

Using the standard conditions of Fast Eddy, we can calculate that his rolling resistance is 36.5 watts at a speed of 40 km/h (c_r = 0.004, m = 75 kg + 8.8 kg bike, g = 9.81 m/s^2 and v = 40/3,6 m/s). This amounts to some 12% of his FTP of 300 watts.

What are the options for Fast Eddy to reduce his rolling resistance and thus to increase his speed? The formula shows that he has two options: reduce his total weight (m, which is the sum of his body weight and the weight of his bike) and to reduce the rolling-resistance factor (c_r). The impact of his body weight and the weight of his bike have been discussed in earlier chapters. In this chapter, we will investigate the impact of c_r.

Which Factors Determine the Rolling-Resistance Factor (c_r)?

According to theory, c_r depends on:

1. Tire type: smooth-running tires are superior
2. Tire width: in practice this has little impact
3. Tube pressure: high pressure is superior
4. Pavement: concrete and asphalt are superior, cobblestones are inferior
5. Wheel diameter: the bigger, the better, but at the cost of aerodynamics
6. Tube: latex is superior for a short time trial

The table below summarizes some data that have been found in practice[44,45,46].

Impact of Surface and Tire Type on c_r	
Condition	c_r
Wooden track, high performance tube, 8 bar	0.002
Road, high performance tube, 8 bar	0.003
Road, average cylinder, 8 bar	0.004
Road, touring tire, 6 bar	0.005
Rough road	0.008
ATB tire 3 bar	0.012

Race Time at the 40-Kilometer Time Trial

Once again, we calculated the impact with our model, using the standard conditions. The results are given in the figure and table. We see that the attainable speed is inversely proportional to the rolling-resistance factor (c_r). If Fast Eddy would replace his average cylinders (c_r = 0.004) by high performance tubes (c_r = 0.003), then his speed would increase by 1% from 40.41 km/h to 40.87 km/h. His total gain on the time trial would be 40 seconds. However, he could lose 40 seconds if he did not inflate his tubes sufficiently (c_r = 0.005). A rough pavement could also cause a significant time loss (171 seconds at a c_r of 0.008).

So, it is definitely worthwhile to select the proper tire and inflate it properly. Of course, the tire type and pressure will also depend on the pavement and the weather. In rainy or hot conditions, safety is more important than speed.

For many years Dutch cyclist Leontien Zijlaard-Van Moorsel held the women's world hour record at 46,065 meters. The rolling resistance has a small, but not negligible, impact in such attempts.

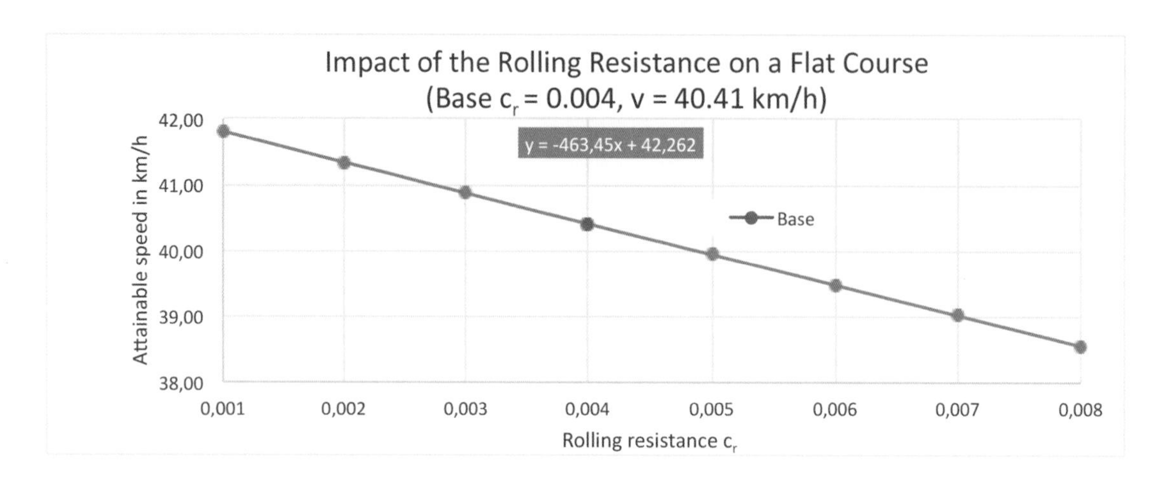

Impact of c_r on a Flat Course			
c_r	v	T 40 km	Difference
(-)	(km/h)	(min)	(sec)
0.001	41.80	57.4	119
0.002	41.34	58.1	80
0.003	40.87	58.7	40
0.004	40.41	59.4	0
0.005	39.94	60.1	-41
0.006	39.48	60.8	-84
0.007	39.02	61.5	-127
0.008	38.56	62.2	-171

Race Time to the Top of the Alpe d'Huez

Once again, the results of our calculations are presented in a similar figure and table. We see that also in this case the attainable speed is inversely proportional to c_r. The impact is almost the same as on the flat (i.e., a gain of 1% or 37 seconds when Fast Eddy reduces his c_r from 0.004 to 0.003). In the case of the Alpe d'Huez, the lower rolling resistance leads to a higher climbing speed and a higher climbing resistance. At the flat time trial, the lower rolling resistance also leads to a higher speed and in this case to a higher air resistance. The total impact is more or less the same for this example.

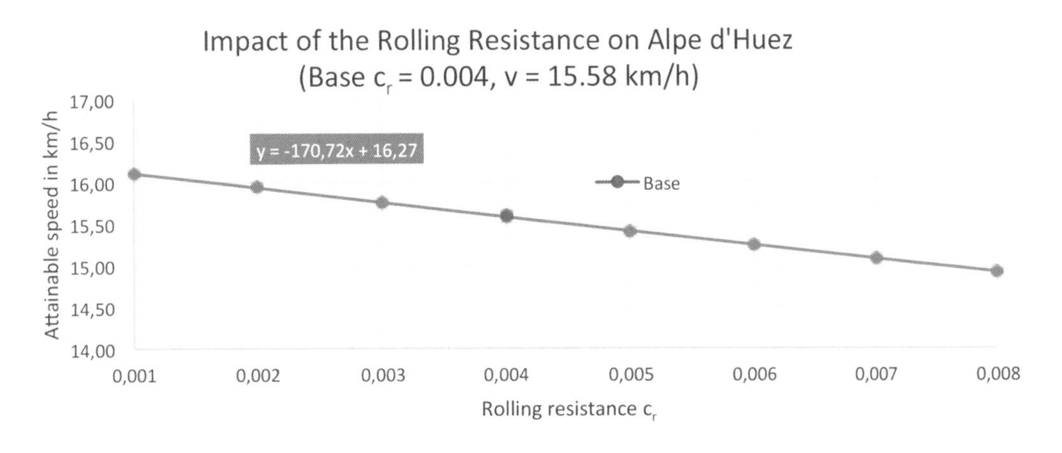

Impact of c_r on Alpe d'Huez			
c_r	v	T Alpe	Difference
(-)	(km/h)	(min)	(sec)
0.001	16.11	53.8	110
0.002	15.93	54.4	74
0.003	15.75	55.0	37
0.004	15.58	55.7	0
0.005	15.41	56.3	-37
0.006	15.24	56.9	-74
0.007	15.08	57.5	-111
0.008	14.92	58.1	-149

40. THE WORLD SPEED RECORD

The bicycle is a curious vehicle. Its passenger is its engine.
–John Howard

In the previous chapter, we learned that the rolling resistance of Fast Eddy is 36.5 watts at a speed of 40 km/h and in the standard conditions. Knowing this, we could answer the question of how fast he could cycle if he only had to surmount the rolling resistance. The simple answer is that this would mean that the rolling resistance should be equal to his total FTP of 300 watts, which would be the case at a speed of 300/36.5*40 = 328 km/h. However, this calculation seems a bit odd, as we all know that in practice the air resistance is dominant, resulting in the attainable speed being substantially lower. But still, there has been someone who approached this extreme speed very closely.

Fred Rompelberg[47]

On October 3, 1995, the Dutch cyclist Fred Rompelberg succeeded in establishing the world speed record at an astonishing 268.83 km/h! He cycled in the wake of a specially designed race car at the salt plains of Bonneville near Salt Lake City. It had taken him eight years of attempts and multiple crashes before he set this record. He used a specially designed bike with a double-reduction gear with a gear rollout of 70/13-60/15! With one stroke of the pedal, he could move 34.8 meters!

Fred Rompelberg cycles his world speed record (268.83 km/h) behind a dragster of the Strasbourg Race Race Team near Salt Lake City.

How Can We Understand and Calculate This Result?

Obviously, Fred's trick was to cycle perfectly in the wake of the car (in the specially designed cage), so that his air-resistance factor (c_dA) would become close to 0. Consequently, he only had to surmount the rolling resistance, as we indicated in the above. We were curious to see if we could reproduce Fred's results with our model and calculate how low his c_dA value actually was.

From Fred's website, we gathered the data that we needed to simulate his world record attempt. These included his body weight, the weight of the bike, the altitude, the air density at that altitude and the rolling resistance of his tires. The table below summarizes these data.

Fred Rompelberg's World Speed Record	
Cyclist weight	77.2 kg
Bike weight	19.5 kg
Altitude	1286 m
ρ	1.03 kg/m^3
c_r	0.008
Age	49 years

How Perfect Was the Aero Drafting?

In order to calculate the c_dA value, we needed to make an educated guess on the power that Fred pushed in the attempt. We assumed that he performed at 85% of the world-class level for his age group, which results in an FTP of 4.73 watts/kg. We reckoned that Fred was a committed cyclist and former professional. In view of the fact that the attempt lasted only one or two minutes, we calculated with a peak factor of 1.85. Consequently, we set his power at 4.73*77.2*1.85 = 675 watts.

Using this power, we prepared the figure below, which gives the relationship between the speed and the c_dA. Since we know that his actual speed was 268.83 km/h, we conclude that his c_dA value was apparently 0.00043 m^2. Considering that the lowest c_dA value in professional time trials is 0.21 m^2, we can conclude that the aero drafting was pretty perfect!

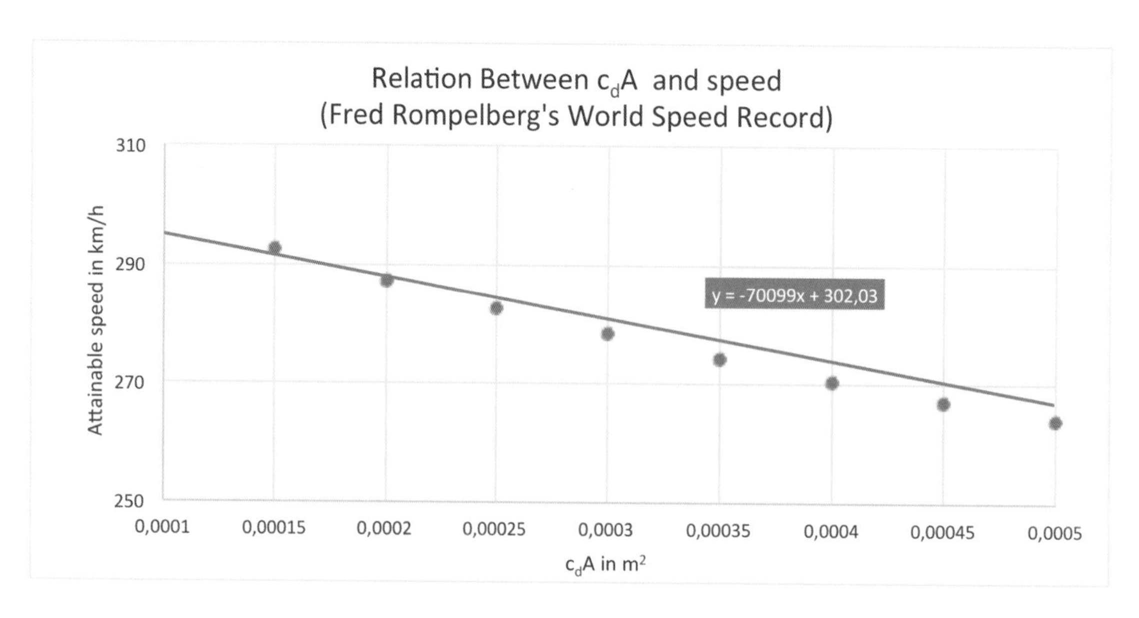

Cobble stones and head wind are bad conditions for fast cycling.

41. THE IMPACT OF THE AIR-RESISTANCE COEFFICIENT

Life is like riding a bicycle. In order to keep your balance, you must keep moving. —Albert Einstein

In the chapter on the cycling formula, we learned that we can calculate the air resistance with the following formula:

$$P_a = 0.5\rho c_d A(v+v_w)^2 v$$

Using the standard conditions of Fast Eddy, we can calculate that his air resistance is 248 watts at a speed of 40 km/h (ρ = 1.205 kg/m^3, $c_d A$ = 0.3 m^2, v = 40/3.6 m/s, v_w = 0 m/s). This is equal to some 83% of his FTP of 300 watts.

This confirms what we know from experience: the air resistance is the dominant factor determining your performance on a flat course. Also we see that the air resistance increases to the cube of the speed. So if you want to increase your speed by 10%, you need to push 33% more power (1.10^3-1)! The major impact of the air resistance is also the reason that it is almost impossible to stay away from a chasing pack, even for world-class cyclists. Obviously, all cyclists in the pack benefit from drafting.

What options does Fast Eddy have to limit his air resistance and thus increase his speed? The formula already shows that the air resistance is determined by three factors: the density of the air (ρ), the air-resistance coefficient ($c_d A$) and the wind speed (v_w). The density of the air itself depends on three other factors: the air pressure, the temperature and the altitude. We will investigate all of these factors in the next chapters. We will start with the impact of $c_d A$ in this chapter.

Which Factors Determine c_dA?

In theory, c_dA depends on:

1. The position on the bike (as streamlined as possible)
2. The bike design (aero wheels, frames and extensions)
3. The body posture (a smaller person has a small advantage)

The table below summarizes some data that have been found in practice[44,45,46].

Attainable Values for c_dA	
	c_dA
Upright position	0.60
Standing on the pedals	0.40
Hands on drops	0.30
Hands on extensions	0.21
Obree position	0.17
Recumbent cyclist	0.02

Race Time at a 40-Kilometer Time Trial

Once again, we calculated the impact with our program, using the standard conditions. The results are given in the figure and table below. As could be expected, the attainable speed depends substantially on the c_dA. If Fast Eddy succeeded in reducing his c_dA from 0.3 to 0.2, then his speed would increase from 40.41 km/h to 45.95 km/h—no less than 14%! At the 40-kilometer time trial he would gain a total of 430 seconds! On the other hand, he would lose 342 seconds if he stood on the pedals (c_dA = 0.40).

The big impact of the c_dA value is also the reason for the success of recumbent bicycles. In October 2013, a team from the TU Delft set the world record for recumbent bicycles at 133.78 km/h! They used a bike with a c_dA as low as 0.025 m^2 and improved the record at an altitude of 1,500 meters in Battle Mountain, USA. Author Guido advised the team and noted that the maximum power during the race was 765 watts. This value matched perfectly with the calculations of our model.

In October 2013, a team from the Delft University of Technology set the world record for recumbent bicycles at 133.78 km/h!

As the aerodynamics have a major impact on your performance, it is certainly worthwhile to optimize your bike design and bike position within the regulations of the UCI. In later chapters, we will discuss concrete possibilities and the advantages in practice. Also, we will analyze the world hour record attempts, including the impact of aerodynamics. Finally, we will show how much you can gain by riding together in a group or with the pack.

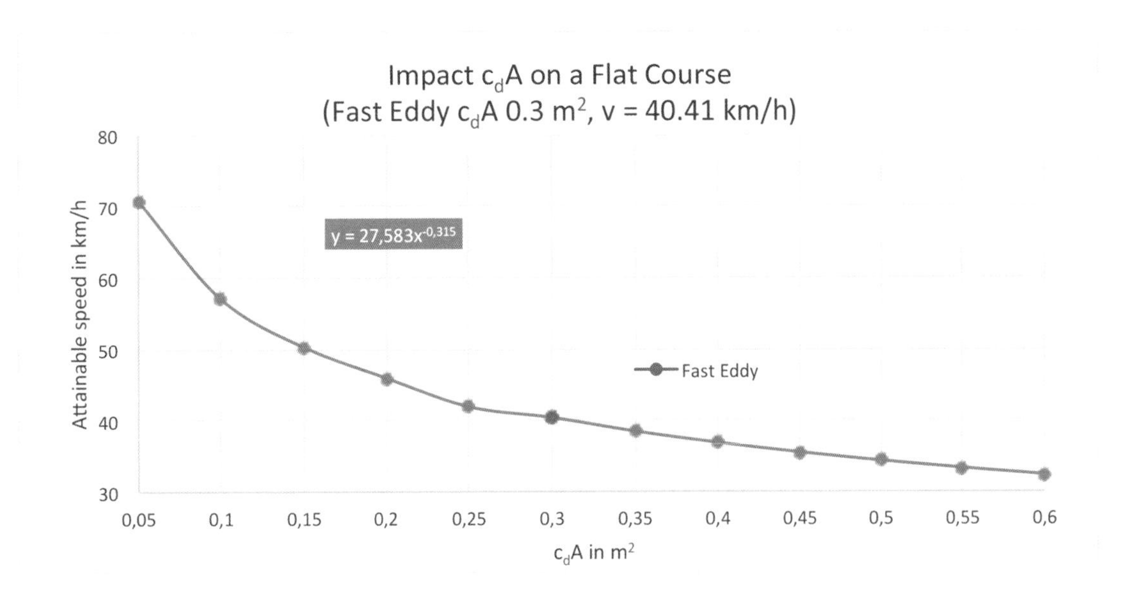

c_dA	v	T 40 km	Difference
m^2	(km/h)	(min)	(sec)
0.05	70.68	34.0	1526
0.1	57.09	42.0	1042
0.15	50.30	47.7	701
0.2	45.95	52.2	430
0.25	41.93	57.2	130
0.3	40.41	59.4	-
0.35	38.47	62.4	-179
0.4	36.87	65.1	-342
0.45	35.50	67.6	-492
0.5	34.33	69.9	-631
0.55	33.29	72.1	-762
0.6	32.38	74.1	-884

Race Time to the Top of the Alpe d'Huez

Once again, the results of our calculations are shown in a similar figure and table. We see that the speed in the mountains depends much less on the c_dA value. A reduction of the c_dA from 0.3 to 0.2 leads to a gain of only 1% or 52 seconds on the climb to the Alpe d'Huez. Obviously, this is caused by the fact that the climbing resistance is the dominant factor in this case.

Finally, we note that standing on the pedals increases the air resistance. In this respect, Froome's climbing style has an advantage over Contador, who is famous for his climbing technique of standing on the pedals.

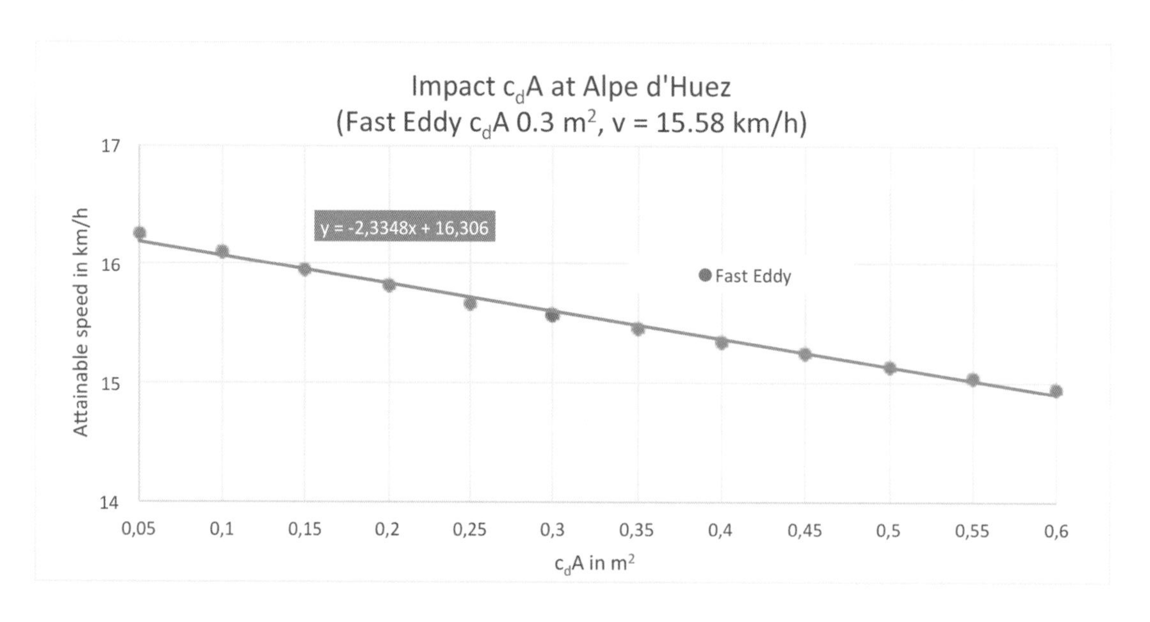

Reducing your air-resistance (c_dA) value is one of the options for riding fast downhill.

c_dA	v	T Alpe	Difference
m^2	(km/h)	(min)	(sec)
0.05	16.25	53.4	137
0.1	16.10	53.9	108
0.15	15.96	54.3	79
0.2	15.83	54.8	52
0.25	15.66	55.4	17
0.3	15.58	55.7	0
0.35	15.46	56.1	-25
0.4	15.35	56.5	-49
0.45	15.25	56.9	-73
0.5	15.14	57.3	-96
0.55	15.04	57.6	-119
0.6	14.95	58.0	-141

Leontien Zijlaard-Van Moorsel optimizes her air-resistance coefficient (c_dA) in a wind tunnel, prior to her world hour record attempt.

42. THE IMPACT OF THE AIR PRESSURE

Melancholy is incompatible with cycling. –James E. Starrs

In the previous chapter, we learned that we can calculate the air resistance with the following formula:

$$P_a = 0.5\rho c_d A(v+v_w)^2 v$$

Using the standard conditions of Fast Eddy, we can calculate that his air resistance is 248 watts at a speed of 40 km/h (ρ = 1.205 kg/m^3, c_dA = 0.3 m^2, v = 40/3.6 m/s, v_w = 0 m/s). This is equal to some 83% of his FTP of 300 watts. In the standard conditions, the air density is 1.205 kg/m^3. Which factors determine the air density and what is the impact of the air density on the attainable speed? In this chapter, we will answer these questions.

Which Factors Determine ρ?

At sea level, the air density depends on the air pressure and the temperature, in accordance with the ideal gas law:

$$\rho = (p*M)/(R*T)$$

In this formula, M represents the molecular weight of air (28.97 g/mole) and R is the molar gas constant (8.314 J/mole/°K). At 20°C (293°K) and the standard air pressure of 101,300 Pa, the air density thus becomes 101,300*28.97/8.314/293/1,000 = 1.205 kg/m^3. When the air pressure is higher than 101,300 Pa (1,013 mbar), the air density becomes higher. Vice versa, the air density is reduced at lower air pressure. We have examined the impact of air pressures between 953 mbar and 1,053 mbar.

Race Time at a 40-Kilometer Time Trial

Once again, we calculated the impact with our program, using the standard conditions. The results are given in the figure and table. We see that the attainable speed increases as the air pressure decreases. However, the impact is small. When the air pressure drops from 1,013 to 1,003 mbar, the speed only increases by 0.3% from 40.41 km/h to 40.53 km/h. The total gain over the 40-kilometer time trial is 11 seconds.

Still, it means that you could gain 68 seconds at the 40-kilometer time trial during a depression (air pressure of 953 mbar)! This could be a nice advantage in a record attempt, such as the world hour record. In a later chapter, we will analyze the world hour record attempts more closely.

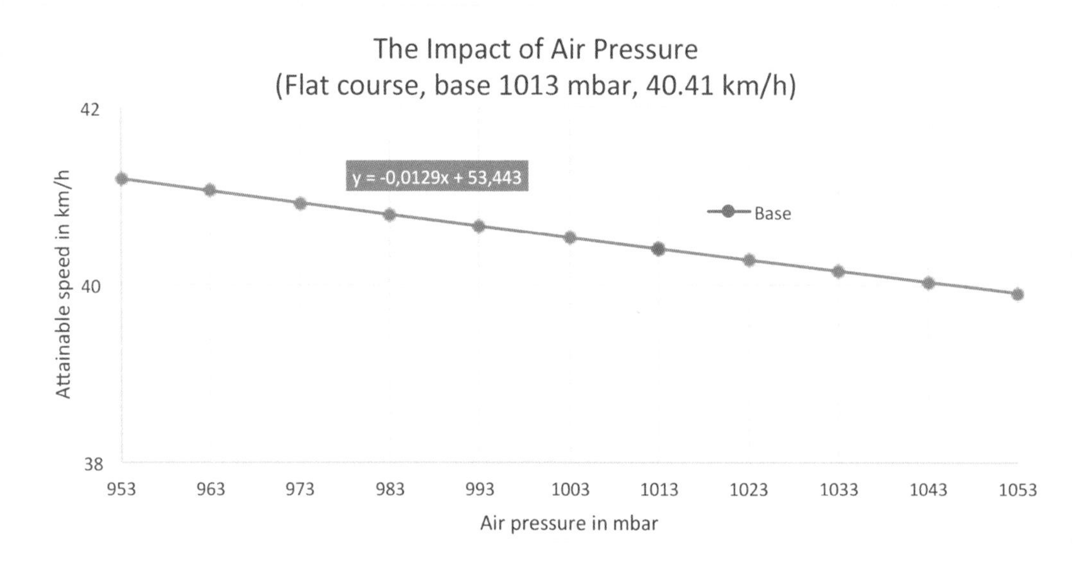

p_0	v	T 40 km	Difference
(mbar)	(km/h)	(sec)	(sec)
953	41.20	58.3	68
963	41.06	58.4	57
973	40.93	58.6	45
983	40.80	58.8	34
993	40.66	59.0	23
1,003	40.53	59.2	11
1,013	40.41	59.4	0
1,023	40.28	59.6	-11
1,033	40.16	59.8	-22
1,043	40.03	59.9	-33
1,053	39.91	60.1	-44

Race Time to the Top of the Alpe d'Huez

Once again, the results of our calculations are shown in a similar figure and table. We see that the speed in the mountains depends even less on the air pressure. A drop in air-pressure from 1,013 to 1,003 mbar will lead to a gain of just two seconds on the climb to the Alpe d'Huez. Obviously, the impact is so small because the climbing resistance determines the climbing time.

We note that so far we have been discussing the impact of the air pressure at sea level. In the mountains, the air pressure decreases with the altitude. As a result, the air becomes thinner with altitude. This has a substantial impact, both on the air resistance and even more on the oxygen uptake in our lungs and consequently on the power output of the human engine. These aspects will be discussed in a separate chapter.

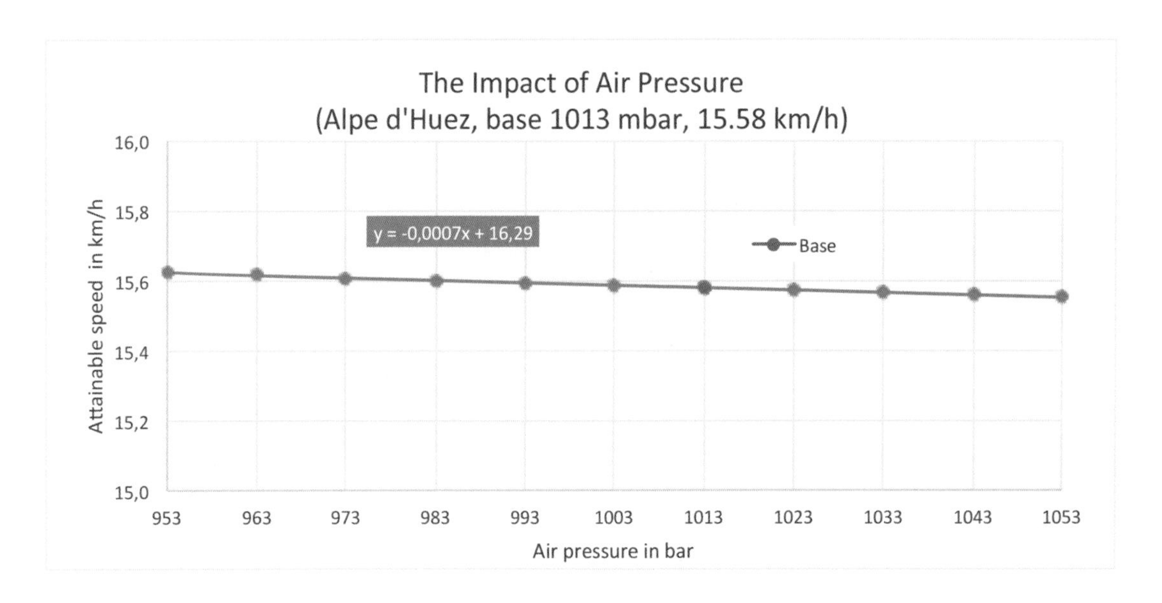

p_0 (mbar)	v (km/h)	T Alpe (min)	Difference (sec)
953	15.62	55.5	9
963	15.61	55.5	8
973	15.61	55.6	6
983	15.60	55.6	5
993	15.59	55.6	3
1,003	15.59	55.6	2
1,013	15.58	55.7	0
1,023	15.57	55.7	-1
1,033	15.57	55.7	-3
1,043	15.56	55.7	-4
1,053	15.55	55.8	-6

Even indoor a world hour record can best be attempted during a low (air pressure).

43. THE IMPACT OF TEMPERATURE

There is no such thing as bad weather, just soft people.
—Bill Bowerman

Earlier, we learned that we can calculate the air resistance with the following formula:

$$P_a = 0.5\rho c_d A(v+v_w)^2 v$$

Using the standard conditions of Fast Eddy, we can calculate that his air resistance is 248 watts at a speed of 40 km/h (ρ = 1.205 kg/m³, $c_d A$ = 0.3 m², v = 40/3.6 m/s, v_w = 0 m/s). This is equal to some 83% of his FTP of 300 watts. In the standard conditions, the air density is 1.205 kg/m³. Which factors determine the air density, and what is the impact of the air density on the attainable speed? In this chapter, we will answer these questions.

Which Factors Determine ρ?

At sea level, the air density depends on the air pressure and the temperature, in accordance with the ideal gas law:

$$\rho = (p*M)/(R*T)$$

In this formula, M represents the molecular weight of air (28.97 g/mole) and R is the molar gas constant (8.314 J/mole/°K). At 20°C (293°K) and the standard air pressure of 101,300 Pa, the air density thus becomes 101,300*28.97/8.314/293/1,000 = 1.205 kg/m³. When the temperature is higher than 20°C, the air density becomes lower. Vice versa, the air density is increased at higher temperatures. We have examined the impact of temperatures from 0°C to 40°C.

We note that, in this chapter, we will limit ourselves to investigating the impact of the temperature on the air density and the air resistance. We will not analyze the impact of the heat or the cold on the performance of your body. This will be discussed in a separate chapter.

Race Time at a 40-Kilometer Time Trial

Once again, we calculated the impact with our program, using the standard conditions. The results are given in the figure and table below. We see that the attainable speed increases as the temperature rises. However, the impact is small. When the temperature rises from 20°C to 25°C, then the attainable speed increases from 40.41 km/h to 40.63 km/h, by just 0.5%. The total gain at the 40-kilometer time trial is 19 seconds.

Still, it means that you could gain 116 seconds on the 40-kilometer time trial at 35°C as compared to 5°C. This could be a nice advantage in a record attempt, such as the world hour record! During the 2012 Olympic Games in London, the temperature in the Olympic Velodrome was purposely increased to 28°C to create record-breaking conditions. In practice, the advantage of the thinner air will have to be weighed against the disadvantage of the heat on the performance of the human body. This will be discussed in a separate chapter. Also, we will analyze the world hour record attempts more closely in a later chapter.

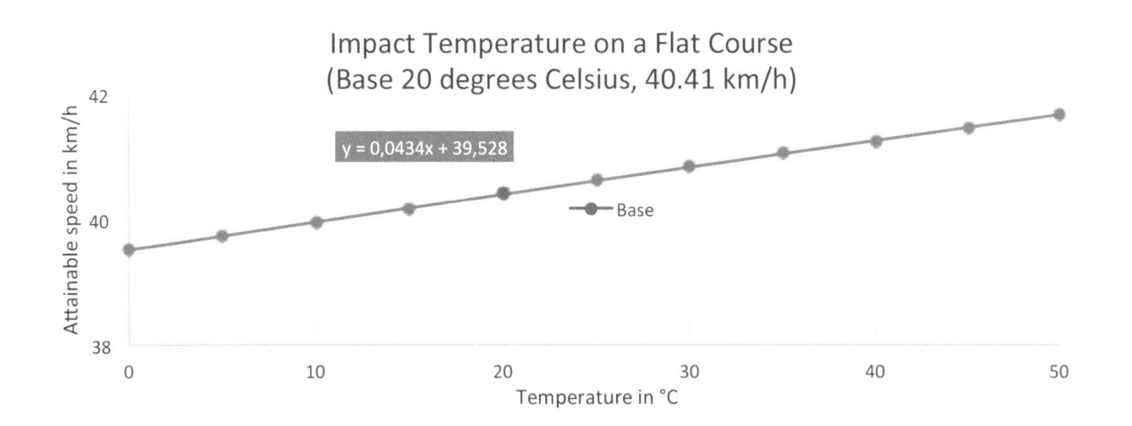

Temperature	v	T 40 km	Difference
(°C)	(km/h)	(min)	(sec)
0	39.51	60.7	81
5	39.74	60.4	60
10	39.96	60.1	40
15	40.19	59.7	20
20	40.41	59.4	-
25	40.63	59.1	-19
30	40.84	58.8	-38
35	41.05	58.5	-56
40	41.26	58.2	-74

Race Time to the Top of the Alpe d'Huez

Once again, the results of our calculations are shown in a similar figure and table. We see that the speed in the mountains depends even less on the temperature. A rise in temperature from 20 to 25°C leads to a gain of just three seconds on the climb to the Alpe d'Huez. Obviously, the impact is so small because the climbing resistance determines the climbing time. Also in this case, the heat will have a negative impact on the performance of the human body as a result of the heat stress and the water loss from sweating. These aspects will be discussed in detail in a later chapter.

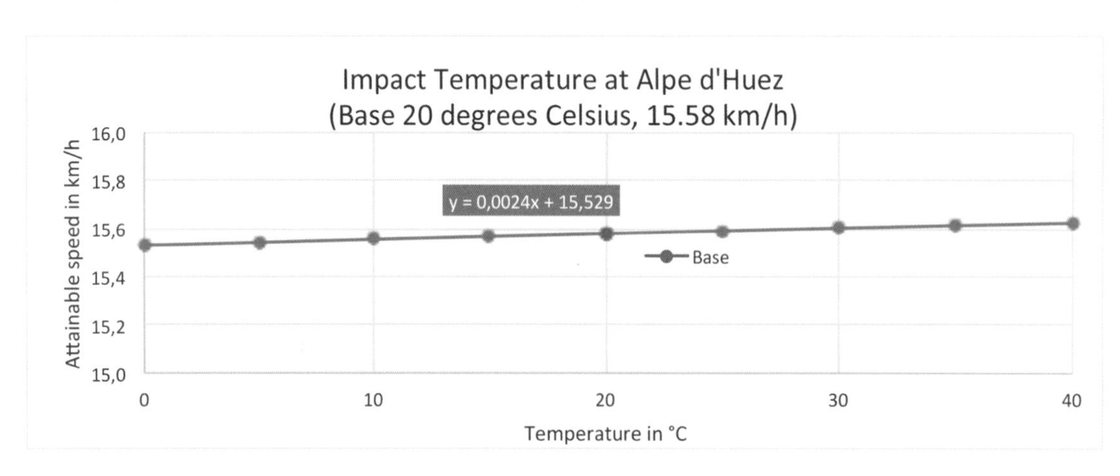

Temperature	v	T Alpe	Difference
(°C)	(km/h)	(min)	(sec)
0	15.53	55.8	11
5	15.54	55.8	8
10	15.55	55.7	5
15	15.57	55.7	3
20	15.58	55.7	0
25	15.59	55.6	-3
30	15.60	55.6	-5
35	15.61	55.5	-7
40	15.62	55.5	-10

The heat has a small positive impact on air resistance. However, the attainable speed will be lower as the power of the human engine is less as a result of the heat stress and the water loss from sweating.

44. THE IMPACT OF ALTITUDE

What does not destroy me, makes me strong.
–Friedrich Nietzsche

In an earlier chapter, we learned that we can calculate the air resistance with the formula:

$$P_a = 0.5\rho c_d A(v+v_w)^2 v$$

This means that at the standard conditions Fast Eddy will have to push 248 watts to overcome the air resistance at a speed of 40 km/h (ρ = 1.205 kg/m^3, $c_d A$ = 0.3 m^2, v = 40/3,6 m/s, v_w = 0 m/s). This is 83% of his FTP of 300 watts. Obviously, at altitude the air density will be lower, so the air resistance of Fast Eddy will be reduced. However, in the thin air the solubility of oxygen in his blood will also be reduced. This compromises the ability of his blood to transport oxygen to the muscles. Consequently, the performance of the human engine is reduced at altitude.

How can we calculate both effects of the altitude? What is the combined impact at different altitudes? We will answer these questions in this chapter.

How Can We Calculate the Air Density?

At sea level, the air density (ρ, in kg/m^3) is determined by the air pressure and the temperature, according to the formula:

$$\rho = (p*M)/(R*T)$$

In this formula, M is the molecular weight of air (28.97 g/mole) and R is the molar gas constant (8314 kJ/mole/°K). At the standard temperature of 15°C (288°K) and the standard air pressure of 101,300 Pa, the air density thus becomes (101,300*28.97(/(8314/288) = 1.226 kg/m^3. In the previous chapters, we have used this value for our calculations.

At altitude, the air pressure is reduced, in accordance with the following formula:

$$p = p_0 * e^{(-Mgh/RT)}$$

Consequently, on top of Alpe d'Huez (altitude (h) = 1,815 meters), the air pressure is only

$101{,}300 * e^{(-28.97*9.81*1815/1000)/(8.314*293))} = 81{,}969$ Pa or about 80% of the sea level air pressure.

The lower air pressure leads to a proportionally lower air resistance. We have calculated the impact of the altitude on the air resistance. The results are given in the figure below. At the altitude of the velodrome in Mexico City (2,336 meters), where Eddy Merckx set his world hour record, the air density is only 0.913 kg/m^3. This is 25% lower than at sea level, a significant advantage!

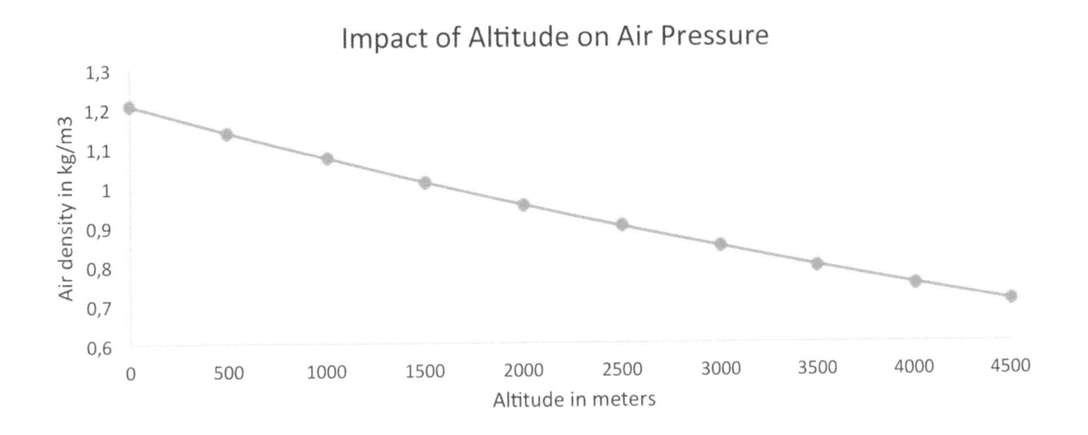

To What Extent Is the Performance at Altitude Reduced?

The solubility of oxygen in the blood is linearly proportional to the air pressure. This means that at Mexico City the blood of the athletes contains 25% less oxygen! As oxygen is essential for the aerobic oxidation of glycogen and fatty acids in the mitochondria, this leads to a significantly reduced power output by the muscles. Consequently, the performance of endurance cyclists at altitude is significantly compromised. Sprinters do not suffer from this phenomenon as they derive their power mainly from the anaerobic glycolysis and the direct conversion of ATP. Both processes do not depend on oxygen.

The impact depends on the adaptation process of the cyclist's body[48,49,50]. Upon arrival at altitude, the body will start to adapt to the lower availability of oxygen by producing more red blood cells. Obviously, the presence of more red blood cells will partly mitigate the impact of the lower solubility of oxygen. The level of hemoglobin may increase up to 10-15%, but this requires time. This process of adaptation is called acclimatization and usually requires about one month.

In the scientific literature[51,52,53,54], several formulas have been published to calculate the reduction of performance as a function of altitude. We have summarized these in the table below.

Performance at Altitude	
(h, in km)	
Basset	Before acclimatization % = 100.352-4.307*h-1.434*h²+0.1781*h³ After acclimatization % = 99.921-1.8991*h-1.1219*h²
Cerretelli	% = 1-11.7*10⁻³h²-4.01*10⁻³*h
Daniels	No explicit formula

As Daniels has not published an explicit formula, we have detailed an example based on a table from his book and compared this to the formulas of Basset and Cerretelli. The results are given in the figure. Based on this comparison, it seems to us that that Cerretelli and Daniels underestimate the impact of the altitude. Consequently, we have used Basset's formulas in our model.

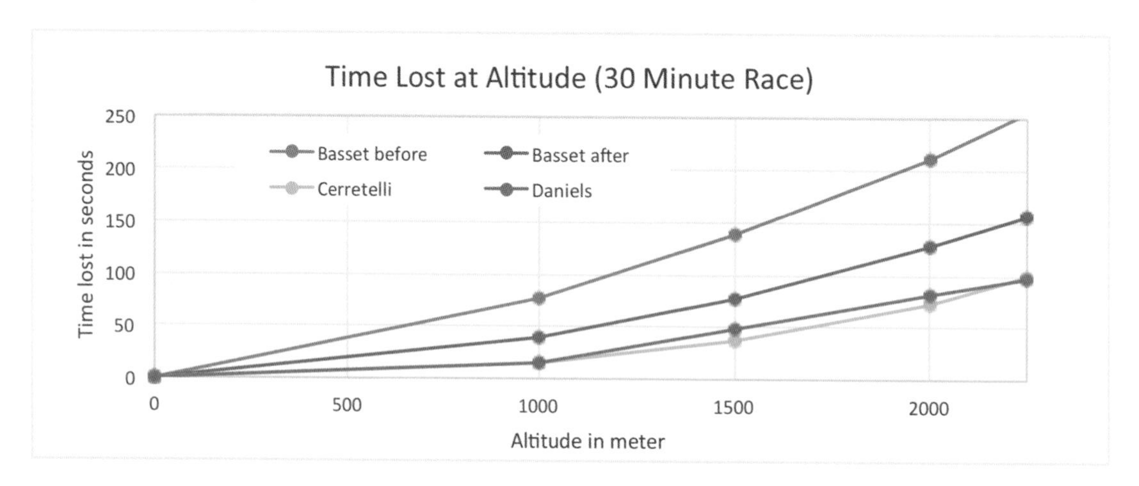

Using Basset's formulas, we have calculated the impact of the altitude on the performce (as FTP). The results are given in the figure. At the top of Alpe d'Huez (1,815 meters), the resulting FTP is 88.9% or 92.8% of sea level (before and after acclimatization). At the altitude of the velodrome in Mexico City (2,335 meters), these values are 84.7% and 89.4%. So the advantage of the lower air resistance can be offset by the disadvantage of the lower performance of the human engine.

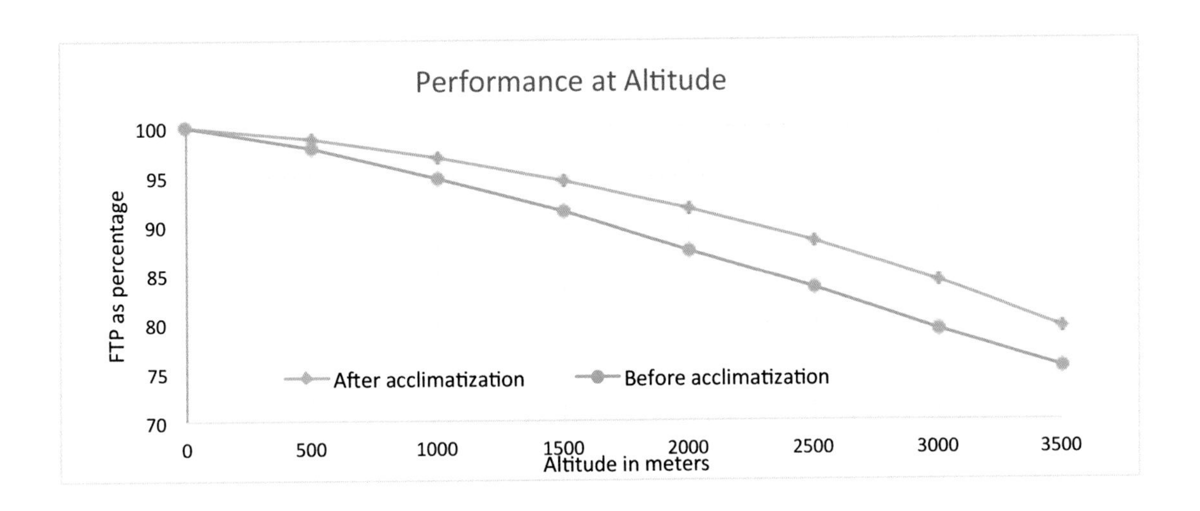

How Big Is the Combined Impact on the Flat?

We have calculated the combined impact of the lower air resistance and the lower FTP at the standard conditions of a flat course, like the 40-kilometer time trial. The results are given in the figure below.

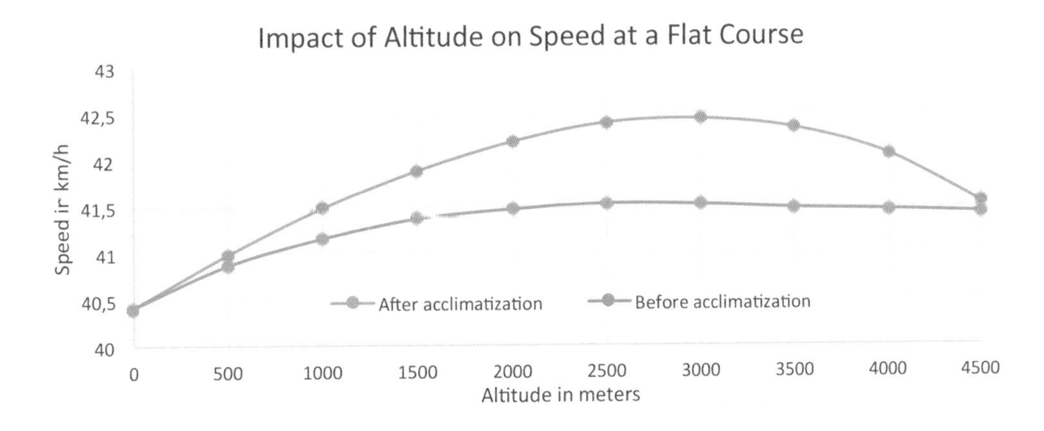

We see that at first the attainable speed increases with altitude. This is caused by the fact that the advantage of the lower air resistance is bigger than the disadvantage of the lower FTP. However, from an altitude of 3,000 meters onwards, the attainable speed starts to decline. At these altitudes the negative impact of the lower FTP predominates.

Leontien Zijlaard-van Moorsel in her successful world hour record attempt in Mexico-City.

At the altitude of the velodrome in Mexico City, the combined impact on the attainable speed is very advantageous (11%)! So, it would be definitely worthwhile for any cyclist wanting to break the world hour record to travel to Mexico! In a later chapter, we will analyze the world hour record attempts of Eddy Merckx and others more closely. There, we will also correct for the impact of the altitude to make a more fair comparison of the real performances of the cyclists.

The table below gives the results of our calculations on the attainable speed and the race time on the 40-kilometer flat time trial for Fast Eddy. We see that Fast Eddy could gain a total of 300 seconds on the time trial if he would cycle at 3,000-meter altitude!

Impact of Altitude on a 40-Kilometer Time Trial			
(After Acclimatization)			
Altitude	v	T 40 km	Difference
(m)	(km/h)	(min)	(sec)
0	40.41	59.4	-
500	40.98	58.6	-50
1,000	41.48	57.9	-92
1,500	41.88	57.3	-125
2,000	42.19	56.9	-150
2,500	42.39	56.6	-166
3,000	42.43	56.6	-170
3,500	42.33	56.7	-162
4,000	42.05	57.1	-139

How Big Is the Combined Impact Uphill?

Again, we made similar calculations of the combined impact of the lower air resistance and the lower FTP at the standard conditions, including a 7.4% gradient over 14.45 kilometers. Obviously, these calculations are very hypothetical as few such climbs will be found at an altitude of 4,000 meters. The results of Fast Eddy are given in the figure and table below.

We see that uphill the combined impact is always negative. The climbing time of Fast Eddy increases substantially, from 55.6 minutes at sea level to 59.2 minutes at the altitude of Alpe d'Huez (1,815 meters), an increase by 6%. This is almost the same percentage as the decrease of his FTP, as the air resistance is of limited importance. In a later chapter, we will analyze more closely the record times of Pantani and others on the climb to the Alpe d'Huez. There, we will also correct for the impact of the altitude to make a more fair comparison of the real performances of the cyclists. We will also show that many of the record performances should be considered as suspect, as they are better than we could theoretically expect at the maximum FTP of 6.40 watts/kg (which we consider to be the ultimate limit of the clean human engine).

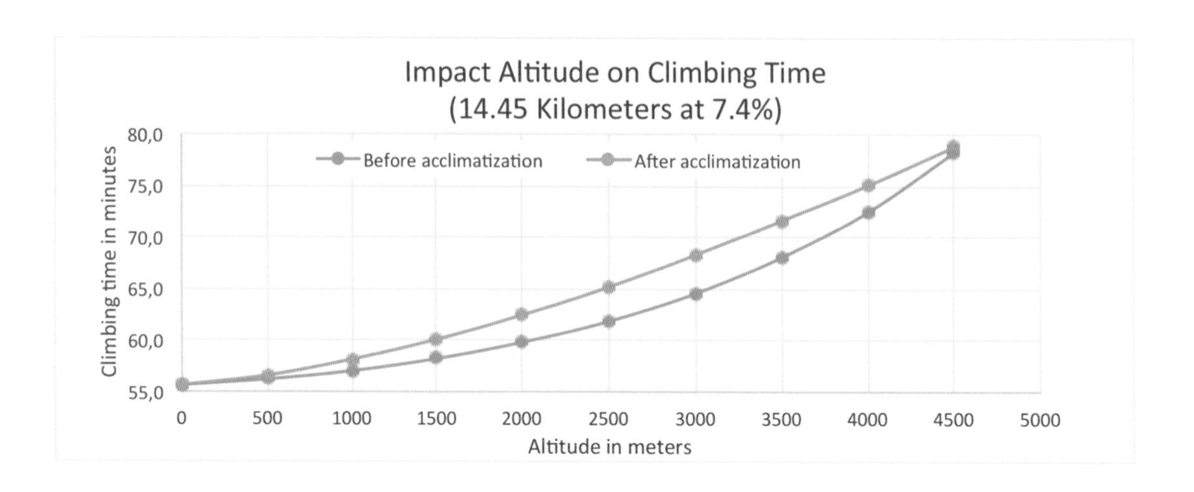

Impact of Altitude on Climbing Time After Acclimatization			
Altitude	v	T Alpe	Difference
(m)	(km/h)	(min)	(sec)
0	15.58	55.6	-
500	15.43	56.2	32
1,000	15.21	57.0	81
1,500	14.9	58.2	152
2,000	14.5	59.8	249
2,500	14.02	61.8	372
3,000	13.43	64.6	535
3,500	12.74	68.1	744
4,000	11.97	72.4	1007

In summary, we conclude that the impact of altitude on the performance of endurance cyclists is substantial. The advantage of the lower air resistance predominates at flat courses up to a 3,000-meter altitude. Consequently, a significant advantage can be gained by attempts to break the world hour record at altitude. However, uphill the substantial disadvantage of the lower power output of the human engine is predominant. As a result, the climbing times to Alpe d'Huez are always negatively impacted. We can calculate both aspects with our model. In the next chapters, we will calculate the exact results, taking into account both aspects of the altitude.

The impact of altitude on the performance of endurance cyclists is substantial. The advantage of the lower air resistance predominates at flat courses up to a 3,000-meter altitude.

45. THE WORLD HOUR RECORD

Eddy Merckx and I won all major classics. I won Paris Tours, he won all the others. –Noël Van Tyghem

The world hour record[55] has always appealed to the imagination of both cyclists and fans. The worldwide media attention boosted when the great Eddy Merckx traveled to Mexico City and improved the record to 49,431 meters. As Eddy was considered to be the all-time best cyclist, it was expected that his record would be untouched by other cyclists for many years.

The Big Impact of Aerodynamics and Altitude

In earlier chapters, we learned that the attainable speed and thus the distance in one hour depends significantly on the aerodynamics (in particular the air-resistance coefficient (c_dA)) and the altitude (as the density of the air is less at altitude).

The first cyclist to improve Eddy Merckx's record was Francesco Moser in 1984. He did this at the same velodrome in Mexico City (an altitude of 2,336 meters above sea level) with a specially designed bike with improved aerodynamics, including disc wheels. We estimate that his c_dA value was only 0.25 m^2, as compared to 0.30 m^2 for Eddy's conventional bike. With our program we have calculated that as a result of the improved aerodynamics, Moser was able to improve Eddy's record by almost three kilometers with less power (362 watts vs. 390 watts).

In later years, other cyclists managed to improve the record by further reducing the c_dA value. An example is the record of Graeme Obree, who used his Obree position with the rider crouched with his chest resting on the bars and his hands tucked under the collar bone. Another example is Chris Boardman, who used the Superman position with the rider's arms straight out front and the torso flat.

In 2000, the UCI banned these extreme aerodynamics and the old world record of Eddy Merckx was reinstated. Later that year Chris Boardman managed to improved Eddy's record by just 10 meters with a conventional bike.

In 2014, the UCI liberalized the rules again and permitted the use of disc wheels and extensions. This has led to renewed interest in the hour record and many attempts have been made in the past years, including the latest improvement by Sir Bradley Wiggins. On June 7, 2015, he cycled an impressive distance of 54,526 meters at the London Olympic velodrome.

How Can We Compare the World Record Attempts?

In order to make a fair comparison of the performance of the cyclists, we have used our program to correct for the significant impact of aerodynamics and altitude. We have used the following data:

1. The c_dA value was estimated, based on literature[56,57] and calculations.
2. The impact of altitude on the air density was calculated as discussed in an earlier chapter.
3. The body weight of the cyclist was checked on the internet.
4. The rolling resistance coefficient (c_r) was set at 0.002.
5. The mechanical efficiency (η) was set at 0.985.

Using these data, we calculated the amount of power (in watts) that the cyclist must have pushed in order to cover his distance in one hour. As the performance of the human engine is reduced at altitude, next we have corrected this wattage to sea level (using Basset's formula, as discussed in a previous chapter). Finally, we have divided the sea level wattage by the body weight of the cyclist to arrive at the specific power in watts/kg. As the duration of the attempt is one hour, this specific power equals the FTP of the cyclist. The table and figures give the results of our calculations.

World Hour Attempts (Men)								
Year	Cyclist	Location	Distance	Altitude	c_dA	Power	Power at sea level	Specific power
			(km)	(m)	(m^2)	(watts)	(watts)	(watts/kg)
1972	Eddy Merckx	Mexico	49.431	2,336	0.30	390	436	6.06
1984	Francesco Moser	Mexico	51.151	2,336	0.25	362	405	5.33
1994	Graeme Obree	Bordeaux	52.713	73	0.17	350	350	4.94
1994	Miguel Indurain	Bordeaux	53.040	73	0.24	497	497	6.15
1994	Tony Rominger	Bordeaux	55.291	73	0.18	400	400	6.17
1996	Chris Boardman	Manchester	56.375	60	0.17	424	424	6.16
2000	Chris Boardman	Manchester	49.441	60	0.25	418	418	6.00
2014	Jens Voigt	Grenchen	51.110	430	0.22	397	401	5.27
2015	Rohan Dennis	Grenchen	52.491	430	0.22	428	433	6.01
2015	Thomas Dekker	Mexico	52.221	1,886	0.22	359	389	5.19
2015	Alex Dowsett	Manchester	52.937	60	0.22	443	443	5.91
2015	Bradley Wiggins	London	54.526	0	0.21	468	468	6.08

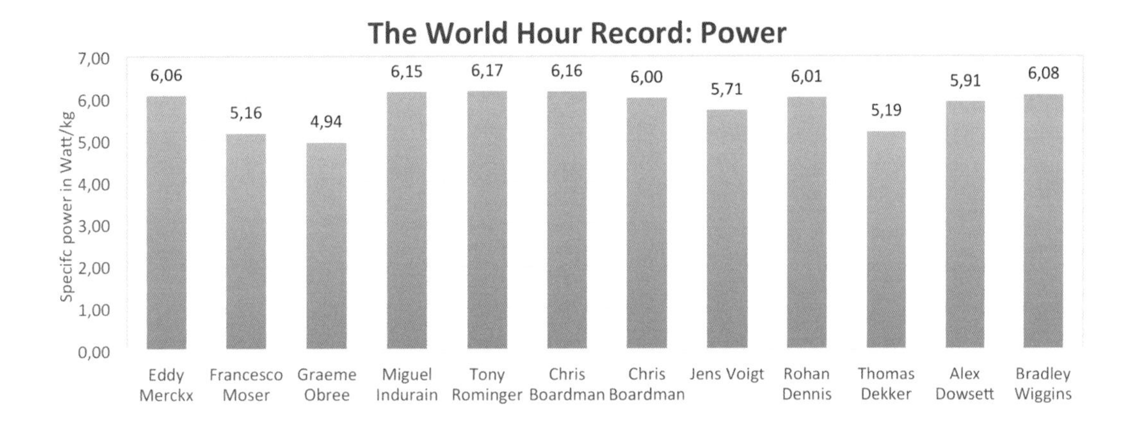

Which Record Is the Best?

From the table and our calculations, we conclude the following:

1. The advantage of the thin air at altitude is significant, as could be expected from theory and the earlier chapter. As an example, we mention that Thomas Dekker cycled almost the same distance as Rohan Dennis, but he needed 17% less power (359 watts vs. 428 watts) as a result of the thin air of Mexico City!
2. The disadvantage of the lower performance of the human engine at altitude reduces the advantage somewhat. In the same example, after correction to sea level, the advantage of Thomas Dekker is reduced from 17% to 10% (389 watts vs. 433 watts).
3. The advantage of improved aerodynamics and a reduced c_dA value is huge. As an example, we mention that Chris Boardman with his Superman position managed to cover almost 2 kilometers more than Sir Bradley Wiggins with 40 watts less power!
4. The values for the specific power (equivalent to the FTP) of the top cyclists are all in the order of 6.0-6.1 watts/kg. Eddy Merckx, Miguel Indurain, Tony Rominger, Chris Boardman, Rohan Dennis and Bradley Wiggins all performed at this high level. Consequently, it seems that these cyclists performed more or less equally. The values of 6.0-6.1 watts/kg are slightly below the maximum of 6.4 watts/kg, which we consider to be the ultimate limit of human performance. We note that we believe that the value of 6.4 watts/kg can only be reached by cyclists with a very low body fat percentage. Climbers are usually skinnier than time-trial specialists, so they have a better chance to approach this level.

We end this analysis with a word of caution. The results of the calculations depend significantly on the assumptions of the c_dA value. Although we have tried to estimate these with the utmost care, this may still affect the outcome to some extent. An example of a suspicious result is the rather high specific power (FTP) of Rohan Dennis; perhaps his real c_dA value was a little lower than the 0.22 m^2 that we used for the calculations.

An In-Depth Analysis of the World Hour Record of Sir Bradley Wiggins

While we were writing this book, Sir Bradley Wiggins smashed the world hour record at the London Olympic velodrome on June 7, 2015. We were thrilled to watch him on TV with his golden helmet, golden shoes and even with his familiar beard shaved off to maximize the aerodynamics. Like an impressive machine he pushed round after round to achieve an impressive new world record of 54,526 meters. His performance inspired us to make an in-depth analysis of his record: what went well and what could have gone even better? We were also curious to see if his record could be improved further in the future. Finally, we wanted to estimate the ultimate limit of the world hour record for a perfect athlete and in perfect conditions.

Bradley Wiggins in the time trial from Bonneval to Chartres in the Tour de France 2012.

How Much Power Did Sir Bradley Push?

With our program we calculated how much power Sir Bradley must have pushed in order to attain the distance of 54,526 meters. We used the data of the table below. From the calculations, we conclude that he must have pushed 468 watts or 6.08 watts/kg. As stated above, this is definitely world-class level and comparable to the performances of Merckx, Indurain, Rominger and Boardman.

World Hour Record of Bradley Wiggins (54.526 Kilometers)		
Standard conditions		
Body weight	77	kg
Bike weight	6.8	kg
$c_d A$	0.21	m^2
c_r	0.002	-
T	28	°C
p	1,030	mbar
η	0.99	-
v_w	0	m/s
P	468	watts

What Went Well and What Could Have Gone Better?

First, it should be noted that the organizers in London had heated the velodrome to a temperature of 28°C in order to reduce the air density. This tactic paid off as the air resistance was reduced. We have calculated that with the same wattage, Sir Bradley would have covered 490 meters less at a temperature of 20°C.

However, Bradley had a stroke of bad luck as the air pressure was a bit high that day (1,030 mbar). According to our calculations, he could have covered 1,200 meters more during a low of 963 mbar!

A further reduction of his $c_d A$ value to 0.20 m^2 would have provided a gain of 870 meters.

Should Bradley have been able to push 10 watts more than the 468 watts, this would have provided a gain of another 400 meters.

By far the best tactic would have been to travel to Mexico City. According to our calculations, he would have covered an additional 2,710 meters there!

Finally, we calculated the impact of a creative (but obviously illegal) idea. Should the organizers have installed fans in the velodrome providing a tail wind of 1 m/s, Bradley would have covered an additional 2,370 meters!

The table and figure show the results of these sensitivity analyses.

We conclude that the record of Sir Bradley—as impressive as it is—will definitely be broken in the near future when he (or another elite time-trial specialist) travels to Mexico City to perform in ideal conditions.

Attainable Distances	Distance	Difference
	(km)	(km)
Base case	54.53	-
No heating (20°C)	54.04	-0.49
Improved aerodynamics (c_dA = 0.20)	55.40	0.87
Higher power (P = 478 watts)	54.93	0.40
Depression (p = 963 mbar)	55.73	1.20
Fans (v_w = 1 m/s)	56.90	2.37
Altitude (h = 2,336 meters)	57.24	2.71

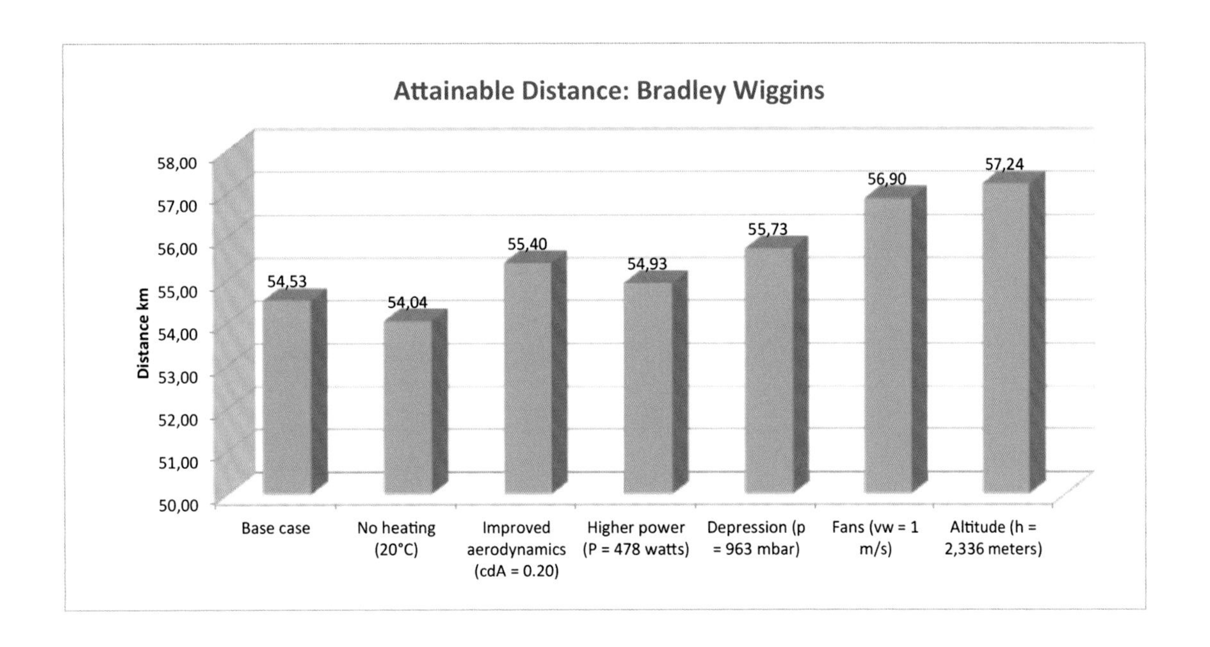

What Is the Ultimate Limit of the World Hour Record?

We were curious to see how much further the world hour record may advance in the future.

Consequently, we made a calculation for the following (extremely favorable) conditions:

1. The FTP of the cyclist will be at the ultimate limit of 6.4 watts/kg and his body weight at 80 kg Consequently, he will be able to push the astonishing power of 512 watts.
2. The location is the old velodrome in Mexico City (at an altitude of 2,336 meters).
3. The $c_d A$ value will be reduced further to 0.19 m^2.
4. The temperature is 30°C.

The result is that in these conditions the record could go to a distance of 61.6 kilometers!

Obviously, these calculations are just theory; the combination of an FTP of 6.4 watts/kg and a body weight of 80 kg seems a bit farfetched. However, a significant improvement of the current record seems quite feasible by going to altitude and further improving the aerodynamics.

46. THE IMPACT OF BIKE POSITION AND BIKE DESIGN

Whoever invented the bicycle deserves the thanks of humanity. –Lord Charles Beresford

In the chapter on the air resistance, we learned that the c_dA has a big impact on the attainable speed, particularly on the flat and somewhat less in the mountains. There we saw that the c_dA depends on:

1. The position on the bike: this should be as streamlined as possible.
2. The bike design: aero wheels, frames and extensions are superior.
3. The body posture: a smaller person has a small advantage.

In this chapter, we will discuss the concrete options and the impact of an improved bike position and bike design in practice.

Review of Concrete Options

The table below gives a review of a number of concrete options regarding bike position and bike design[44,45,46]. We have indicated the impact on the c_dA value, as reported in literature.

Impact of Bike Position and Bike Design		
	c_dA (m^2)	Difference with base
Position		
Upright	0.6	0.3
Standing on pedals	0.408	0.108
Bending forward	0.401	0.101
Tucked down	0.324	0.024
Arms on drops	0.307	-
Aerobars	0.291	-0.009
Aerobars optimized	0.268	-0.032
Wheels		
Standard	0.0212	-
Aero rim	0.0144	-0.0068
Composite	0.0127	-0.0085
Disk	0.008	-0.0132
Forks		
Standard round	0.0215	-
Oval	0.0149	-0.0066
Airfoil shaped	0.0103	-0.0112
Handlebars		
Standard		-
Semi-aero	-0.0126	-0.0126
Full aero	-0.0181	-0.0181
Frames		
Standard	0.0913	-
Semi-aero	0.084	-0.0073
Aero	0.0656	-0.0257
Total		
Standard	0.2914	
Semi-aero		
Aero	0.1993	-0.0921

Author Guido Vroemen explains how to improve the bike position.

Aero-optimized time-trial bike.

Race Time at a 40-Kilometer Time Trial

Once again, we calculated the impact with our program and using the standard conditions. The results are given in the figure and table below. As could be expected, the bike position has a big impact on the attainable speed. If Fast Eddy were to sit upright, his speed would drop from 40.41 km/h to 32.38 km/h, by 20%. At the 40-kilometer time trial this corresponds to a loss of 884 seconds. You might be more interested to see that he could gain a total of 334 seconds with an optimal bike design and an optimal bike position. The data from the table may help you in deciding how to spend your budget.

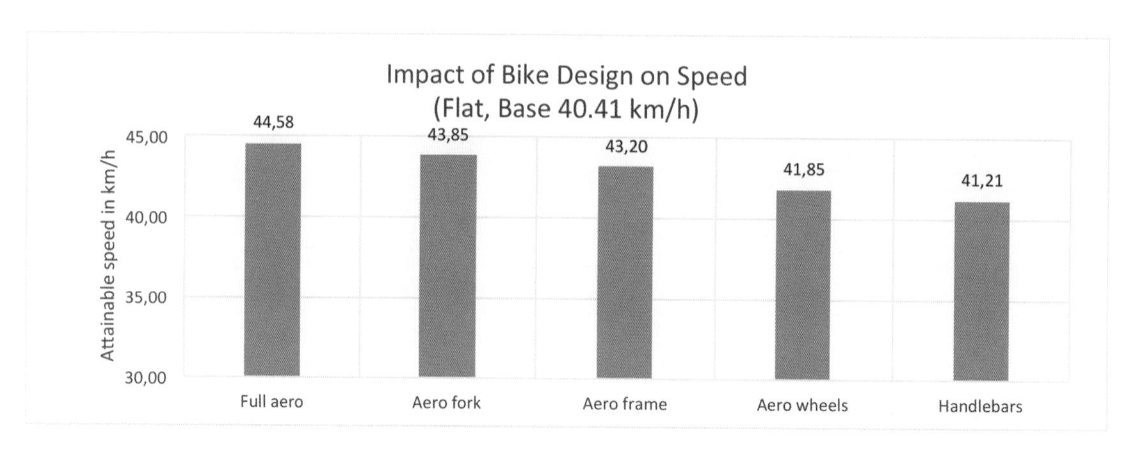

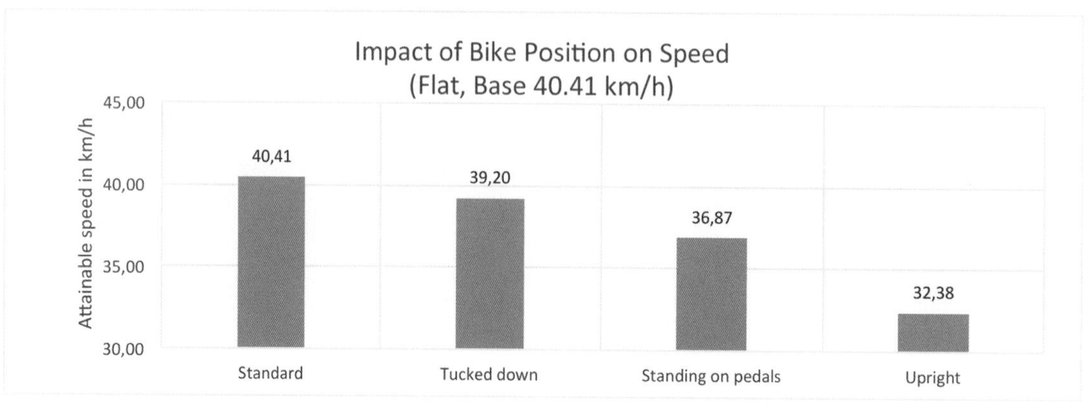

Aero	c_dA	v	T 40 km	Difference
		(km/h)	(min)	(sec)
Full aero	0.220	44.58	53.8	-334
Aero fork	0.232	43.85	54.7	-280
Aero frame	0.243	43.20	55.6	-231
Aero wheels	0.269	41.85	57.4	-123
Handlebars	0.282	41.21	58.2	-70
Standard	0.300	40.41	59.4	-
Tucked down	0.330	39.20	61.2	110
Standing on pedals	0.400	36.87	65.1	342
Upright	0.600	32.38	74.1	884

Race Time to the Top of the Alpe d'Huez

Once again, the results of our calculations are shown in a similar figure and table. We see that the impact in the mountains is much less. With a full aero bike Fast Eddy can only gain 41 seconds on the climb to the Alpe d'Huez. Obviously, this is caused by the fact that the climbing resistance is the dominant factor in this case.

Finally, we note that in this chapter we have looked at the impact of the bike design on the air resistance only. An optimal bike design also includes reducing the weight. Obviously, this leads to a substantial gain in the mountains. This has already been discussed in a previous chapter.

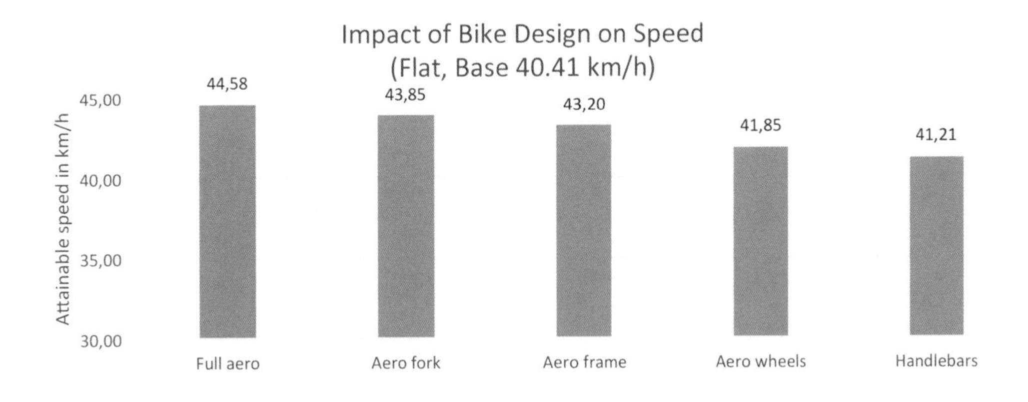

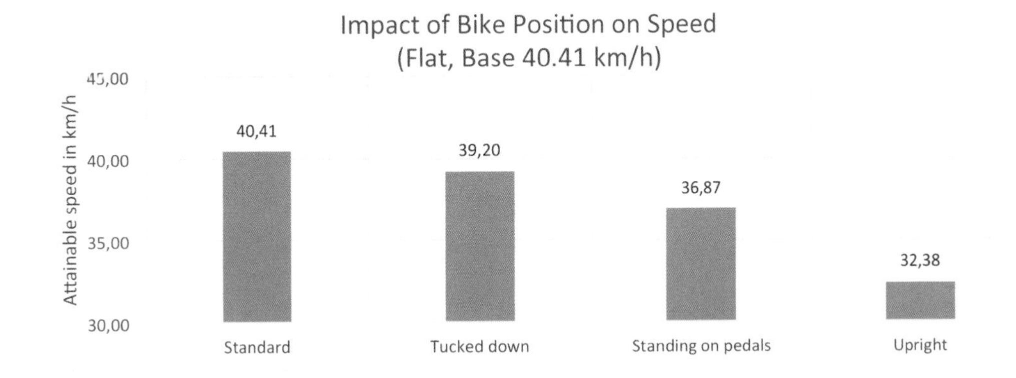

Aero	c_dA	v	T Alpe	Difference
		(km/h)	(min)	(sec)
Full	0.220	15.78	55.0	-41
Aero fork	0.232	15.75	55.1	-35
Aero frame	0.243	15.72	55.2	-29
Aero wheels	0.269	15.65	55.4	-16
Handlebars	0.282	15.62	55.5	-9
Standard	0.300	15.58	55.7	0
Tucked down	0.330	15.51	55.9	15
Standing on pedals	0.400	15.35	56.5	49
Upright	0.600	14.95	58.0	141

For perfect bike fitting, advanced tools are available.

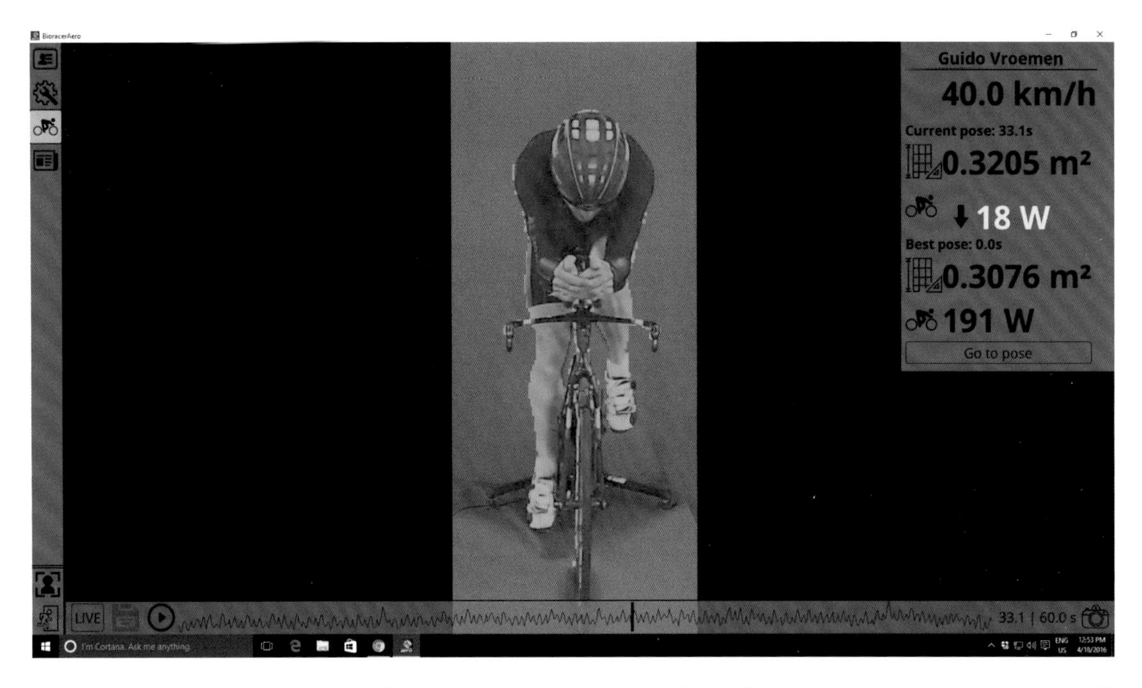

The frontal area (A) can also be measured with a camera system and software to calculate the power needed to cycle at a certain speed with predefined circumstances (e.g., $c_d A$, wind, temperature).

47. THE IMPACT OF WHEEL SUCKING

Half of my time I bike, the other half is wasted.

In the chapter on the cycling formula, we learned that we can calculate the air resistance with the following formula:

$$P_a = 0.5\rho c_d A(v+v_w)^2 v$$

Using the standard conditions of Fast Eddy, we can calculate that his air resistance is 248 watts at a speed of 40 km/h (ρ = 1.205 kg/m^3, c_dA = 0.3 m^2, v = 40/3.6 m/s, v_w = 0 m/s). This is equal to some 83% of his FTP of 300 watts.

This confirms what we know from experience: air reswwistance is the dominant factor determining the performance on a flat course. Also we see that the air resistance increases to the cube of the speed. So, if you want to increase your speed by 10%, you need to push 33% more power (1.10^3-1)!

The major impact of the air resistance is also the reason that it is almost impossible to stay away from a chasing pack, even for world-class cyclists. Cycling within the pack is relatively easy, as your c_dA is then reduced by some 40%. Consequently, when Fast Eddy cycles 40 km/h within the pack, he only has to push 0.6*248 = 140 watts. This is around 47% of his FTP, so this poses no problem at all.

Joop Zoetemelk in the wheel of Eddy Merkcx. Joop was a great cyclist and had an (undeserved) reputation as a wheel sucker. Joop completed the Tour de France 16 times and finished in second place six times. In 1980 Joop won the Tour.

How Big Is the Advantage of Drafting?

We have summarized the literature on the advantage of drafting in the table below[44,45,46]. The table shows that two cyclists always have an edge on a single cyclist. The back rider of the two has an advantage of 25% (so his c_dA is 25% lower), but even the front rider has an advantage of some 10%, because the back rider pushes the air in front of him. Consequently, two cyclists can maintain a 5% higher speed as compared to a solo cyclist. The advantage increases with the number of cyclists. Five cyclists can already maintain a 10% higher speed than a single cyclist. Therefore, breakaway groups of five cyclists stand a decent chance against the pack. However, the pack always has the upper hand as more cyclists can share the hard work at the front. Next to the physical advantage of drafting, wheel sucking also has an important psychological impact. The front rider will always worry that the wheel sucker behind him can save his strength and beat him at the finish. The back cyclist will feel rested and strong and be confident of the outcome of the final sprint.

Impact of Drafting	
	c_dA
	(m^2)
One cyclist	0.3
Two cyclists, front rider	0.27
Two cyclists	0.255
Two cyclists, back rider	0.225
Five cyclists	0.200
Pack	0.18

Race Time at a 40-Kilometer Time Trial

Once again, we calculated the impact with our program and using the standard conditions. The results are given in the figure and table. As could be expected, the attainable speed of Fast Eddy increases substantially when he gets the chance to ride in the pack or a group. In the pack he can cycle 47.50 km/h, 17% faster. At the 40-kilometer time trial, he can gain no less than 532 seconds! In a group of five, he can maintain a speed of 45.94 km/h, much faster than the 40.41 km/h he can cycle solo. Even with just one other cyclist, the chances for Fast Eddy to stay ahead of the pack increase significantly. If he could manage to keep the back position, he could cycle 44.27 km/h.

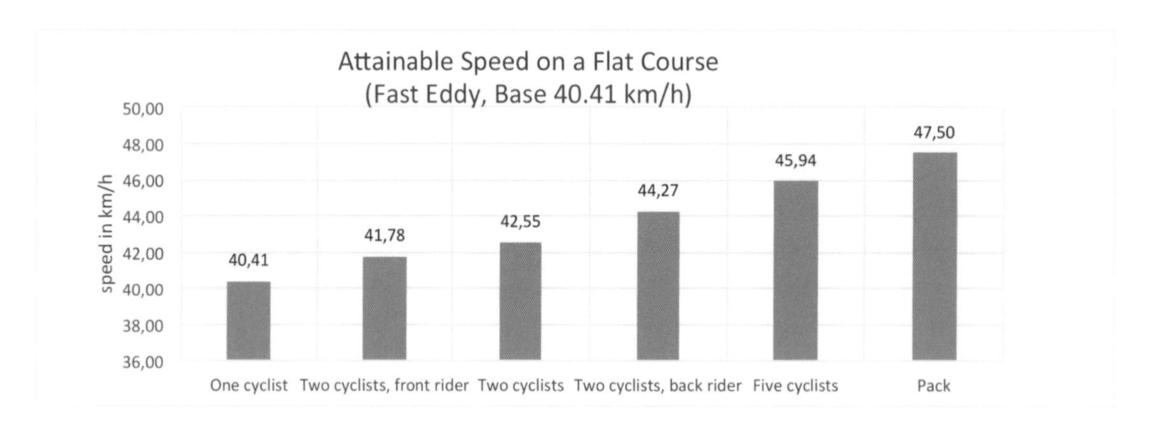

Impact of Drafting				
	c_dA	v	T 40 km	Difference
	(m^2)	(km/h)	(min)	(sec)
One cyclist	0.3	40.41	59.4	-
Two cyclists, front rider	0.27	41.78	57.4	117
Two cyclists	0.255	42.55	56.4	179
Two cyclists, back rider	0.225	44.27	54.2	311
Five cyclists	0.200	45.94	52.2	429
Pack	0.18	47.50	50.5	532

The advantages of drafting are well illustrated in team time trials.

Race Time to the Top of the Alpe d'Huez

Once again, the results of our calculations are shown in a similar figure and table. We see that the impact in the mountains is much less. The speed of a pack, who have the same specifications as Fast Eddy, will be 15.88 km/h, only slightly higher than the 15.58 km/h he can ride solo. The total gain of the pack of Fast Eddys is only 63 seconds on the climb to the Alpe d'Huez. Obviously, this is caused by the fact that the climbing resistance is the dominant factor in this case.

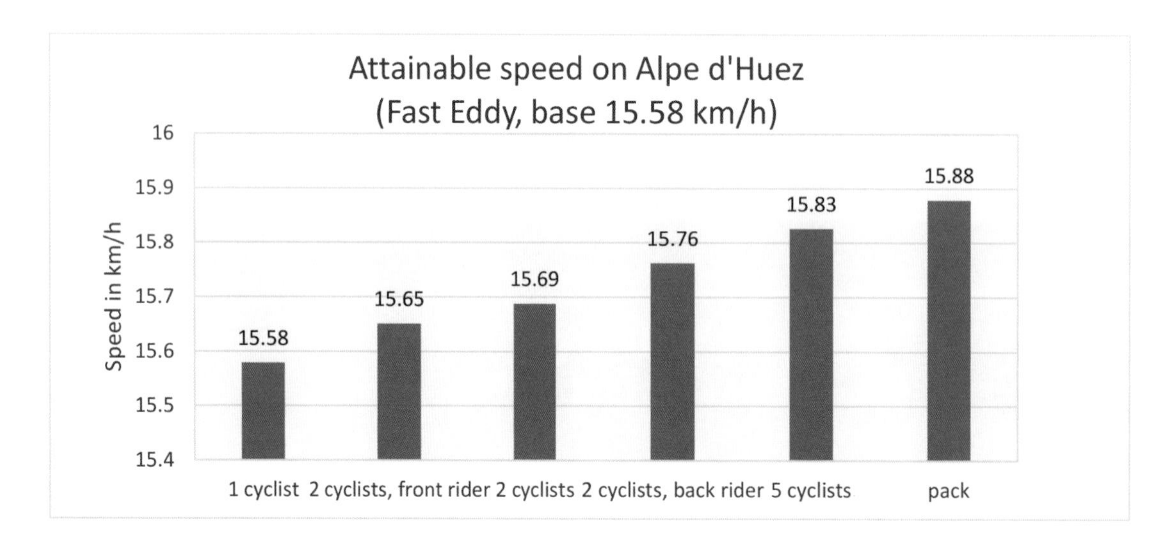

Impact of Drafting				
	c_dA	v	T Alpe	Difference
	(m^2)	(km/h)	(min)	(sec)
One cyclist	0.3	15.58	55.7	-
Two cyclists, front rider	0.27	15.65	55.4	-15
Two cyclists	0.255	15.69	55.3	-23
Two cyclists, back rider	0.225	15.76	55.0	-39
Five cyclists	0.2001	15.83	54.8	-52
Pack	0.18	15.88	54.6	-63

Joop Zoetemelk won the Alpe d'Huez stage of the Tour de France twice. Bend 20 (1976) and bend 16 (1979) in the road from Bourg d'Oisans to Huez are named after Joop.

48. THE IMPACT OF THE WIND

May the road rise up to meet you. May the wind be always at your back. –Irish proverb

In the chapter on the cycling formula, we learned that we can calculate the air resistance with the following formula:

$$P_a = 0.5\rho c_d A(v+v_w)^2 v$$

Using the standard conditions of Fast Eddy, we can calculate that his air resistance is 248 watts at a speed of 40 km/h (ρ = 1.205 kg/m^3, c_dA = 0.3 m^2, v = 40/3.6 m/s, v_w = 0 m/s). This is equal to some 83% of his FTP of 300 watts.

Obviously, this result is valid for windless conditions. However, in practice we frequently have to face windy conditions. From experience, we know that this has a big impact on our speed. When we face a strong head wind, our speed drops significantly, sometimes to pedestrian pace. On the other hand, we seem to fly when we are lucky enough to benefit from a strong tail wind.

How big is the impact of a head wind and a tail wind on the attainable speed of Fast Eddy? We have made calculations for a range of wind speeds from -50 km/h (a head wind) to +50 km/h (a tail wind). The table shows the Beaufort scale[58] of the wind force, which is used frequently in practice. A wind speed of 50 km/h corresponds to wind force 6 or 7 at the Beaufort scale (strong breeze or high wind).

Wind force (Beaufort)	Description	Wind speed (km/h)
0	Calm	0-1
1	Light air	1-5
2	Light breeze	6-11
3	Gentle breeze	12-19
4	Moderate breeze	20-28
5	Fresh breeze	29-38
6	Strong breeze	39-49
7	High wind	50-61
8	Gale	62-74
9	Strong gale	75-88
10	Storm	89-102

Race Time at the 40-Kilometer Time Trial

Once again, we calculated the impact with our program and using the standard conditions. The results are given in the figure and table. Facing a head wind, the speed drops by 61.6% of the wind speed. At a head wind with a speed of 20 km/h, Fast Eddy's speed drops to 28.83 km/h, by 29%. Consequently, it will take him 83.2 minutes to complete the 40-kilometer time trial instead of 59.4 minutes in windless conditions! On the other hand, with a tail wind of 20 km/h, he can reach a speed of 77.24 km/h, so he will reach the finish after 31.1 minutes! This illustrates clearly that the wind is a dominant factor in the attainable speed at a flat time trial.

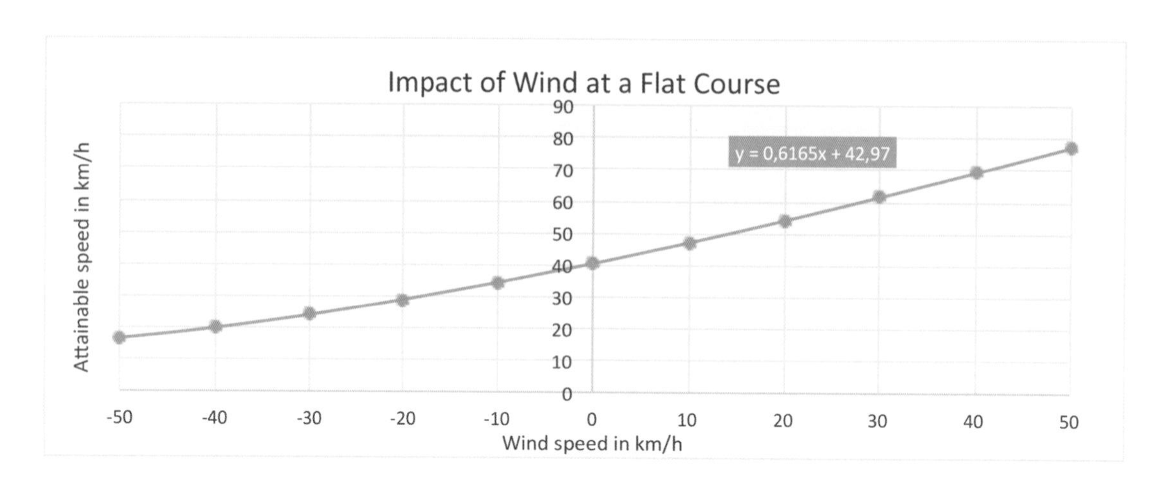

Impact of Wind on Speed at a Flat Course			
v_w	v	T 40 km	Difference
(km/h)	(km/h)	(min)	(%)
-50	16.30	147.2	147.9
-40	19.80	121.2	104.1
-30	23.97	100.1	68.6
-20	28.83	83.2	40.2
-10	34.32	69.9	17.7
0	40.41	59.4	-
10	47.01	51.1	-14.0
20	54.07	44.4	-25.3
30	61.49	39.0	-34.3
40	69.23	34.7	-41.6
50	77.24	31.1	-47.7

Stage of Olympia's Tour through the Netherlands on the windy Afsluitdijk.

Race Time to the Top of the Alpe d'Huez

Once again, the results of our calculations are shown in a similar figure and table. We see that the impact in the mountains is less, but still significant. Facing a head wind of 20 km/h, the speed of Fast Eddy drops from 15.58 km/h to 13.23 km/h, by 15%. His climbing time to the top increases from 55.6 to 65.6 minutes. On the other hand, Fast Eddy may benefit uphill from a tail wind. With a tail wind of 50 km/h, he can reach the top in 39.1 minutes, almost as fast at the record of Marco Pantani! It should be noted that these calculations are just theory, as it is not possible to benefit continuously from a tail wind as a result of the hairpins in the climb. Nevertheless, the impact of the wind on the climbing times will still be significant.

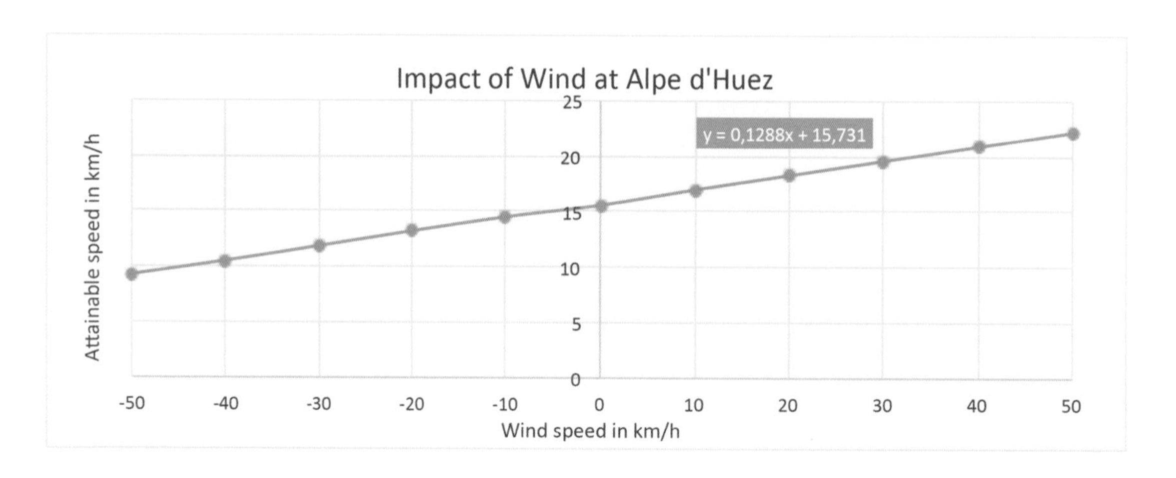

Impact of Wind on Speed at Alpe d'Huez			
v_w	v	T Alpe	Difference
(km/h)	(km/h)	(min)	(%)
-50	9.30	93.2	67.5
-40	10.55	82.2	47.7
-30	11.88	73.0	31.2
-20	13.23	65.5	17.8
-10	14.51	59.8	7.4
0	15.58	55.6	0.0
10	17.00	51.0	-8.4
20	18.30	47.4	-14.9
30	19.60	44.2	-20.5
40	20.90	41.5	-25.5
50	22.20	39.1	-29.8

The Impact of the Wind in Practice

Obviously, in the real world you will never be so lucky as to have a tail wind continuously. As the direction of the course will never be a straight line, you will have to cope with different wind conditions. The net impact of wind on your speed and race time will usually be negative, because you lose more time from a head wind than you can gain from a tail wind. This is illustrated in the figure that shows the impact on the race time for the hypothetical case of a course with 50% head wind and 50% tail wind.

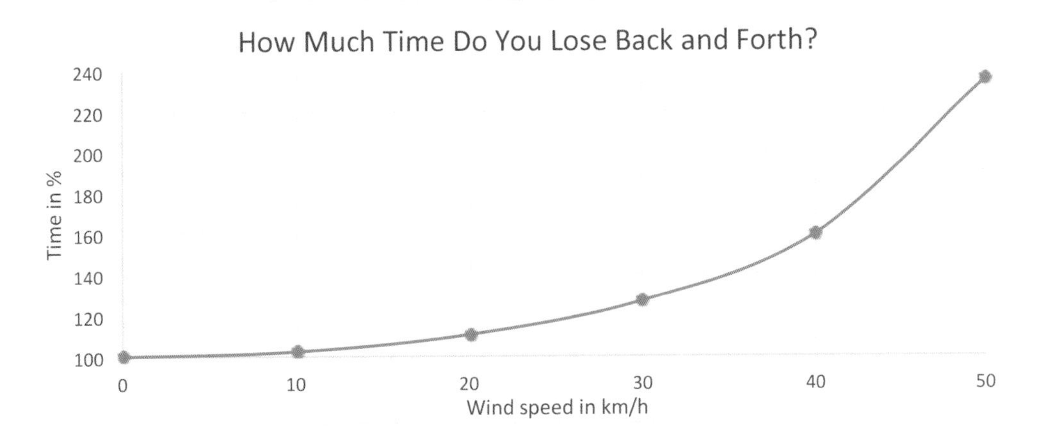

How Hard Is Cycling Against a Head Wind?

The figure illustrates that it can indeed be quite hard to face a head wind. The figure shows the cases where the wind resistance and the climbing resistance are equal. As an example, we see that cycling against a head wind of 72 km/h (wind force 8 of the Beaufort scale, a gale) is just as hard as climbing the Alpe d'Huez! Of course, we should note that we rarely have to cycle continuously against a head wind of 72 km/h.

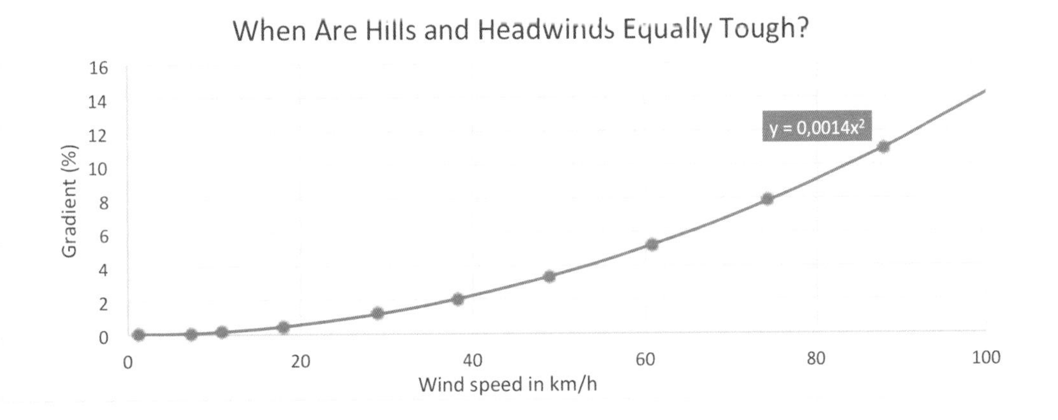

49. THE IMPACT OF THE CLIMBING RESISTANCE

Who stays in the valley will never see the other side of the mountain. –José de Cauwer

In the chapter on the cycling formula, we learned that we can calculate the climbing resistance with the formula:

$$P_c = (i/100)mgv$$

As an example, we calculate the climbing resistance for Fast Eddy in the standard conditions. The result is 677 watts at the climb to the Alpe d'Huez with a speed of 40 km/h ($i = 7.41\%$, $m = 83.8$ kg, $g = 9.81$ m/s^2, $v = 40/3.6$ m/s). As this is more than his FTP of 300 watts, we can conclude that he cannot maintain a speed of 40 km/h uphill. This confirms what we already know from experience: uphill the speed drops significantly, sometimes even to such a low level that the spectators can run along the cyclists for a while.

What are the options available to Fast Eddy to limit his climbing resistance? As we can see from the formula, he has just one option: to reduce his weight (m, the combined weight of his body and his bike). We have discussed the impact of the weight already in earlier chapters, both for flat and hilly courses. There, we concluded that reducing the weight has a favorable impact on the specific power (P/m, in watts/kg) of your human engine. This specific power determines your speed, particularly in the mountains.

In this chapter, we will study the impact of the gradient percentage (i). Obviously, Fast Eddy cannot change this, but the gradient does have a huge impact on his speed.

The Impact of the Gradient on the Speed

Once again, we made the calculations for the standard conditions (ρ = 1.205 kg/m^3, m = 83.3 kg, c_dA = 0.30 m^2, v_w = 0 m/s). In this case, we varied the gradient percentage (i) between -6% and +20%. We used the FTP of Fast Eddy (4 watts/kg), so the results are the speed that he can maintain for one hour. We refer to the figure and table for the results of the calculations.

The figure and table show that at a gradient between -5% and +5%, the speed drops linearly by a factor of 4.3 times the gradient. Consequently, Fast Eddy's speed of 40.4 km/h at the flat increases to 49.6 km/h at a downhill gradient of -2%. His speed decreases to 31.4 km/h at an uphill gradient of 2%.

At gradients above 5%, the curve deviates more and more from a straight line. This is caused by the fact that the air resistance becomes less important. At a steep gradient of 20%, the speed is reduced to just 6.3 km/h.

At steep descents (i.e., high negative gradients), the cycling formula is no longer valid and Fast Eddy more or less falls downward. This will be discussed in a later chapter.

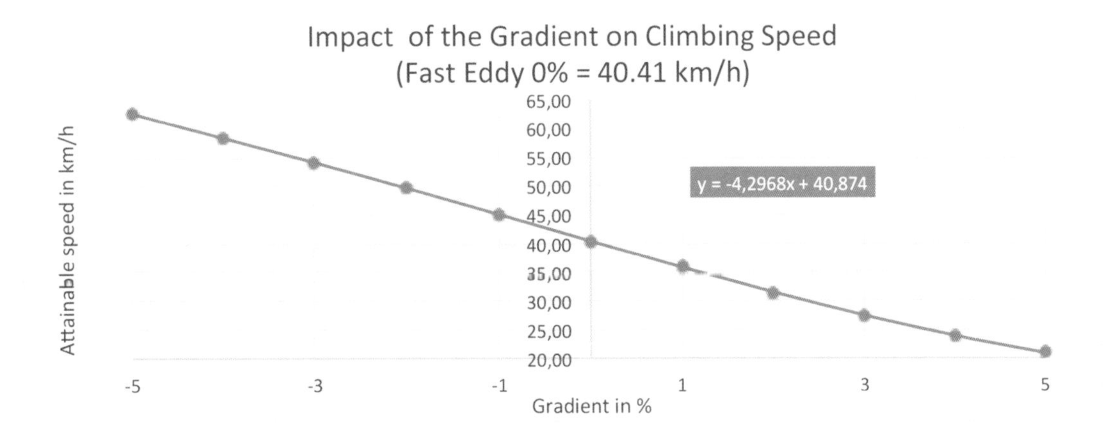

Impact of the Gradient (i)	
i	v
(%)	(km/h)
-6	66.59
-5	62.59
-4	58.43
-3	54.11
-2	49.64
-1	45.05
0	40.41
1	35.82
2	31.43
3	27.40
4	23.87
5	20.87
6	18.37
7	16.31
8	14.62
9	13.21
10	12.03
11	11.04
12	10.19
13	9.45
14	8.81
15	8.26
16	7.76
17	7.32
18	6.93
19	6.58
20	6.26

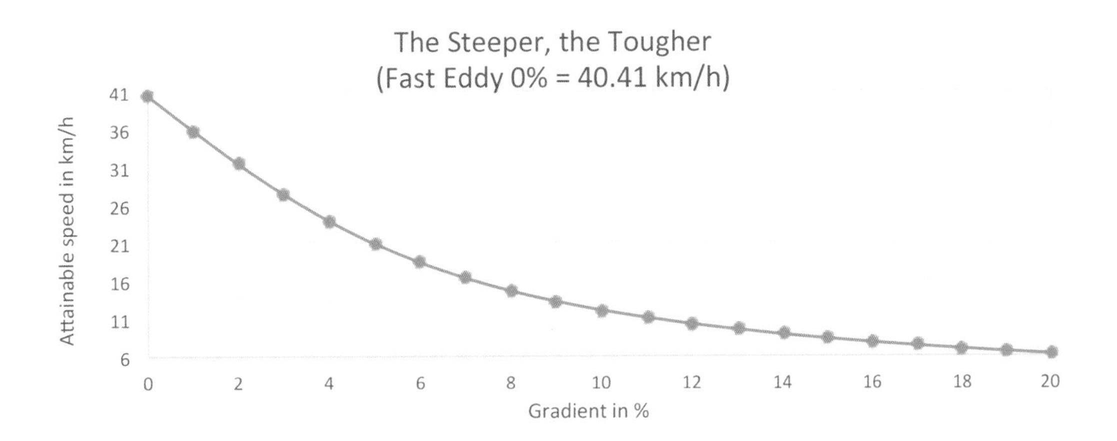

The road from Allemond to Huez.

50. HOW FAST CAN YOU CLIMB?

What the ideal pro looks like? Take the legs of Eddy Merckx, the head of Eddy Merckx, the muscles of Eddy Merckx and the mentality of Eddy Merckx.
–Jacques Anquetil

In the earlier chapter on the climbing resistance, we learned that we calculate this with the formula:

$$P_c = (i/100)mgv$$

Also, we saw that Fast Eddy had to push 677 watts in order to climb the Alpe d'Huez with a speed of 40 km/h in the standard conditions ($i = 7.41\%$, $m = 83.8$ kg, $g = 9.81$ m/s^2, $v = 40/3.6$ m/s). As this is 226% of his FTP of 300 watts, we concluded that he cannot maintain a speed of 40 km/h uphill. With our program, we then calculated that Fast Eddy can maintain a speed of 15.58 km/h and reach the top of the climb after 55.6 minutes.

Rule of Thumb

There is also an easier way to calculate how fast you can climb. Neglecting the rolling resistance, the air resistance and the mechanical resistance, we only have to calculate with the climbing resistance. Rewriting the above formula gives the result:

$$P_c/m = (i/100)gv$$

Next, we consider that (1/100)v represents the vertical climbing speed (v_v, the gain in altitude in m/s) and we substitute P_c/m (in watts/kg) by the FTP (also in FTP). The result is the following formula for the vertical climbing speed that you can maintain for one hour:

$$v_v = 3.6/9.8 * FTP = 0.37 * FTP$$

In this formula, v_v is expressed in km/h. As an example, Fast Eddy with his FTP of 4 watts/kg can climb with a vertical speed of 0.37*4 = 1.48 km/h. So, in one hour, he can gain 1,480 meters in altitude.

Similarly, we can now calculate the climbing time:

$$t = h/v_v = h/(0.37*FTP)$$

In this formula h is expressed in kilometers. As an example, Fast Eddy can climb to the top of the Alpe d'Huez (an altitude gain of 1,071 meters) in 1.071/(0.37*4) = 0.72 hour or 43.4 minutes. The formula shows clearly that your climbing time is inversely proportional to your FTP.

Which Factors Did We Neglect and What Is the Impact?

We see that the climbing time calculated with the simplified formula is too low, 43.4 minutes instead of the 55.6 minutes that we calculated with our program. This is caused by the fact that we neglected the rolling resistance, the air resistance and the mechanical resistance. Also, we did not include the weight of Eddy's bike in the calculations. Finally, Eddy's FTP will be somewhat reduced in the mountains as a result of the thin mountain air.

To illustrate the impact of these factors, we have prepared a figure. It gives four lines for the climbing speed as a function of the FTP:

1. The theoretical line according to the rule of thumb.
2. Additionally, 15% has been added for the rolling resistance, the air resistance and the mechanical resistance.
3. Additionally, 10% has been added for the weight of the bike.
4. Additionally, 11% has been added for the impact of the thin mountain air.

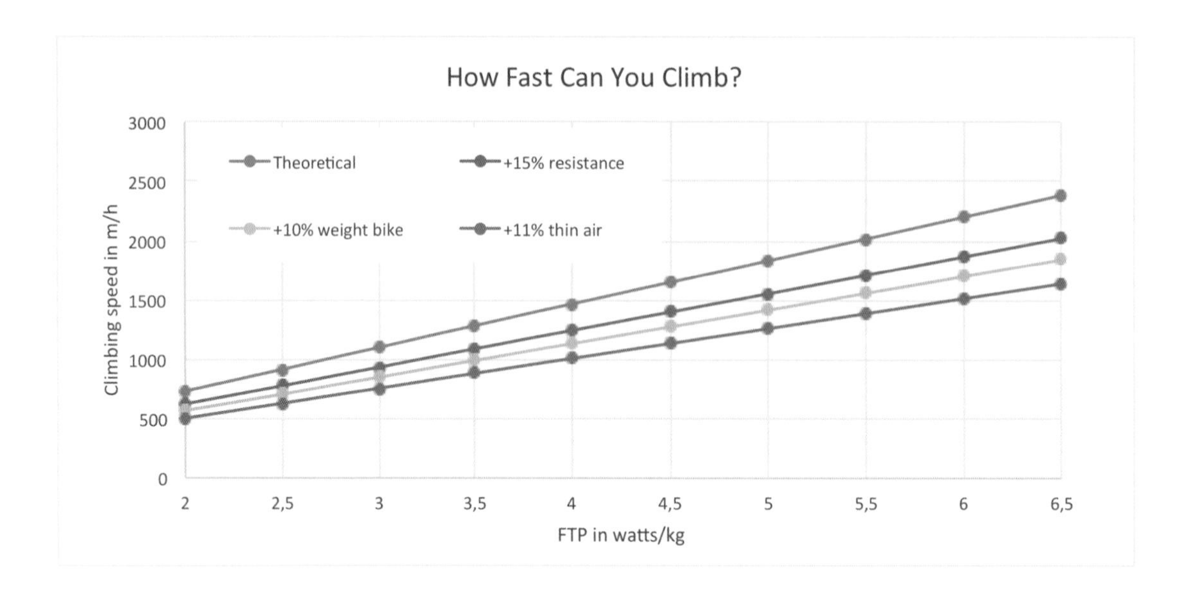

This figure allows you to estimate your climbing speed as a function of your FTP.

The Impact of Your Body Weight and the Weight of Your Bike

What are the options available to Fast Eddy to limit his climbing resistance? As we can see from the formula, he has just one option: to reduce his total weight (m, this is the sum of his body weight and the weight of his bike). To illustrate the impact, once again we have made calculations with our program. We have compared six cases, using the standard conditions (body weight = 75 kg and bike weight = 8.8 kg) and alternatives in which Eddy gains or loses 5 kg of body weight and 2 kg of bike weight. The figure and table below give the results. We see that Eddy can gain 238 seconds on the climb when he reduces his body weight by 2 kg and buys a 2-kg lighter bike.

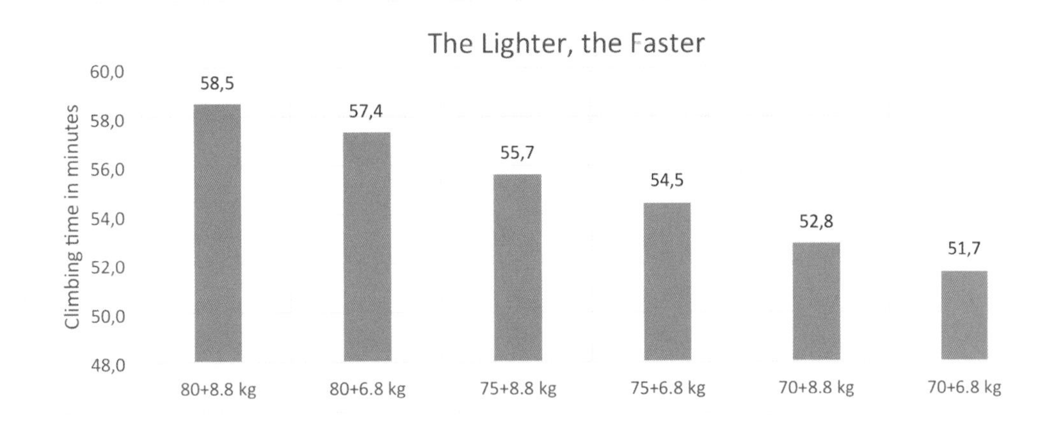

Impact of Weight on Alpe d'Huez			
	v	T Alpe	Difference
	(km/h)	(min)	(sec)
80+8.8 kg	14.81	58.5	-173
80+6.8 kg	15.11	57.4	-104
75+8.8 kg	15.58	55.7	-
75+6.8 kg	15.91	54.5	69
70+8.8 kg	16.42	52.8	171
70+6.8 kg	16.78	51.7	238

There is just one option to reduce the impact of the climbing resistance: reduce your total weight (the sum of your body weight and the weight of your bike).

51. THE ALPE D'HUEZ

If it hurts me, it must hurt the others twice as much!
–Jens Voigt

The climb to the Alpe d'Huez is one of the most famous cycling events in the world. No less than 27 times did a stage of the Tour de France finish on the summit. The climb starts in the village of Le Bourg d'Oisans at an altitude of 744 meters above sea level. The finish at Alpe d'Huez is at an altitude of 1,815 meters, so the total gain in altitude is 1,071 meters. The length of the climb is 13.2 kilometers, but usually the climbing length is measured at 14.45 kilometers from the top. Consequently, the gradient of the actual climb is 8.1%, but including the flat run-up it is only 7.41%.

The climb comprises of 21 officially numbered hairpin bends. At every bend a sign lists the name of one or two stage winners, including the Dutchmen Hennie Kuiper, Joop Zoetemelk and Peter Winnen, who all won the stage twice. The mythical image of the climb ensures large crowds along the course, cheering the cyclists.

Throughout this book, we have used the Alpe d'Huez as an inspiring example. In this chapter, we will use the top ten climbing times as a basis for our calculations. We were curious to see how high the FTP of the ten cyclists had been. Were the FTPs of Marco Pantani and Lance Armstrong close to the limit of 6.4 watts/kg? As discussed earlier, we consider this number to be the ultimate limit of the power of the clean human engine.

Alpe d'Huez really is the Mecca of cycling. An average of 400 cyclists per day accept the challenge of the climb with 21 hairpins bends.

The Top Ten Climbs

We have used the official list of the top ten climbs as the basis for our calculations[59]. The table below shows the riders and their record climbing times. Marco Pantani holds the record with a time of 37 minutes and 35 seconds. Unfortunately, we now know that both Pantani and all the other top ten cyclists have been found guilty of or have confessed to using doping at some point in their career. Of course, this sheds a dark shadow on their performances.

Record Climbs to Alpe d'Huez	
	Time
	(min:sec)
Marco Pantani (1997)	37:35
Lance Armstrong (2004)	37:36
Marco Pantani (1994)	38:00
Lance Armstrong (2001)	38:01
Marco Pantani (1995)	38:04
Jan Ullrich (1997)	38:23
Floyd Landis (2006)	38:34
Andreas Klöden (2006)	38:35
Jan Ullrich (2004)	38:37
Richard Virenque (1997)	39:02

The Calculations of the FTP of the Top Ten Cyclists

We have made a complete calculation of the performances of the top ten cyclists, including:

1. The complete cycling formula, including the rolling resistance, the air resistance, the climbing resistance and the mechanical resistance
2. Both aspects of the thin mountain air: the small advantage of a lower air resistance due to the lower air pressure and the bigger disadvantage of the lower performance of the human engine due to the lower availability of O_2

3. A correction for the fact that the climbing time is less than one hour, so the specific power will be higher than the FTP (which represents the power that can be maintained for one hour)

The table below gives the results. First, we have used the climbing speed and the body weight to calculate the power that the cyclist must have pushed. Next, we corrected this for the altitude by calculating the equivalent sea-level power. Finally, we corrected this for the time (and the body weight), so we calculated the sea-level equivalent FTP (in watts/kg).

The results are striking: all riders from the top ten had equivalent FTP values near or even above the limit of 6.4 watts/kg. When we consider that the equivalent FTP values of all the world records In athletics are between 6.30 and 6.36 watts/kg (and these records have been set at specially prepared record races in ideal conditions), it seems clear that the top ten cyclists may have used doping to achieve these performances at the end of a tough stage. When we divide the extreme value of Pantani (6.88) by the limit of 6.4, one might say that apparently the use of EPO has led to an increase of his FTP (and thus his performance) of at least 8% (100*(6.88/6.4-1)).

Record Climbs to Alpe d'Huez

	Time	v	Weight	P	$P_{sea\ level}$	$FTP_{sea\ level}$
	(min:sec)	(km/h)	(kg)	(watts)	(watts)	(watts/kg)
Marco Pantani (1997)	37:35	23.07	57	375	404	6.88
Lance Armstrong (2004)	37:36	23.06	75	466	502	6.50
Marco Pantani (1994)	38:00	22.82	57	370	398	6.79
Lance Armstrong (2001)	38:01	22.81	75	460	495	6.41
Marco Pantani (1995)	38:04	22.78	57	369	397	6.77
Jan Ullrich (1997)	38:23	22.59	72	439	473	6.38
Floyd Landis (2006)	38:34	22.48	68	417	449	6.41
Andreas Klöden (2006)	38:35	22.47	63	393	423	6.52
Jan Ullrich (2004)	38:37	22.45	72	437	470	6.35
Richard Virenque (1997)	39:02	22.21	65	398	428	6.40

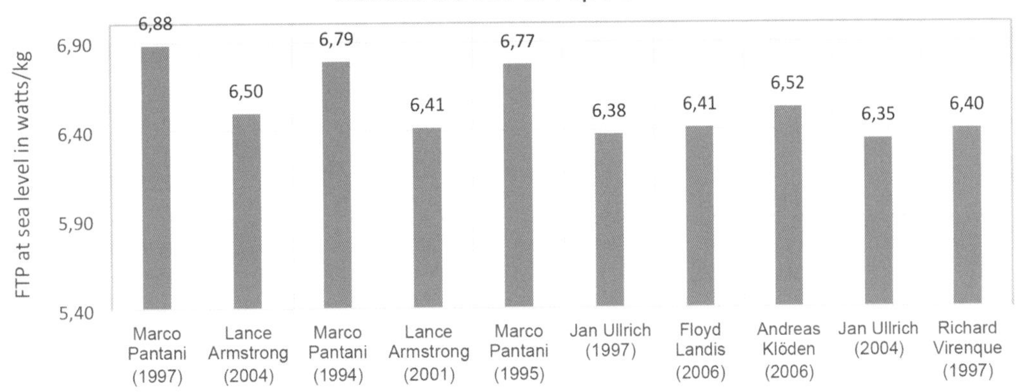

The climb to Alpe d'Huez counts 21 bends. Dutch spectators traditionally gather in bend #7.

52. HOW FAST CAN YOU RIDE DOWNHILL?

Crashing is part of cycling as crying is part of love.
–Johan Museeuw

In the earlier chapter on the climbing resistance, we learned the following formula:

$$P_c = (i/100)mgv$$

The gradient (i) is positive uphill and negative downhill. This means that the climbing resistance becomes negative in a descent and actually supports the power of your human engine. Consequently, we can rewrite the cycling formula to:

$$P+P_c = P_r+P_a+P_m$$

As the climbing resistance can now be added to your own power, your speed will increase significantly downhill. At steep descents, the support by gravity becomes so big that you don't have to pedal anymore. In this case, we can rewrite the cycling formula to:

$$P_c = P_r+P_a+P_m$$

Neglecting the mechanical resistance, we get the following formula:

$$(i/100)mgv = c_r mgv+0,5\rho c_d Av^3$$

Dividing by v and some rewriting leads to the formula describing the maximum descent speed:

$$v = \sqrt{(2g(i/100-c_r)m/\rho c_d A)}$$

As an example, we use the standard conditions for Fast Eddy ($m = 75+8.8$ kg, $g = 9.81$ m/s^2, $\rho = 1.205$ kg/m^3 and $c_d A = 0.3$ m^2). His descent speed at Alpe d'Huez ($i = 7.41\%$) thus becomes 64.3 km/h.

The Impact of Your Body Weight

The formula shows that the descent speed increases with the body weight. We have illustrated the impact of the body weight in the table and figure below. Both show that heavyweights have an edge as their descent speed is significantly higher. So we see that the disadvantage of a higher bodyweight uphill is partly compensated by an advantage downhill. Unfortunately, the impact of the higher descent speed will be limited as you will probably have to brake in the hairpin bends.

Speed of Descent in km/h				
Weight (kg)	**v at i = 5%**	**v at i = 10%**	**v at i = 15%**	**v at i = 20%**
60	46.49	67.16	82.83	95.97
70	49.85	72.01	88.81	102.90
80	53.00	76.56	94.41	109.39
90	55.96	80.85	99.70	115.52
100	58.78	84.92	104.73	121.34

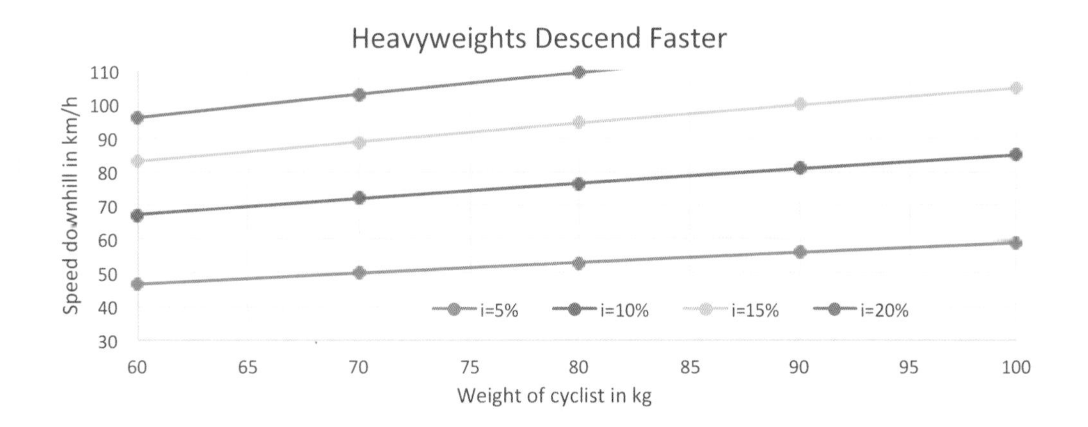

53. THE IMPACT OF THE MECHANICAL RESISTANCE

Cycling provides a context for looking at the world.

In the chapter on the cycling formula, we learned that the impact of the mechanical resistance is that less than 100% of the power of your human engine is transferred to the axis of your bike. This is expressed by the mechanical efficiency (η), which is slightly less than one. The cycling formula including the mechanical efficiency is given below:

$$P\eta = c_r mgv + 0.5\rho c_d A(v+v_w)^2 v + (i/100)mgv$$

In the standard condition, η is 0.975, which means that 97.5% of the pedaling power of Fast Eddy (300 watts) is available to surmount the rolling resistance, the air resistance and the climbing resistance.

What are the options available to Fast Eddy to limit his mechanical resistance and increase his mechanical efficiency?

Which Factors Determine η?

Theoretically, the mechanical efficiency (η) depends on:

1. Bike design: in particular crankshaft, derailleur, chain, hub and bearings
2. Bike maintenance: cleaning and lubricating
3. Pedaling power: at higher power the efficiency increases somewhat
4. Gear and pedaling frequency

The table summarizes some data that have been found in practice[44,45,46].

Mechanical efficiency (η)	
Top bike pro cyclist at time trial	0.990
Top bike pro cyclist average	0.980
Standard at time trial	0.975
Standard average	0.965
Touring bike at time trial	0.960
Touring bike average	0.950

Cleaning and lubricating are the easiest options available to limit mechanical resistance and increase mechanical efficiency.

Race Time at the 40-Kilometer Time Trial

Once again, we calculated the impact with our model, using the standard conditions.

The results are given in the figure and table. We see that the attainable speed is higher when the mechanical efficiency (η) increases. If Fast Eddy could increase his mechanical efficiency from 0.975 to 0.985, then his speed would increase from 40.41 km/h to 40.56 km/h, by 0.3%. His total gain in the time trial would be 13 seconds. On the other hand, he could lose 13 seconds if his mechanical efficiency were to drop from 0.975 to 0.965.

So, it is definitely worthwhile to keep your bike clean and in top condition. You may even want to buy a top bike, depending on your budget.

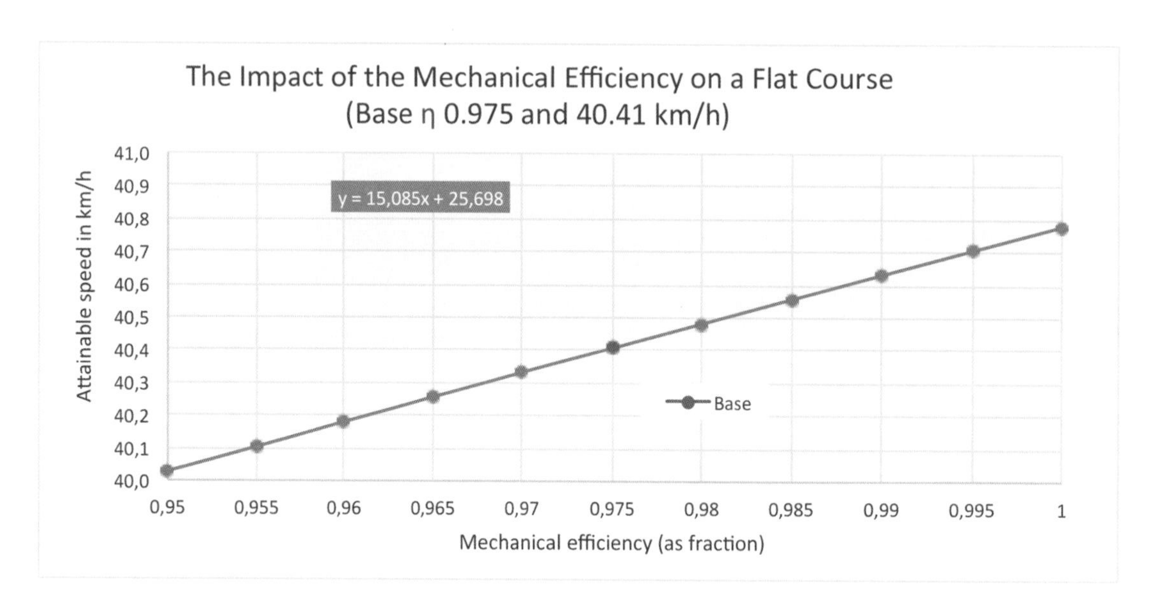

Impact of Mechanical Efficiency on a Flat Course			
η	v	T 40 km	Difference
(-)	(km/h)	(min)	(sec)
0.95	40.03	60.0	34
0.955	40.10	59.8	27
0.96	40.18	59.7	20
0.965	40.26	59.6	13
0.97	40.33	59.5	7
0.975	40.41	59.4	0
0.98	40.48	59.3	-7
0.985	40.56	59.2	-13
0.99	40.63	59.1	-20
0.995	40.71	59.0	-26
1	40.78	58.9	-33

Race Time to the Top of the Alpe d'Huez

Once again, the results of our calculations are presented in a similar figure and table. We see that in this case the attainable speed is higher when the mechanical efficiency increases. The impact is a little more than on the flat (a gain of 1% or 30 seconds when Fast Eddy increases his η from 0.975 to 0.985). In the case of the Alpe d'Huez, the lower mechanical resistance leads to a higher climbing speed and a higher climbing resistance. At the flat time trial, the lower mechanical resistance also leads to a higher speed and in this case to a higher air resistance. As the air resistance increases to the cube of the speed, the increase in speed on the flat is less than on the climb.

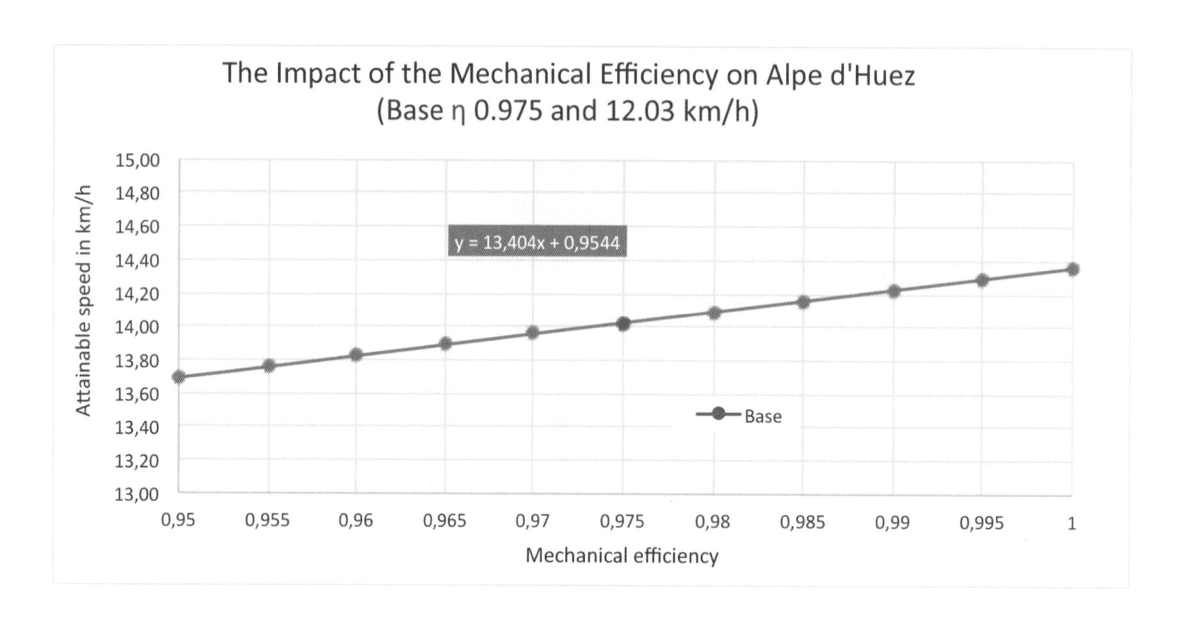

Impact of Mechanical Efficiency on Alpe d'Huez			
η	v	T Alpe	Difference
(-)	(km/h)	(sec)	(sec)
0.95	13.69	54	-77
0.955	13.76	54	-62
0.96	13.82	53	-46
0.965	13.89	53	-31
0.97	13.96	53	-15
0.975	14.02	53	0
0.98	14.09	52	15
0.985	14.16	52	30
0.99	14.22	52	45
0.995	14.29	52	59
1	14.36	51	74

The mechanical efficiency (η) depends primarily on bike design, in particular crankshaft, derailleur, chain, hub and bearings.

54. GEARS, PEDALING RATE AND CRANK LENGTH

Whenever I see an adult on a bicycle, I do not despair for the human race. –H.G. Wells

Gears, pedaling rate and crank length are popular topics in cycling literature and at the regular table in the cycling pub. Which gears are the best for you? How can you cycle the desired speed without wasting your legs? What is your optimum pedaling rate? Is your crank length correct? Most cyclists will have experienced what works for them, but we want to understand the fundamental theory behind these matters as well.

The Relationship Between Gear Ratio and Speed

This is the most fundamental principle of the modern bicycle. Ever since the invention of the chain and gears, we can increase the speed of the bike by using a larger gear ratio. The relationship between speed and gear ratio can be described by the following formula:

$$v = \pi D_w * PR * (n_f / n_r)$$

As an example, we use a wheel diameter (D_w) of 0.71 meter (28 inches), a pedaling rate (PR) of 100 rpm (revolutions per minute) and a gear ratio (n_f / n_r, the ratio of the number of teeth at the front cog and the rear cog) of 3, so the speed (v) becomes 41.29 km/h. The figure below gives the relationship. We see that a large gear ratio is required to attain a high speed.

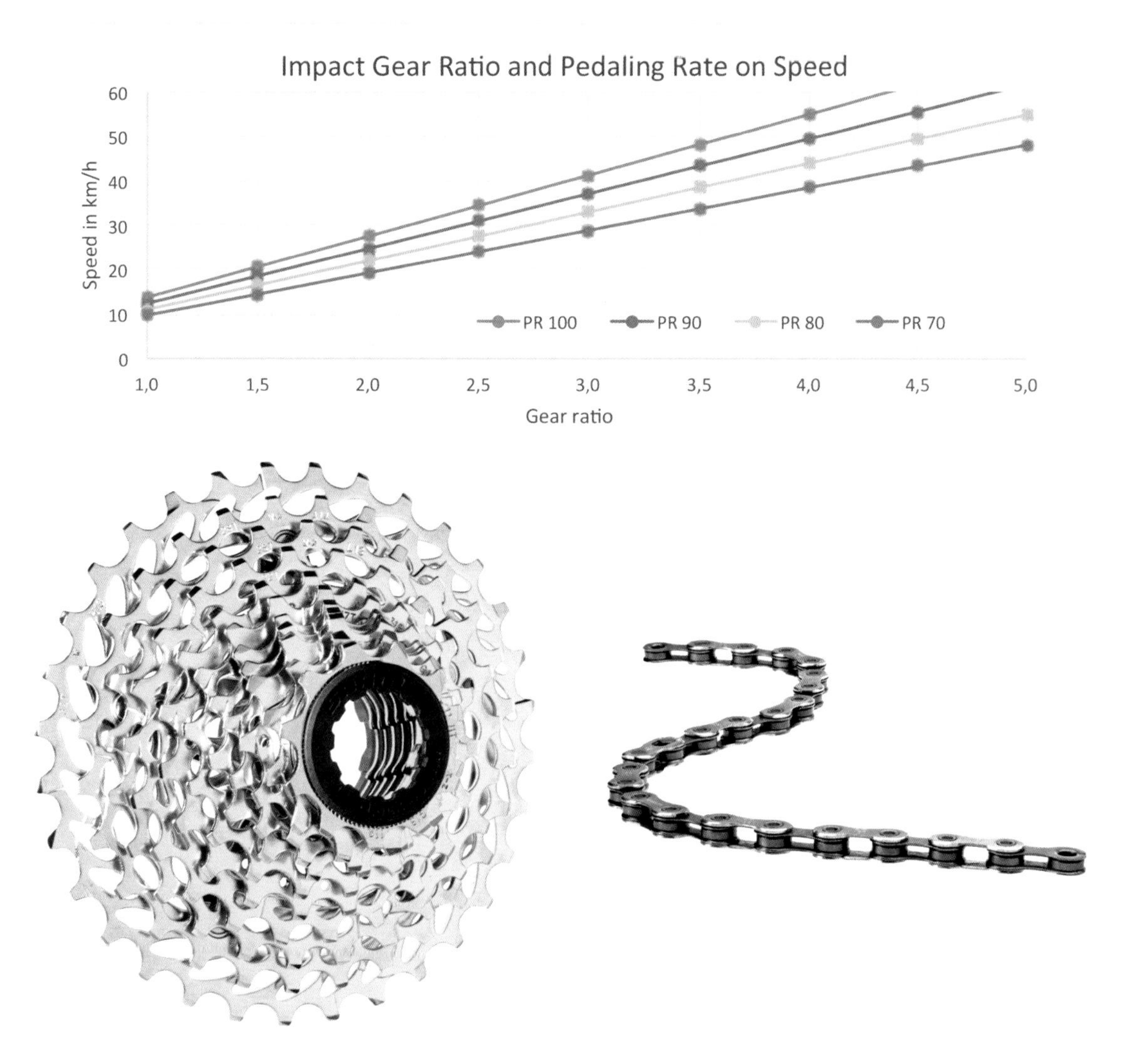

Ever since the invention of the chain and gears, we can increase the speed of the bike by using a larger gear ratio.

The Relationship Between Gear Ratio and Power

A large gear ratio is a prerequisite to attain a high speed, but you can only use it if you are capable of pushing the required power. In order to illustrate how much power is required as a function of the gear ratio, we assume that the air resistance is the dominant factor so we neglect the rolling resistance, the climbing resistance and the mechanical resistance. Consequently, the relationship between power and speed during windless conditions is as follows:

$$P = 0.5\rho c_d A v^3$$

As an example, we use the standard conditions ($\rho = 1.205$ kg/m^3, $c_dA = 0.3$ m^2), so the required power to attain a speed of 41.29 km/h becomes 273 watts.

Substituting the above relationship between v and gear ratio (nf/nr) we get:

$$P = 0.5\rho c_d A(\pi D_w * PR * (n_f/n_r))^3$$

We see that the required power increases to the cube of the gear ratio. The relationship is given in the figure below. This figure clearly shows that you need an awful lot of power to push a high gear ratio!

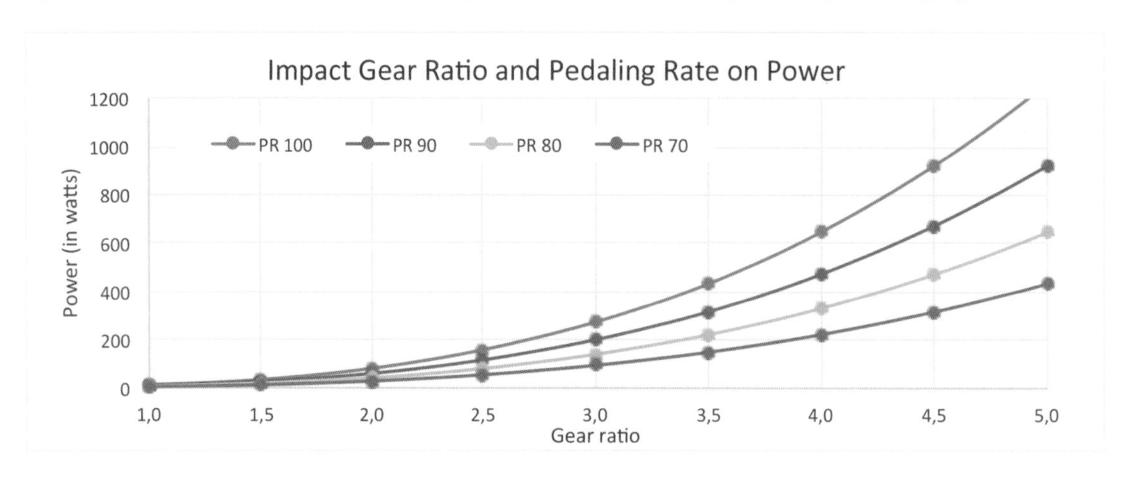

The Relationship Between Gear Ratio and Pedaling Force

We can also illustrate how hard it is to push a large gear ratio by looking at the relationship between gear ratio and the required pedaling force. This can be described by the following formula:

$$F_p/F = (D_w/D_c)*(n_f/n_r)$$

As an example, we use a wheel diameter (D_w) of 0.71 meter, a crank diameter of 0.35 meter and a gear ratio (n_f/n_r) of 3. The result is that your pedal force (F_p) is six times the propulsion force (F). In the above example the propulsion force (F) is used to overcome the air resistance, so it can be calculated by the following equation:

$$F = 0.5\rho c_d A v^2$$

The figure below gives the relationship between the gear ratio and the pedaling force.

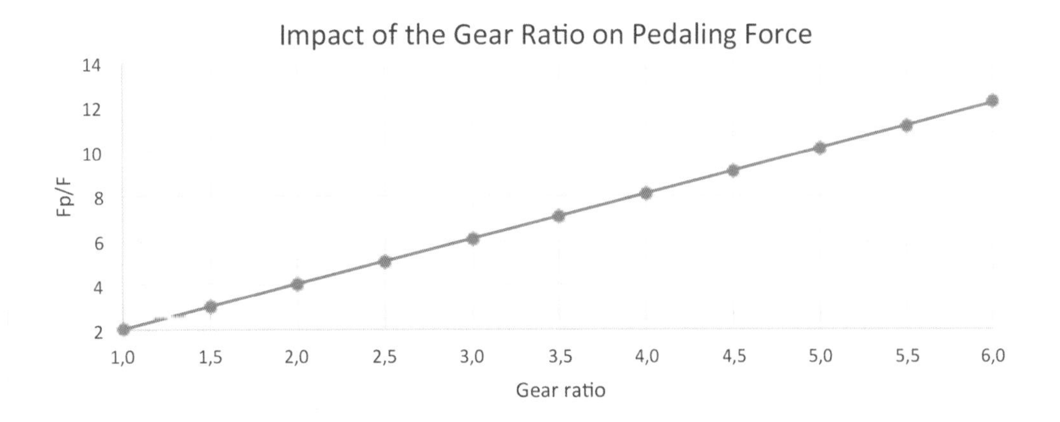

It seems obvious that the pedaling force is the decisive factor in the choice of the gear ratio. This becomes even more clear when we express the pedaling force as a percentage of the body weight.

The following relationships apply:

$$P = F_p*v$$

$$v = \pi D_w*PR*(n_f/n_r)$$

$$P/m = F_p/m* \pi D_w*PR*(n_f/n_r)$$

As an example, we use a gear ratio (n_f/n_r) of 3, a pedaling rate (PR) of 100 rpm and a wheel diameter (D_w) of 0.71 meter. The result is that at a specific power (P/m) of one watt/kg, the required pedaling force (F_p) becomes 6.68% of the body weight (m). This relationship between pedaling force and specific power is given in the figure below.

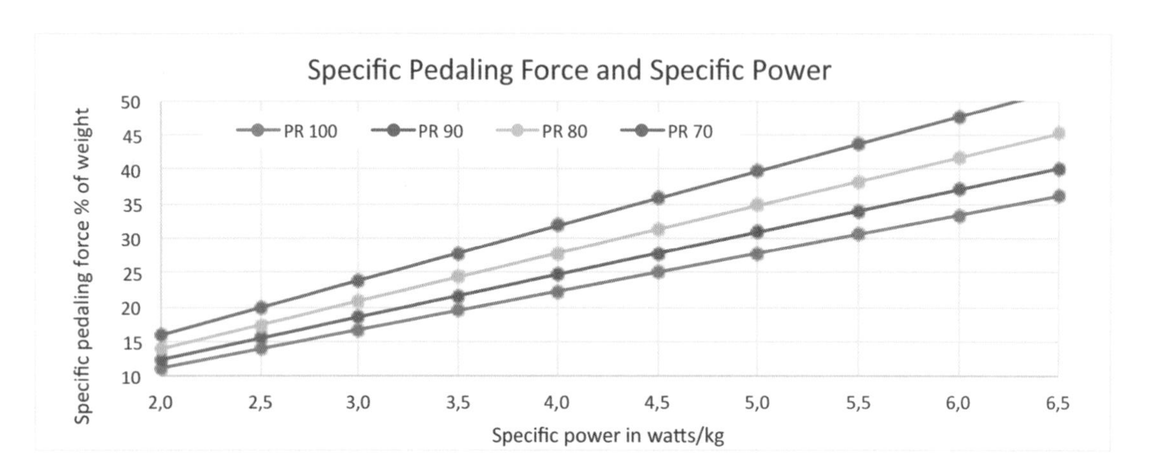

We see that the world-class cyclists with a specific power of 6.4 watts/kg need to develop a pedaling force of some 45% of their body weight (at a PR of 80 rpm). This comes close to the maximum value of 50%, considering that force can only be developed during the downward cycle of the pedal.

What Is the Optimal Pedaling Rate?

From the above, it can be seen that it is difficult to choose the optimal gear ratio and pedaling rate. This depends on the desired speed (and thus on the race conditions) and on the capacities of your human motor (output of power and force). Most cyclists prefer a smaller gear ratio and a higher pedaling rate. This reduces the required pedaling force and saves the legs. Usually, a pedaling rate of 100 rpm on the flat and 70 rpm in the mountains is considered optimal, but this need not be the case for all cyclists.

Recently, a good paper[61] was published on research into the optimal pedaling rate. The authors concluded that instead of the pedaling rate, the cyclic rate should be optimized. They defined the cyclic rate as the product of the pedaling rate and the pedal speed. The research showed that the cyclists were most efficient at a cycling speed of 4-5 (Hz*m/s).

When we consider that the pedal speed equals the bike speed times the ratio of the wheel diameter and the crank diameter, we can describe the cyclic rate by the following formula:

$$v_c = PR/60*v/3.6*(D_w/D_c)$$

As an example, we use the optimal cyclic speed (v_c) of 4.5 (Hz*m/s), a PR of 100 rpm, a speed (v) of 40 km/h and a D_w of 0.71 m. The result is that the optimal D_c becomes 0.17 meter. Obviously, this is quite commonly used. From the formula, we can also derive that at a higher speed the optimal PR decreases. The figure below gives the relationship between speed and optimal pedaling rate according to this research (based on D_w = 0.71 and D_c = 0.175).

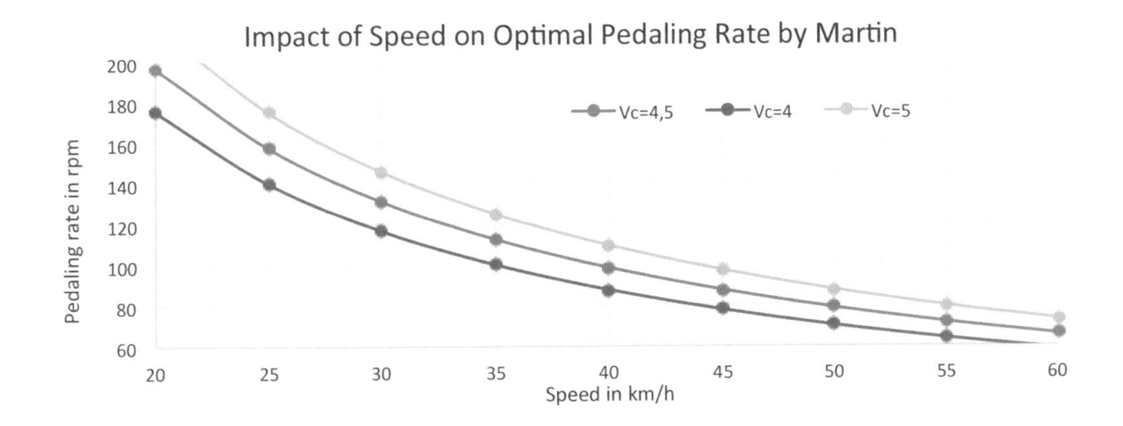

55. BENDS, THE TRACK AND THE PROLOGUE

Ride a bike. Ride a bike. Ride a bike. –Fausto Coppi, on how to improve

Bends require special attention. As a result of the centripetal force, you may literally jump the curve. The centripetal force is proportional to the square of your speed (v) and inversely proportional to the radius of curvature of the bend (R):

$$F_{centr} = mv^2/R$$

Balance Angle

As we all know from experience, we can moderate the centripetal force by leaning under an angle ϕ. This creates a balance between the centripetal force and the horizontal component of the gravity force:

$$F_{centr} = F_g \tan(\phi)$$

As F_g equals mg, we arrive at the following equation:

$$\tan(\phi) = v^2/(gR)$$

As an example, we use v = 40 km/h and R = 20 meter, so $\tan(\phi) = 0.63$ and the balance angle ϕ is 32°.

The figure gives the impact of the speed and the radius on the angle of lean. We see that at high speeds and small radii you have to lean very far to prevent jumping the curve. In order to prevent falling, in practice the angle of lean should be smaller than 45°. At a wet and slippery pavement it should be smaller than 35°. Consequently, you will be forced to slow down before the bend, in particular on a slippery road.

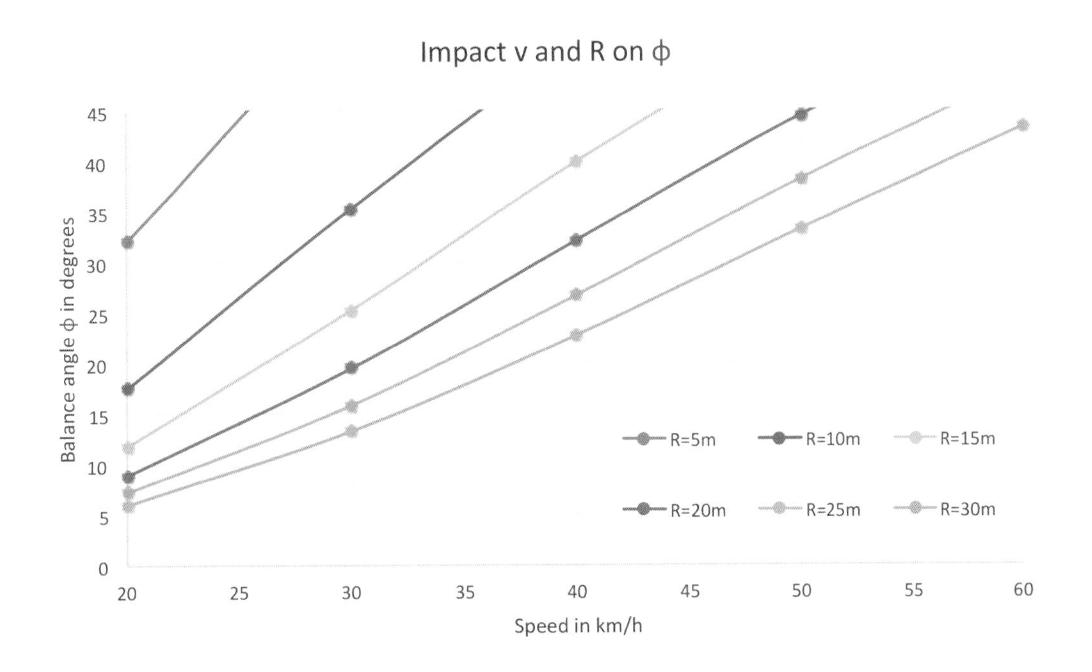

Equilibrium Speed at a Velodrome

In a velodrome the curves have been constructed at an oblique angle β. This means that the centripetal force and the gravity force are exactly in equilibrium when ϕ is equal to β. Substituting this in the equation above gives:

$$v_e = \sqrt{(gR\tan(\beta))}$$

As an example, we use β = 45° and R = 20 meter, so the equilibrium speed (v_e) is equal to 50.5 km/h. This means that if you cycle slower than 50.5 km/h, you run the risk of slipping down by gravity. If you cycle faster, you run the risk of sliding upward due to the centripetal force. The figure below gives the equilibrium speed as a function of β and R.

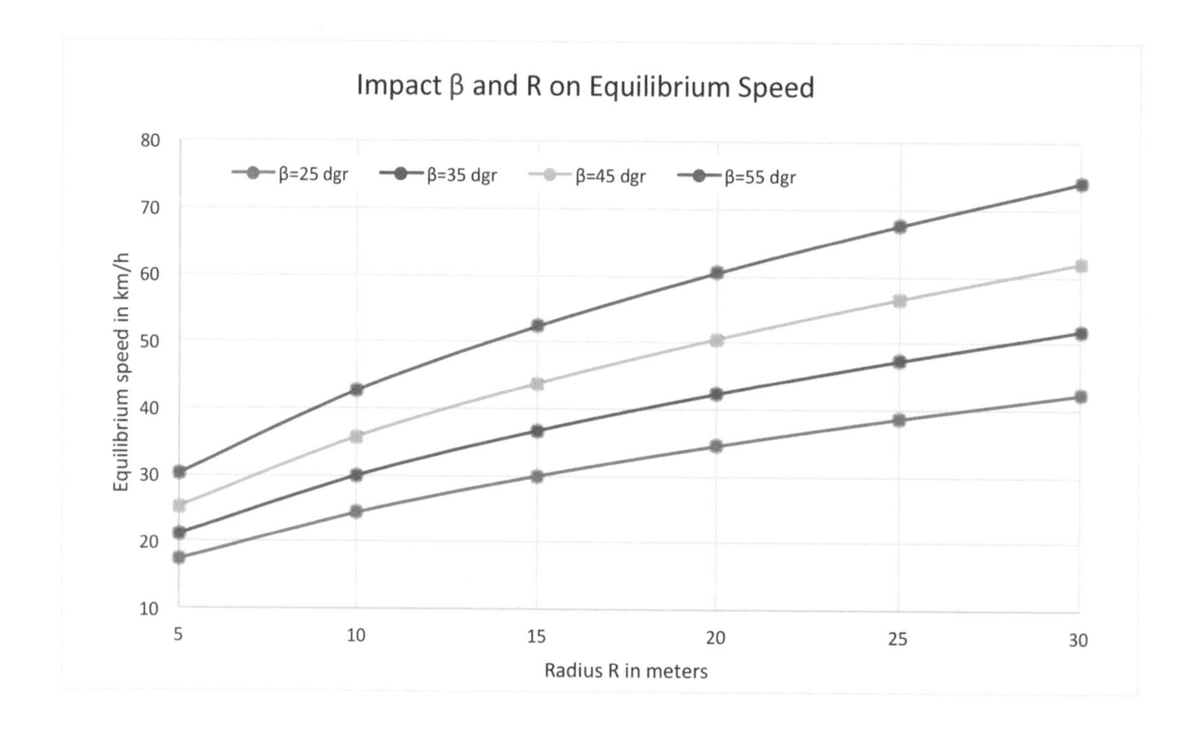

How Big Is the Impact of the Increased g-Force in the Bends?

In the bends you encounter the combination of the centripetal force and the gravity force. As a result, you actually face a combined and increased g-force:

$$g_b = \sqrt{(1+(v^2/gR)^2)}$$

As an example, we use again a speed (v) of 40 km/h and a radius (R) of 20 meters, so the g_b value becomes 1.18. In other words, you are exposed to a g value of 1.18 times gravity. The figure gives the g_b value as a function of v and R. We see that the g_b value can increase significantly at high speeds and in sharp bends.

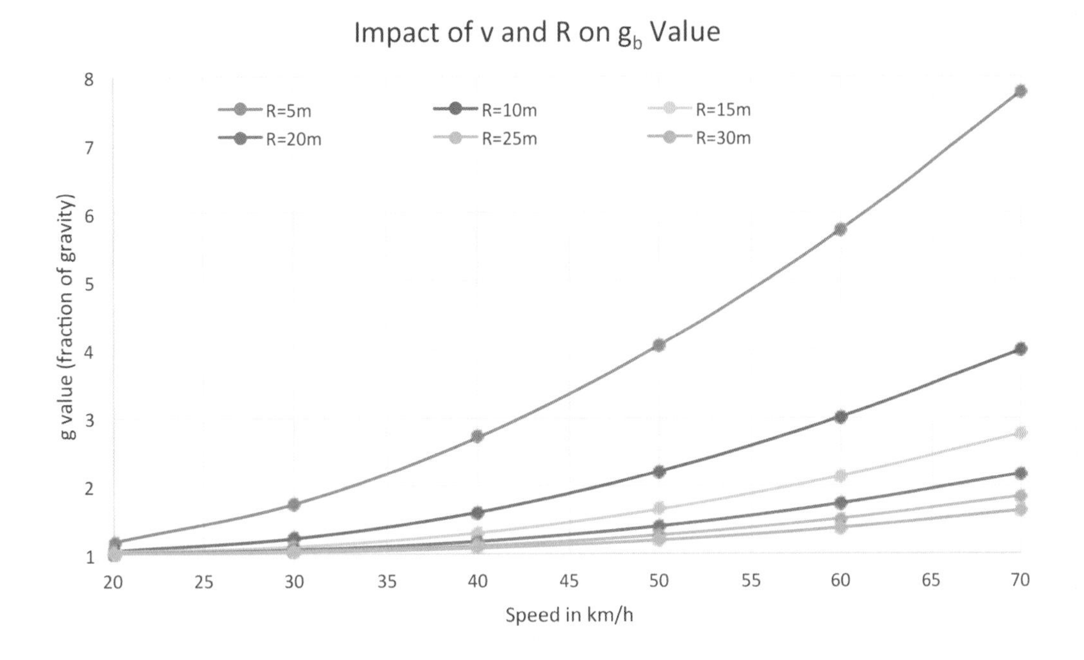

We have calculated how big the impact of the increased g-force has been during the world hour attempt by Dutchman Thomas Dekker in Mexico on February 25, 2015. The velodrome in Mexico has an R of 21 meters and Thomas cycled at a speed of 52 km/h, so in the bends he encountered a g_b value of 1.44 times gravity. As both bends together have a length of 132 meters and the total length of the track is 250 meters, on average his rolling resistance was increased by a factor of 1.23 (i.e., ((132*1.44+118)/250)). Consequently, his rolling resistance was increased by 5 watts. This seems small, but nevertheless it amounts to 1.5% of the total power output by Dekker during the attempt (which was 367 watts). In this respect, a velodrome with wider bends would have been better.

In bends you encounter the combination of the centripetal force and the gravity force, actually resulting in an increased g-force.

How Big Is the Impact of Bends in a Prologue?

The impact of bends can be significant in a short prologue. As an example, we use a 10K prologue with five sharp bends. We assume that the radius of the bends is so small that the cyclists are forced to slow down to 30 km/h (5.55 m/s). We further assume that it takes them 25 meters to slow down before the bend and also 25 meters to accelerate after the bend to a cruising speed of 52 km/h (14.44 m/s). Without the bend, the 50 meters would have taken them 50/14.44 = 3.5 seconds. With the bend, it takes them 50/5.55 = 9 seconds. Consequently, they lose 5.5 seconds per bend and in total 5*5.5 = 27.5 seconds. With a cruising speed of 52 km/h, the cyclist would finish a 10K prologue without bends in 10,000/14.44 = 692.5 seconds. With bend it will take him 720 seconds. This means his race time increases by 4% and his average speed decreases by 4%. This is a big impact and even more so when we consider that a 4% higher speed is equivalent to a 12% higher power output!

As an example, we looked at the prologue of the Tirreno Adriatico in 2015, which was won by Fabian Cancellara with an average speed of 53.26 km/h. When we calculate this with our program (m = 81 kg+ 6.8 kg bike, c_dA = 0.25, c_r = 0.003, altitude = 23 m, temperature = 20°C), the result is that Fabian must have pushed 545 watts. When we make the same calculations with a 4% higher speed, we find that his power output would have been 610 watts! For Fabian, the 610 watts is equivalent to a specific power output of 7.5 watts/kg and an FTP of 6.3 watts/kg. These data seem somewhat high, even for a world-class time-trial specialist like Cancellara, but this can be explained by our assumption for his c_dA (which can ideally be as low as 0.21 m^2).

Fabian Cancellara in the Grand Départ (prologue) of the 2015 Tour de France in Utrecht.

56. ACCELERATIONS AND THE SPRINT FINISH

As long as I am riding, I know that I am the luckiest guy in the world. –Mark Cavendish

So far, we have made all the calculations for the equilibrium condition. In this condition, the power output of the cyclist is equal to the sum of the rolling resistance, the air resistance, the climbing resistance and the mechanical resistance. As a result of this equilibrium condition, the speed remains constant.

Obviously, this is not the case during accelerations and the sprint finish. At these moments, the cyclist mobilizes a very high pedaling force and a very high power output, so his speed increases rapidly. We can calculate this acceleration as the result of the excess force (i.e., the difference between the pedaling force and the force required to surmount the rolling resistance and the air resistance (in cases without climbing resistance)):

$$m*a = F_p-F_r-F_a$$

As an example, we use F_p = 114 N, F_r = 2 N, F_a = 33 N and m = 83.8 kg (75 kg body weight and 8.8 kg bike weight). The result is that the acceleration a becomes 0.97 m/s^2. Consequently, the speed increases by 3.5 km/h in one second. Obviously, the cyclist can maintain such a large force for only a few seconds, so his jump needs to be well timed to be successful.

In the Tour de France there is a classification for intermediate sprints. At these moments the cyclist mobilizes a very high pedaling force and a very high power output.

An Example of a Sprint Finish

To illustrate this, we have calculated an example of a sprint finish. Once again we used the standard conditions (ρ = 1.205 kg/m^3, c_dA = 0.3 m^2, c_r = 0.004, m = 75 kg+8.8 kg bike). Also we have assumed that the pack has gone into the sprint finish at a speed of 60 km/h. In the pack, the air resistance of our cyclist is reduced by 40% as a result of drafting. When he jumps ahead, he will lose this advantage. We have calculated with our program that our cyclist needs to push 543 watts, when he is still cycling in the pack. Next, we assumed that our cyclist is a world-class sprinter who can mobilize a maximum sprinting power (during five seconds) of 6 watts/kg*75 kg*4.23 (peak factor) = 1,903 watts.

Now, we can calculate his acceleration from the difference between his peak power of 1,903 watts and the base power of 543 watts:

$$a = (P_p - P_b)/v*m$$

In the example v = 60 km/h and m = 83.8 kg, so his acceleration (a) becomes 0.97 m/s^2. The figures below give the development of his speed and power during the sprint finish. After five seconds, the cyclist can no longer maintain the peak power, so his power reduces strongly. As a result, his speed also starts to decrease slowly. We also see the impact of the increased air resistance when the sprinter jumps ahead of the pack. His c_dA value increases and his attainable speed decreases (from 73.4 km/h to 72.0 km/h in the example).

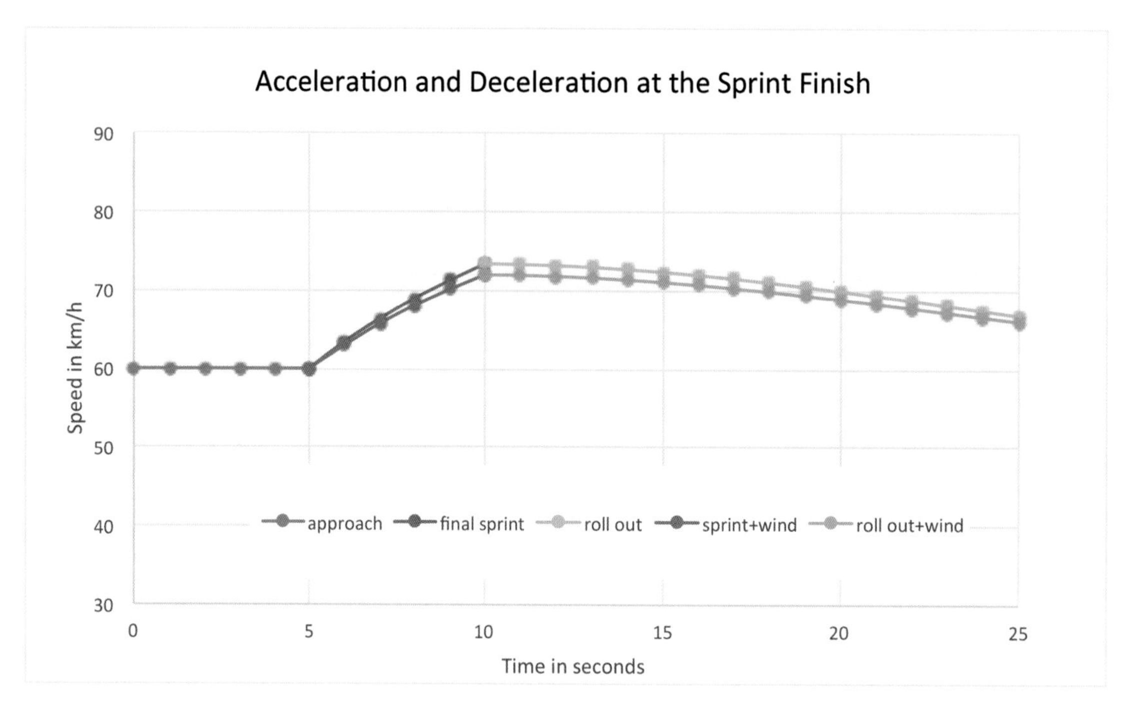

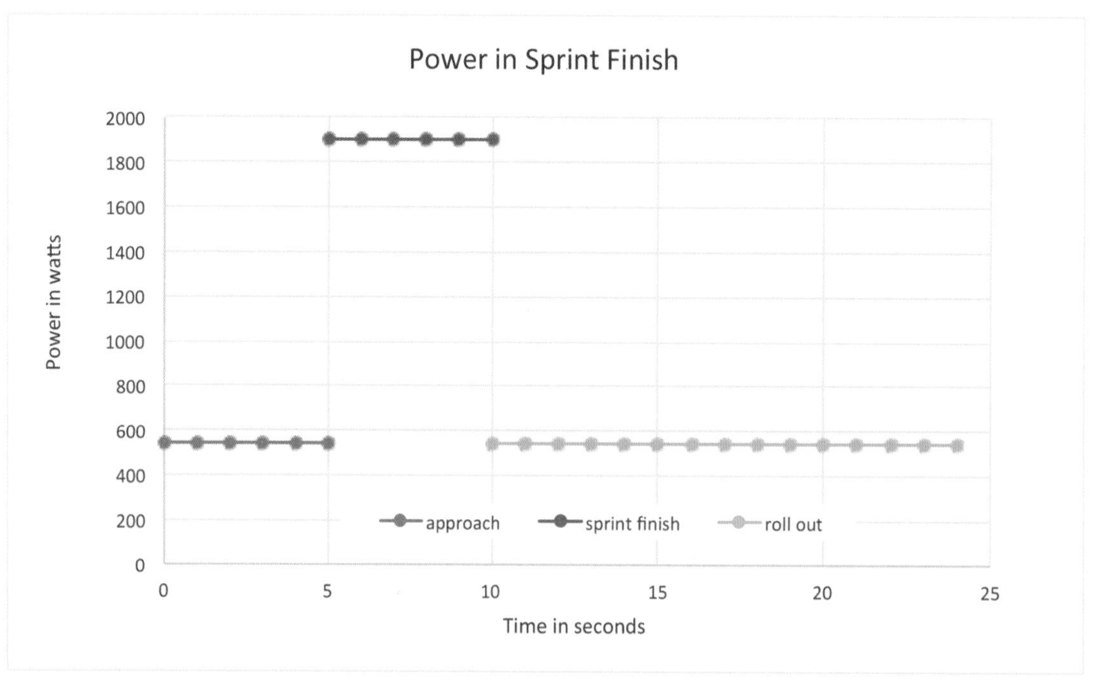

The Impact of the Inertia of the Wheels

Strictly speaking, we should not have made the above calculations using just the sum of the body weight and the bike weight (in our example 75+8.8 kg = 83.8 kg), but we should have added the moment of inertia of the wheels. This moment of inertia determines the force required to increase the wheel speed. In practice, this plays only a minor role as the moment of inertia of the wheels is in the order of 2 kg, so we should have made the calculations with 85.8 kg. This means that the acceleration will in practice be 2% less. This does not make a difference to the example. However, a sprinter who buys wheels with a lower moment of inertia may gain an edge. In practice, he needs to balance this against other factors, such as aerodynamics, rolling resistance and cost.

In most cases the best strategy is to maintain constant power during the entire race.

57. THE IMPACT OF PACE AND RACE STRATEGY

Last thought before a race: "Why am I doing this?"
First thought after a race: "When can I do this again?"

So far, we have limited our analysis to the equilibrium situation with constant power and constant speed. The only exception to this was the chapter on the sprint finish, where we saw that it is possible to mobilize additional power during five seconds, enabling you to make the final jump to the finish.

However, in practice our power and speed are usually not constant. In training, we deliberately change both during interval sessions. In races, both may change as a result of chases alternated with slow trotting sections or the final kick to the finish. How should we analyze these variations? What is their impact on our training load and efficiency? And finally, which pacing strategy should you adopt to get the best race results?

Normalizing Power

As the reader will sense, variations in pace require additional energy and power. Consequently, cycling at a steady pace is the best strategy to save energy and minimize the required power. This is caused by the fact that accelerations and decelerations waste energy.

We can express variations in power with the notion of the normalized power P_n. This notion indicates how much more power is required for variations in power as compared to the average power. The normalized power (P_n) is defined by the following formula[7]:

$$P_n = ((1/t)*(\sum P_i^4 t_i))^{0.25}$$

In order to illustrate the formula, we use an example of an interval training of Fast Eddy. During this one-hour training, he alternates eight minutes of easy cycling at 150 watts with five minutes of hard work at 600 watts. The table and figure below show the values for P_n as compared to the average power (P_{av}). The table shows that P_n is always higher than P_{av}, as expected. In the example, the ratio of the two is 1.52. This clearly illustrates that variations require additional energy and power.

Example of Interval Training (Four Five-Minute Intervals Per Hour)				
T_i	P_i	$\sum(PiTi)^4$	P_n	$P_n/P_{average}$
(sec)	(watts)		(watts)	
480	150	2.43E+11	150	1.00
780	600	3.9123E+13	473	1.46
1260	150	3.9366E+13	420	1.63
1560	600	7.8246E+13	473	1.46
2040	150	7.8489E+13	443	1.57
2340	600	1.1737E+14	473	1.46
2820	150	1.1761E+14	452	1.54
3120	600	1.5649E+14	473	1.46
3600	150	1.5674E+14	457	1.52

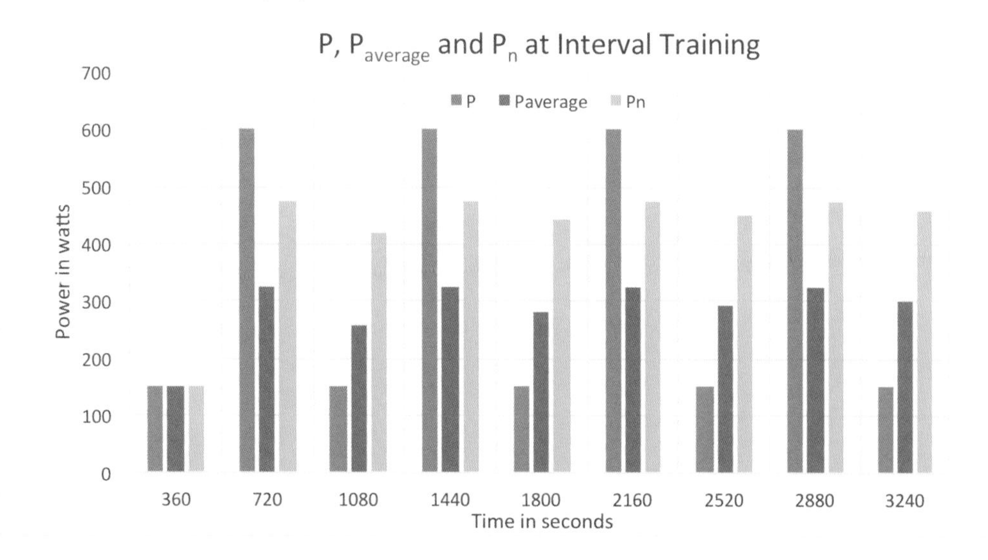

Normalizing Intensity

In earlier chapters, we learned the importance of training at a high intensity. The best way to express intensity is by comparing the normalized power with the FTP. Consequently, the normalized intensity (I_n) is defined by the following formula:

$$I_n = P_n/FTP$$

In the trivial example that you should cycle an entire training or race with a P_n at the level of your FTP, your normalized intensity (I_n) would thus be one. The table and figure give the values of In as a function of the percentage of FTP. Obviously, a normalized intensity of one can be considered as very hard, as it is means that you have cycled at the level of your FTP.

I_n as a Function of %FTP and P_n

%FTP	$P_n/P_{av}=1$	$P_n/P_{av}=1.2$	$P_n/P_{av}=1.5$
30	0.3	0.36	0.45
40	0.4	0.48	0.6
50	0.5	0.6	0.75
60	0.6	0.72	0.9
70	0.7	0.84	1.05
80	0.8	0.96	1.2
90	0.9	1.08	1.35
100	1	1.2	1.5

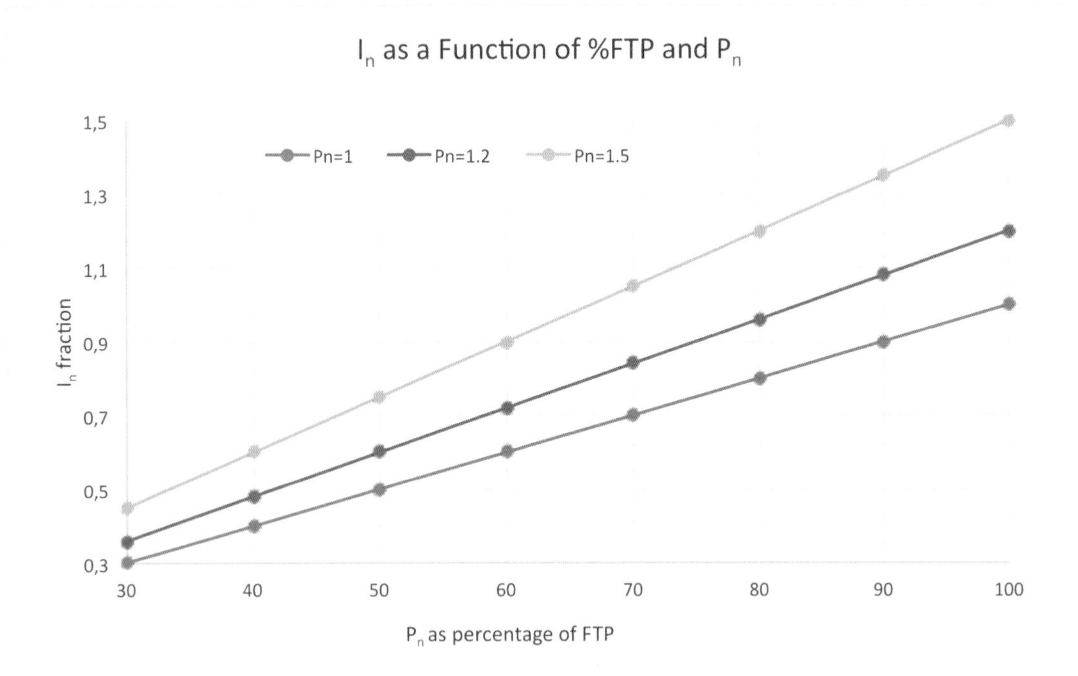

In practice, the following classification is used for I_n:

- » $I_n < 0.75$: easy, recovery training
- » I_n 0.75-0.85: normal endurance training
- » I_n 0.85-0.95: tempo training, long intervals, longer races
- » I_n 0.95 1.05: short intervals, short races
- » I_n 1.05-1.15: speed training
- » $I_n > 1.15$: prologue or track races

Normalizing Training Load

The stress that a training or race imposes on your body is not just determined by P_n and I_n, but also by a third factor, the duration (t, in hours). The three parameters (P_n, I_n and t) can be combined in the so-called total stress score (TSS), which is defined by the following formula:

$$TSS = 100*t*I_n^2$$

The table and figure below give the values for TSS as a function of I_n and t (in hours).

TSS as a Function of I_n and t				
I_n	t=1 hour	t=2 hours	t=4 hours	t=6 hours
0.3	9	18	36	54
0.5	25	50	100	150
0.7	49	98	196	294
0.9	81	162	324	486
1.1	121	242	484	726
1.3	169	338	676	1014
1.5	225	450	900	1350

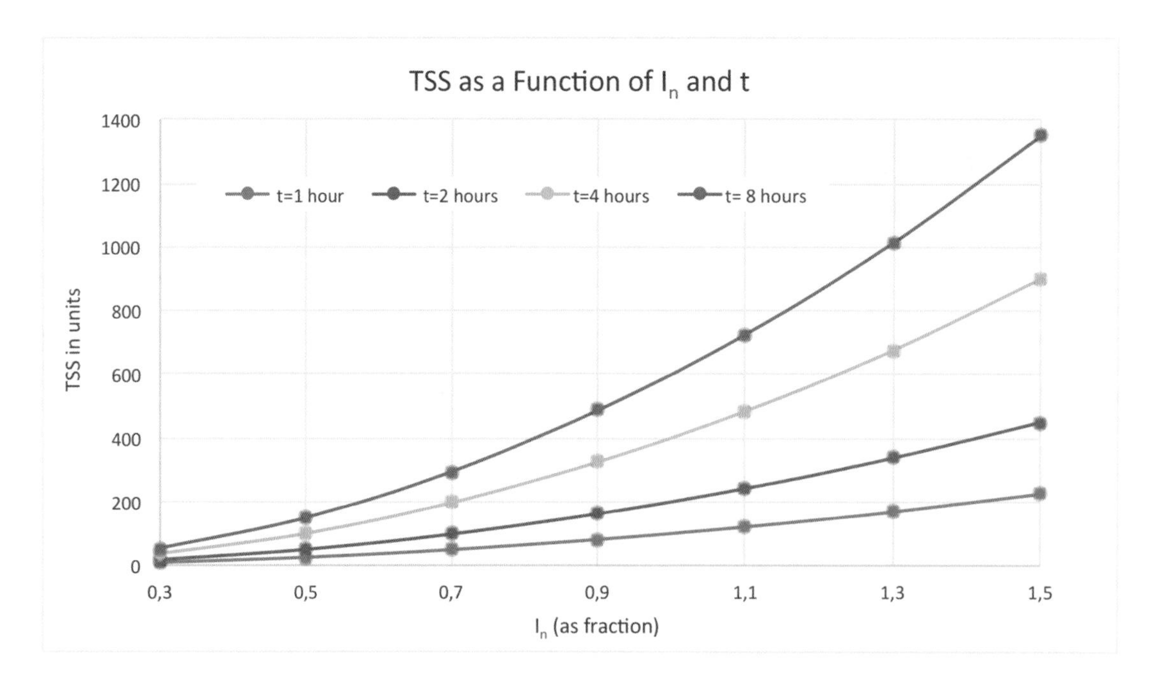

TSS values of more that 150 only occur at very strenuous training sessions or races. It goes without saying that it is physiologically impossible to maintain an I_n of one for longer than one hour. In practice, the following classification for TSS is used:

- TSS < 150: light, recovery training
- TSS 150-300: normal training that can be done on a daily basis
- TSS 300-450: strenuous training that requires recovery the next day
- TSS > 450: very strenuous workouts or races that require longer recovery

What Is the Best Racing Strategy?

From the theory of the human engine and the above, it follows that your race performance is determined primarily by two factors:

1. **The duration of the race**
   In a short race, you can cycle at an I_n of 1.15, so with a power of 15% above your FTP. At a longer race your power will drop to your FTP (at a one-hour race) or lower (0.88 FTP at a two-hour race). This means you will have to judge carefully the power and pace that you can maintain during the entire race. If you start too fast, you will pay the price in the later part of the race! If you start too slow, you may not use your full potential.

2. **The variations in pace and power**
   As we learned from the notion of normalized power, it is always best to limit variations in power as much as possible; try to cycle with constant power throughout the race. At a flat course and in windless conditions, constant power also means constant pace. However, when the conditions change during the race (e.g., because of hills or wind), constant power is not equivalent to constant pace! Uphill constant power means you will slow down, just like everybody else around you. Don't worry about this! Just hold on to the strategy of keeping your power constant throughout the race.

So, what all of the above boils down to is that it is always the best strategy to judge the power and pace that you can maintain during the entire race correctly. This will require self-knowledge, but you can also use the data from your power meter to your advantage!

The only exception to the above rule is determined by the fact that you always lose more time on the slower sections of the course. Consequently, it may be wise to use some additional power on the hard sections (e.g., uphill or facing headwind). You may gain valuable time there that you could use to recover in the easier sections. However, you should be prudent with this strategy as it may get you in the red. The last thing you would want is to get into trouble due to an accumulation of lactic acid! So don't push yourself too hard and only use this strategy before a section where you can recover.

58. NUTRITION BEFORE AND DURING THE RACE

Cycle tracks will abound in Utopia. –H.G. Wells

During the 15th stage of the 1975 Tour de France, the unbeatable Eddy Merckx once more cycled ahead of his competitors. Everybody expected him to finish victoriously in his yellow jersey at the climb to Pra Loup. But suddenly, the great champion hit the wall. From one moment to the next, he collapsed and could not push even the lightest gear ratio. He was overtaken by Joop Zoetemelk and Bernard Thevenet and lost minutes in the final kilometers. That day cost him his sixth overall victory of the Tour de France. That is what can happen when you hit the wall. What is it exactly, and how can we understand it and prevent it from happening to us?

It is important to maintain your fluid balance, as you may lose up to 1.5 liters of sweat per hour in warm conditions.

What Happens When You Hit the Wall?

Hitting the wall is the phenomenon that happens when your muscles run out of glycogen or carbohydrates. At that moment, the muscles are forced to switch over to fatty acids as fuel. However, the power output from the conversion of fatty acids is much less (only 30%) compared to that of glycogen, as the table from an earlier chapter shows. This means that from one moment to the next, your power output drops significantly! From that moment onwards, you will indeed have problems with even the lightest gear ratio. When you hit the wall, the race is over and lost for you!

The Power Output of the Four Human Engines

	P	P/m
	(mmol ATP/s)	(watts/kg)
ATP/CP		
ATP → ADP $C_{10}H_{16}N_5O_{13}P_3 \rightarrow C_{10}H_{15}N_5O_{10}P_2$	73	24.64
Anaerobic conversion of glycogen		
$C_6H_{12}O_6 + 3ADP \rightarrow 2C_3H_6O_3 + 3ATP$	40	13.50
Aerobic conversion of glycogen		
$C_6H_{12}O_6 + 6O_2 + 38ADP \rightarrow 6CO_2 + 6H_2O + 38ATP$	23	7.76
Aerobic conversion of fatty acids		
$CH_3(CH_2)_{14}COOH + 23O_2 + 130ADP \rightarrow 16CO_2 + 16H_2O + 130ATP$	7	2.36

What Can You Do to Avoid Hitting the Wall?

To avoid hitting the wall, you have to make sure that the supplies of glycogen in your muscles are adequate. It is possible to increase the stock of glycogen by adapting your nutrition, in particular during the last days before a big race. In the 1970s, the Swedish researcher B. Saltin[5] was the first to observe that the glycogen level in the muscles of athletes could be increased by eating food containing a high amount of carbohydrates for a few days. This was the origin of the marathon diet or carbo-loading. Carbo-loading comprises of changing the diet during the last 2-3 days before the race in such a way as to increase the level of carbohydrates to 70%. In practice, it means that the consumption of fats—and to some extent proteins—has to be reduced strongly. Instead, products rich in carbohydrates have to be eaten, like vegetables, fruits, whole-wheat bread, potatoes, pasta, honey, figs and so on. During these final days, you should avoid products like butter, cheese, fat meat, chocolate, cake and fried snacks. This carbo-loading will lead to an increase in the glycogen level in your muscles and liver (also known as super compensation). This effect will be strengthened by the fact that you will reduce the training significantly during these final days (known as tapering). Research has shown that by carbo-loading it is possible to increase the stock of glycogen in the liver and muscles by almost a factor of two, as shown in the table below.

Available Stock of the Four Fuels		
	(kJ)	Remarks
ATP/CP		
ATP → ADP $C_{10}H_{16}N_5O_{13}P_3 \rightarrow C_{10}H_{15}N_5O_{10}P_2$	13	
Anaerobic conversion of glycogen		
$C_6H_{12}O_6 + 3ADP \rightarrow 2C_3H_6O_3 + 3ATP$	23	
Aerobic conversion of glycogen	21	Blood plasma
$C_6H_{12}O_6 + 6O_2 + 38ADP \rightarrow 6CO_2 + 6H_2O + 38ATP$	366-680	Liver
	1300-2375	Leg muscles
Aerobic conversion of fatty acids		
$CH_3(CH_2)_{14}COOH + 23O_2 + 130ADP \rightarrow 16CO_2 + 16H_2O + 130ATP$	13,200	2% fat

Save Your Energy and Power!

Equally important as carbo-loading is avoiding spending too much energy and power in the early parts of the race. In practice, your muscles always use a fuel mix of glycogen and fatty acids. At rest and while pedaling at a low speed, the fuel mix consists mainly of fatty acids, as shown in the figure[23]. An example is that you pedal easily in the pack at 50% of your VO_2 max. The figure shows that in this case the fuel mix consists of 35% glycogen and 65% fatty acids. This means that you save your stock of glycogen for later in the race. Should you race from the start at your FTP (equivalent to 88% of your VO_2 max), the fuel mix would consist of 74% glycogen and 26% fatty acids. This will lead to a rapid depletion of your glycogen

stock and a high risk of hitting the wall.

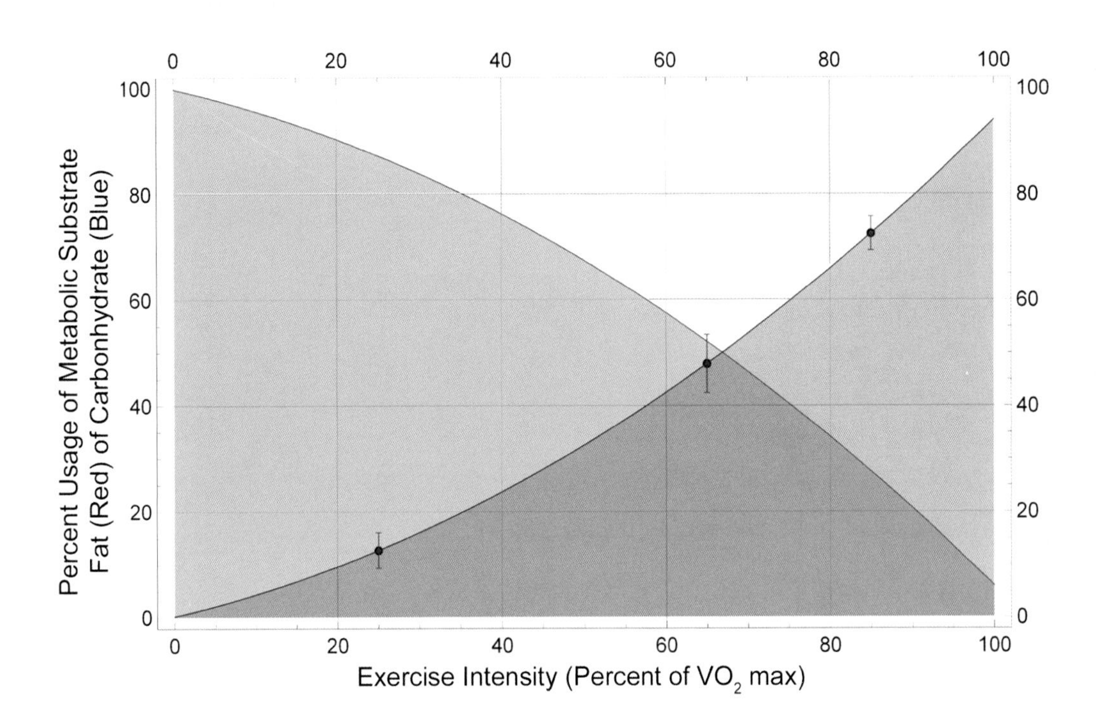

Fuel mix in muscles according to Rapaport[23].

How Long Will Your Glycogen Stock Last?

As an example, we use Fast Eddy. His FTP is 300 watts, so at this level he produces 300*3,600/1,000 = 1,080 kJ of energy per hour. At the level of his FTP, the fuel mix contains 74% of glycogen, so he produces 0.74*1,080 = 799 kJ of energy from glycogen per hour. Without carbo-loading, his glycogen stock is 21+366+1300 = 1,687 kJ, so he would hit the wall in 1,687/799 = 2.1 hour. With carbo-loading, his glycogen stock would increase to 21+680+2,375 = 3,076 kJ, so he can postpone hitting the wall to 3,076/799 = 3.8 hour.

In the case that Eddy pedals easily in the pack, the glycogen content in the fuel mix drops to 35%, so he uses only 0.35*1,080 = 378 kJ of energy from glycogen per hour. This means that even without carbo-loading, he can now postpone hitting the wall to 1,687/378 = 4.5 hour!

These examples show the importance of carbo-loading and saving energy in the early parts of the race.

Refueling During the Race

You should also stock up your supplies of glycogen during the race by eating and drinking regularly. In the early parts of the race it should not be a problem to digest carbohydrates likes cake, bananas and gels. Of course, it will take some time before the carbohydrates are taken up by the blood and the muscles, so you should start eating early in the race. It is also important to maintain your fluid balance, as you may lose up to 1.5 liters of sweat per hour in warm conditions.

In extreme races like the Tour de France, it is difficult if not impossible to prevent a negative energy balance. The energy cost of long stages can be 6,000 kJ or more. This means you have to eat and drink as much as you can digest! Modern sports drinks have a concentration of 70 grams of carbohydrates per liter, so they are isotonic. As a result they are taken up quickly in the blood. If you drink one liter of sport drink, this provides 70*4 = 280 kJ of energy. Theoretically, this amount of energy can postpone hitting the wall for 280/799 = 0.35 hour (while cycling at the FTP). Lightweights have an edge as they use less energy, so the same amount of carbs can sustain them longer.

You should refuel during a race by eating regularly.

Body Weight Increase

In the last days before a big race, you have to be careful not to wolf down too much carbs. This may lead to an undesirable increase in body weight, in particular as one gram of carbohydrates also binds three grams of water. Author Hans gained more than 2 kg of body weight as a result of carbo-loading before the Rotterdam Marathon. After five days his body weight had returned to normal, as shown in the figure below. The body weight increase of 2.2 kg is equivalent to 2.2/4 = 0.55 kg of carbohydrates. This matched well with the additional amount of honey, bananes, pasta and sweets that Hans ate in the last few days before the marathon. He concluded that he had overdone the carbo-loading! In later marathons, he reduced the carbo-loading somewhat and was able to manage his weight increase to 1 kg.

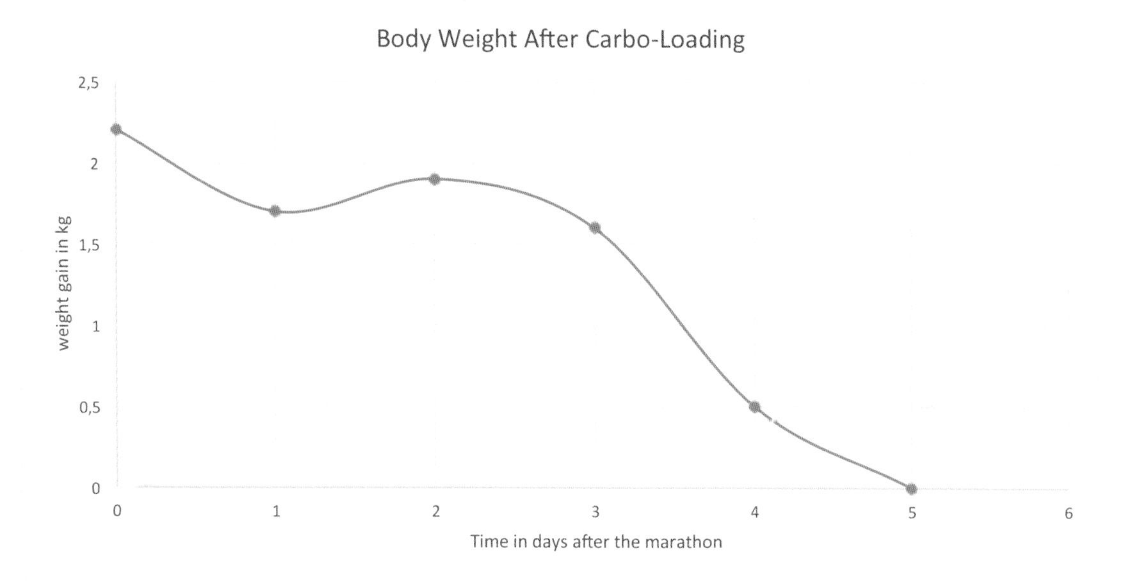

Sports Breakfast

Finally, we note that you should take an alimentary breakfast on the morning of the big race, some three hours before the start. This will stock up the glycogen stores in the liver. During the night, these stores are reduced, so it is neccesary to complement them. The stock in the muscles are not reduced during the night, so you don't have to worry about this.

59. THE IMPACT OF THE HEAT

He who suffers most will win.

Almost all cyclists will have experienced an ideal race: fast course, no hills, windless conditions and perfect weather. But what is actually the ideal temperature, how high or how low should it be to provide the best race times? And how big is the impact of non-ideal temperatures on the race times? In this chapter, we will answer these questions. In an earlier chapter, we already learned that at a higher temperature, we can benefit from the lower air resistance as a result of the lower air density. In this chapter, we will look into the impact of the temperature on the performance of the human engine. We have used our experiences in running as well as the literature on cycling for this chapter.

The impact of the temperature on the cycling performance is determined by at least two factors:

1. When the temperature gets too low, we are forced to wear additional clothing to protect us from the cold. Additional clothing increases our weight and consequently the energy cost of cycling. Moreover, it may hinder our motion.
2. When the temperature gets too high, it becomes more difficult to release the heat our body produces as a result of cycling. Consequently, we run the risk of overheating and of dehydration from sweating. The processes of overheating and dehydration depend strongly on the distance.

What Is the Impact of a High Temperature on Our Body?

We should differentiate between the impact of the heat on the body core temperature (hyperthermia) and on the dehydration. When we cycle, we usually produce more heat than we use. Consequently, our body temperature will increase and we start to sweat in order to release the excess heat from our body. At a low temperature, we may lose a considerable amount of heat to the air by means of convection, so the need for sweating is reduced. At a high temperature, we need to sweat much more, which may lead to dehydration. At severe weather conditions (high temperature and high humidity of the air), sweating can become increasingly difficult, so we cannot release the excess heat any more. This may lead to a sunstroke or collapse.

As a result of the increase in body temperature, the skin blood vessels will dilate, which will lead to increased blood flow to the skin where it may release heat. However, it means that less blood is available for other functions, including the leg muscles. In effect our cardiovascular capacity has been reduced and so has our cycling capacity. We may note this from the cardiac drift of our HR monitor: at the same HR we cycle more slowly or at the same speed our HR becomes higher. The increase of the body core temperature also leads to a decrease in the resistance to fatigue and an increase in the ratio of glycogen and fatty acids in the fuel mix of the muscles.

The sweat loss leads to a decrease in the blood (plasma) volume, as a result of which the stroke volume and the cardiac output decrease. Ultimately, this may lead to extremely low pressures in the vena, which may endanger the return blood flow to the ventricles. When the body core temperature rises above 39.5°C, the symptoms of sunstroke may occur (fainting, extreme fatigue, reduced sweating ability).

The Impact of the Temperature in Running a Marathon

Several studies[72,73,74] have been reported in literature on the statistical relationship between the temperature and the racing times in the marathon. We think the study of Helou et al.[73] is particularly useful. They have analyzed the results of over 1.7 million finishers of six big city marathons (Berlin, Boston, Chicago, London, New York and Paris) between 2001 and 2010. The temperature ranged between 1.7 and 25.2°C during these events. The authors found a statistically significant relationship between the finish times and the wet-bulb temperature[75]. In winter the wet-bulb temperature is almost equal to the normal air temperature. However, in summer the wet-bulb temperature can be much lower than the air temperature, particularly at low humidity.

The figure gives the impact of the wet-bulb temperature on the marathon race times of world-class runners and of normal runners like our Marathon Man.

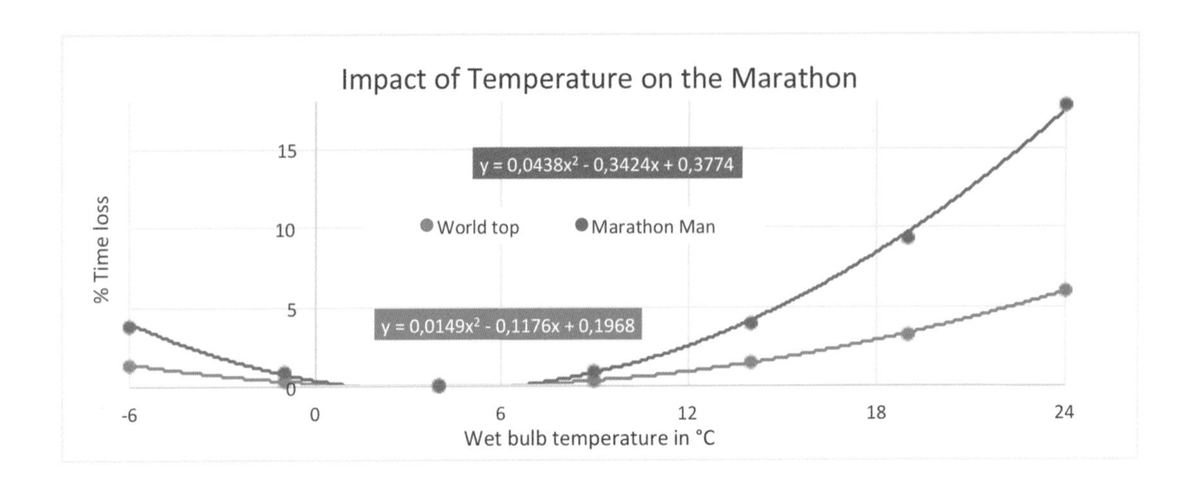

The results can be summarized as follows:

- The optimum temperature is around 5°C (world-class runners 4°C, normal runners 7°C).
- In the cold (-5°C) the speed is reduced by 3% (world-class runners 2%, normal runners 4%).
- In the heat (25°C) the speed is reduced by 6% (world-class runners) up to 18% (normal runners).

For women the optimum temperature is slightly higher (9°C) and the speed loss is slightly smaller (13% at 27°C). Apparently, women are a little better resistant to the heat.

What Is the Ideal Temperature at Shorter Running Distances?

It makes sense that runners suffer most from the heat at the marathon. Obviously, at a short distance, the problem of overheating will not manifest itself. On the other hand it is well-known that sprinters thrive best in warm conditions. They need some heat to warm up their muscles so they can mobilize maximum peak power in a few seconds. In literature, a study has reported the optimal temperature for various distances[63]. The results are given in the table and figure.

Optimal Temperature		
Distance	Men	Women
(km)	(°C)	(°C)
0.1	22.1	23.0
0.2	22.6	22.3
0.4	20.8	17.7
0.8	19.0	18.4
1.5	22.2	19.4
5	18.3	17.2
10	16.8	19.0
21.1	14.3	13.4
42.195	9.7	11.0

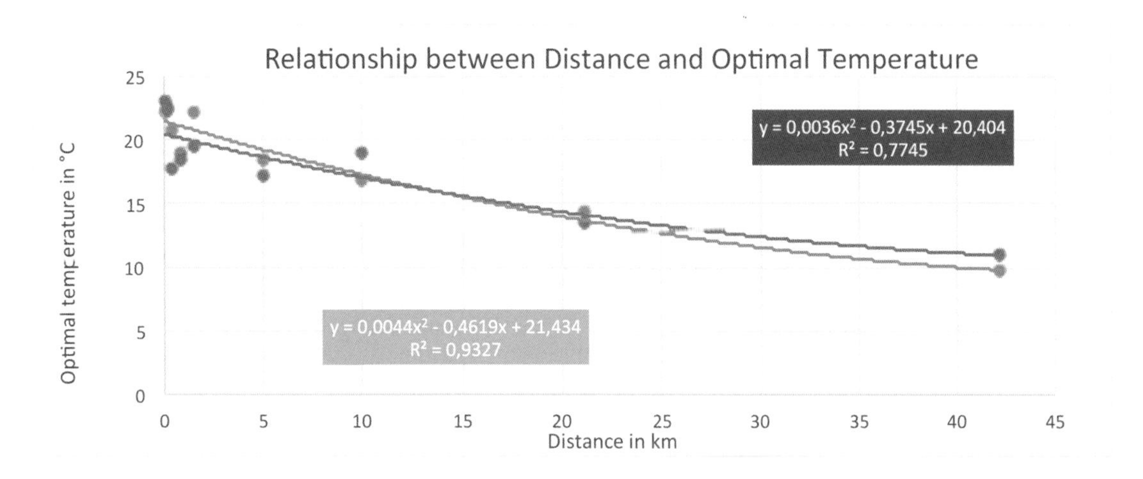

The relationship in the figure makes sense. Sprinters thrive in warm weather, whereas distance runners need cold weather to get rid of the excess heat that they produce. Too low temperatures should always be avoided as it increases the risk of hypothermia, particularly during rain and windy conditions.

How Can We Transfer the Experiences From Running to Cycling?

It goes without saying that there are big differences in the heat balance for running and for cycling. In cycling we benefit from additional air cooling as a result of the high speed of cycling. Before we discuss this in detail, we first need to look into the notion of the wet-bulb temperature.

The Wet-Bulb Temperature

In summer, we may experience one of those tropical, humid days when our clothing gets wet and sticky. Those days really bother us, much more than days with dry heat. This is caused by the fact that we cannot release excess heat to humid air. On such days, our problems are not so much related to high air temperatures, but to high wet-bulb temperatures.

What is the wet-bulb temperature[66]? When we expose water to the air, it starts to evaporate and so the humidity of the air increases. This continues until the air becomes saturated with water, so condensation may start. The wet-bulb temperature is defined as the temperature when condensation starts. This means that in humid air, the wet-bulb temperature can be equal to the air temperature. However, in dry air the wet-bulb temperature will be much lower than the air temperature. In practice, the conditions become severe at a wet-bulb temperature above 15°C. Sweating becomes more or less impossible and conditions become dangerous at a wet-bulb temperature above 22°C.

Obviously, the difference between the air temperature and the wet-bulb temperature depends on the relative humidity of the air. The wet-bulb temperature T_{wb} (in °C) can be calculated from the air temperature (T, in °C) and the relative humidity (RH, in %) with the following formula[67]:

$$T_{wb} = T*\arctan(0.151977*(RH+8.313659)^{0.5})+\arctan(T+RH)-\arctan(RH-1.676331)+ 0{,}00391838*RH^{1.5}*\arctan(0.023101*RH)-4.686035$$

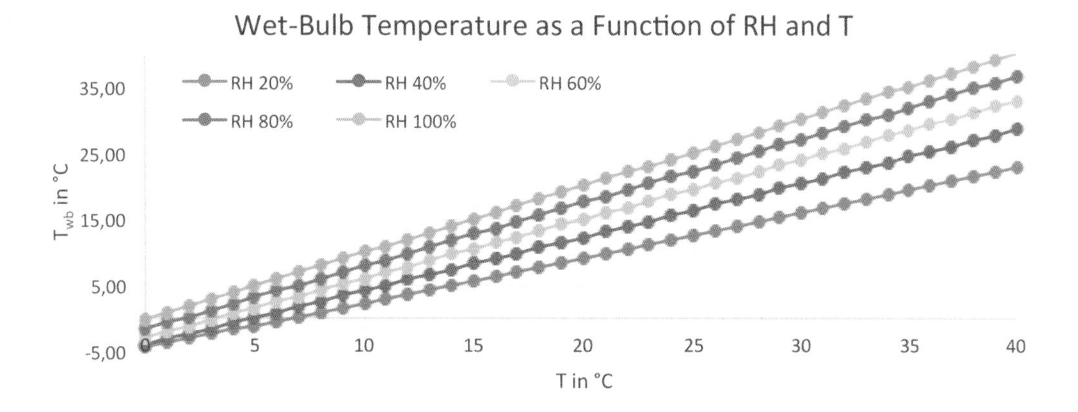

The figure gives the relationship between T, RH and T_{wb}. In winter, the RH is usually high, so the T_{wb} will not deviate much from T. However, in summer, on days with dry heat, RH will be low, so T_{wb} can be 10°C or more below T. The figure shows that the dangerous level of T_{wb} = 22°C may not even be reached on days with an air temperature of 40°C, provided the RH is sufficiently low! These are the hot dry days that are still quite tolerable.

Heat Balance for Cycling

The heat balance for cycling is given in the box.

Heat Balance for Cycling

$E = H - R - C$

E is net heat production per unit of time (J/s = watts).

H is heat production by cycling in watts.

R is heat loss by radiation in watts.

C is heat loss by convection in watts.

The Heat Production during Cycling (H)

We can calculate the heat production during cycling easily from the FTP. As we learned earlier, we can maintain the FTP for about one hour. Our Fast Eddy weighs 75 kg and has a specific FTP of 4 watts/kg, so he can cycle for about one hour with his FTP of 4*75 = 300 watts. As the metabolic efficiency is 25%, this means that the total power produced by Fast Eddy is 300/0.25 = 1,200 watts. It also means that 75% of his total power (or 900 watts) is transferred into excess heat! This excess heat has to be released from his body in order to prevent his body from overheating! As the heat production is linearly proportional to the weight, heavyweights produce more heat and have more problems releasing the excess heat.

The Heat Loss by Radiation (R)

From literature[62], it is known that we can calculate the heat loss by radiation (R) with the following formula:

$$R = 9.1 * (T_{skin} - T_{wb})$$

The formula shows that R depends on T_{wb}. As an example, we use T_{skin} of 34°C and T_{wb} of 20°C. R then becomes 127 watts. In cold weather we may lose a lot of heat by radiation. However, at high wet-bulb temperatures the heat loss by radiation can be small or even negative. The formula also shows that R is independent of the weight. This means that heavyweights, who produce more heat as we saw earlier, cannot release more heat by radiation.

The Heat Loss by Convection (C)

From literature[62], it is known that we can calculate the heat loss by convection (C) with the following formula:

$$C = 12.5 * v^{0.6} * (T_{skin} - T_{wb})$$

The formula shows that C does not only depend on T_{wb}, but also on the speed (v). As an example, we use a v of 40 km/h. C then becomes 747 watts. We also note that C gets very small at high wet-bulb temperatures, again confirming the problems of releasing excess heat during these conditions.

The Net Heat Production (E)

Now that we have determined all the parameters of the heat balance, it is easy to calculate the net heat production from the balance:

$$E = H - R - C$$

In cycling E will be much smaller than in running (e.g., 300 watts vs 700 watts). This is caused by the impact of the air cooling (which results from biking at a high speed) on the heat loss by convection (C).

The Heat Stress Index

Finally, we should look at one additional factor that is relevant in tropical conditions (i.e., the fact that is can be hard or impossible to sweat in humid air). This means you lose the ability to release your excess heat and you could suffer from a heat collapse. This risk is determined by the heat stress index (HSI). The HSI can be calculated by the following formula[62]:

$$HSI = E/E_{max}$$

In this formula E_{max} is the maximum amount of heat that can be released to the ambient air. This is another very important difference between cycling and running. In cycling E_{max} is much higher as a result of the air cooling. Obviously, the HSI needs to be less than one to prevent the accumulation of heat and overheating. To illustrate the concept, we have calculated the HIS for running and for cycling. The results are given in the figures below.

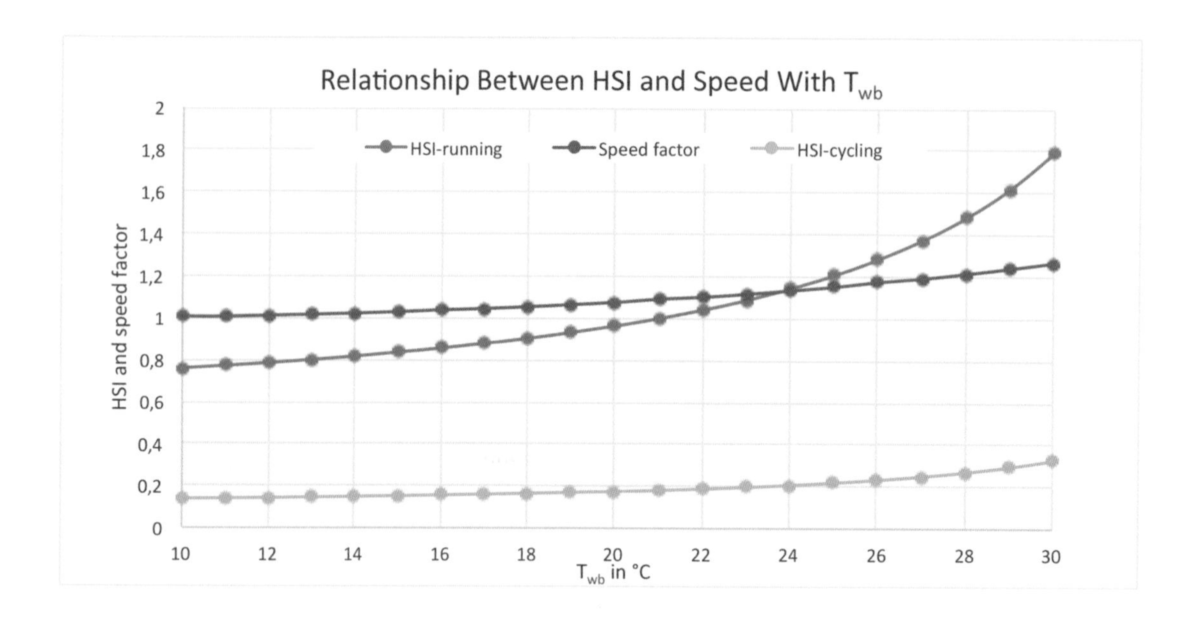

The figures show clearly that for running the HSI can be around one, whereas for cycling it usually is much lower, around 0.2. Also we see a clear relationship between the HSI and the speed decline in running, as we discussed earlier.

Based on these observations, we believe we can conclude that in cycling the impact of the temperature on the performance of the human engine will be much smaller than in running. In general the impact will be negligible. Exceptions to this general conclusion can be found in the following cases:

1. Extreme mountain climbs. When the speed drops to pedestrian levels, the air cooling effect will be lost.
2. Extreme tropical weather conditions. At a high RH, even in cycling the HSI may become high and problems with overheating may occur.

Sweat Loss and Liquid Balance

The sweat loss follows directly from the heat balance. As an example, we use a net heat production for Fast Eddy of 325 watts. As the heat of evaporation of water (sweat) is 2,249 kJ/l, we can calculate the sweat production (S, in liters per hour) from the heat balance with the following formula:

S*2249*1000 = E*3600, or S = 0.0016*E

Consequently, the net sweat loss for Fast Eddy amounts to 0.0016*325 = 0.5 l/h. In practice, the actual sweat loss is determined by:

1. **The FTP**
   A world-class cyclist produces more heat and will lose more sweat, around 0.8 l/h.
2. **The speed**
   As the speed drops in the mountains to 12 km/h, the sweat loss by Fast Eddy increases to 1.1 l/h.
3. **The temperature**
   At a temperature of 34°C, the sweat loss of Fast Eddy will increase to 1.8 l/h.

The impact of sweating depends mostly on the humidity. In dry air sweating is not so much of a problem, you just have to make sure you drink enough to make up the fluid balance. In humid air, sweating can become almost impossible and the danger of overheating becomes imminent. In those conditions, you can easily suffer a sunstroke or collapse. Races should be banned in such tropical conditions as the risks are excessive!

Effect of Precooling

Recent research[65] has revealed that in extreme conditions (temperatures of 32-35°C with an RH of 50-60%) the power output could be boosted by 3% as a result of the combination of precooling with ice towels and drinking ice slurry during cycling.

At cycling the temperature only impacts the performance of the human engine under extreme conditions.

60. THE IMPACT OF THE RAIN, THE WIND AND THE COLD

Cycling allows you to explore the world!

In the previous chapter, we already learned that the performance in running is significantly reduced in the cold, in the order of 4% as shown in the figure below. This is partly caused by the fact that in the cold additional clothing is required to prevent hypothermia. Additional clothing increases our weight and reduces our freedom of motion.

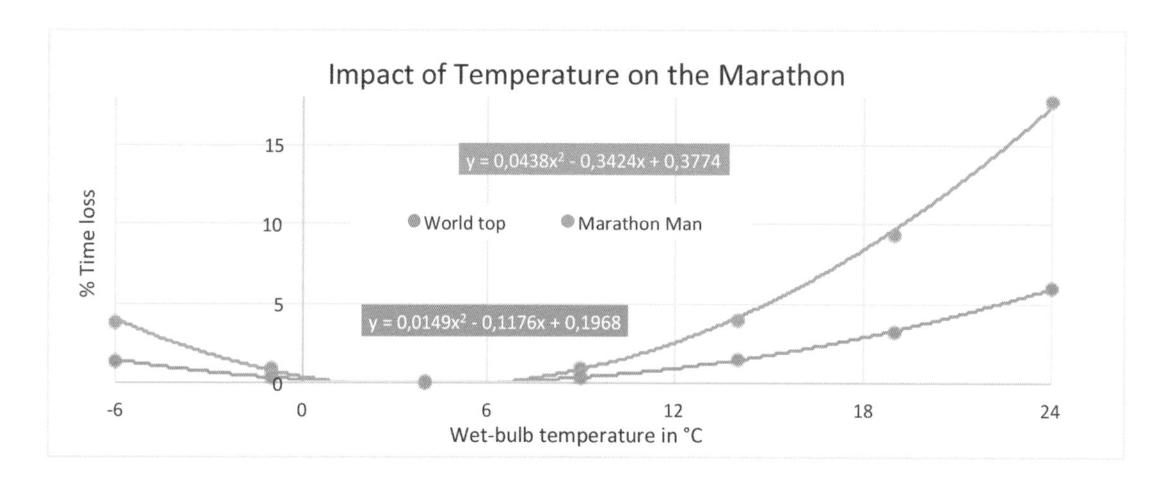

How Can We Transfer the Experiences From Running to Cycling?

As we saw earlier, the heat balance of running and cycling is quite different. In the heat the air-cooling effect of cycling has a favorable impact on the heat stress index. Consequently, the impact of the heat is much less in cycling as compared to running.

In the cold, we can distinguish two essential differences between running and cycling:

1. In cycling, it is easier to wear additional clothing to protect us from the cold. The additional weight has only a limited effect on the performance, particularly on a flat course.
2. In cycling, we lose much more heat to the air as a result of the higher speed. This is known as the windchill effect and is very important in practice.

The Wind Causes Windchill

As a result of wind the perceived temperature at our skin can be much lower than the air temperature. This perceived decrease in temperature is called the windchill. It is caused by the fact that wind blows away the insulating layer of air around our skin. The windchill temperature (T_{wc}) can be calculated with the following formula[68]:

$$T_{wc} = 13.12+0.6215T_a-11.37v^{0.16}+0.3965T_a v^{0.16}$$

In this formula T_a is the air temperature and v is the wind speed in km/h. The figure below gives T_{wc} as a function of the air temperature and the wind speed.

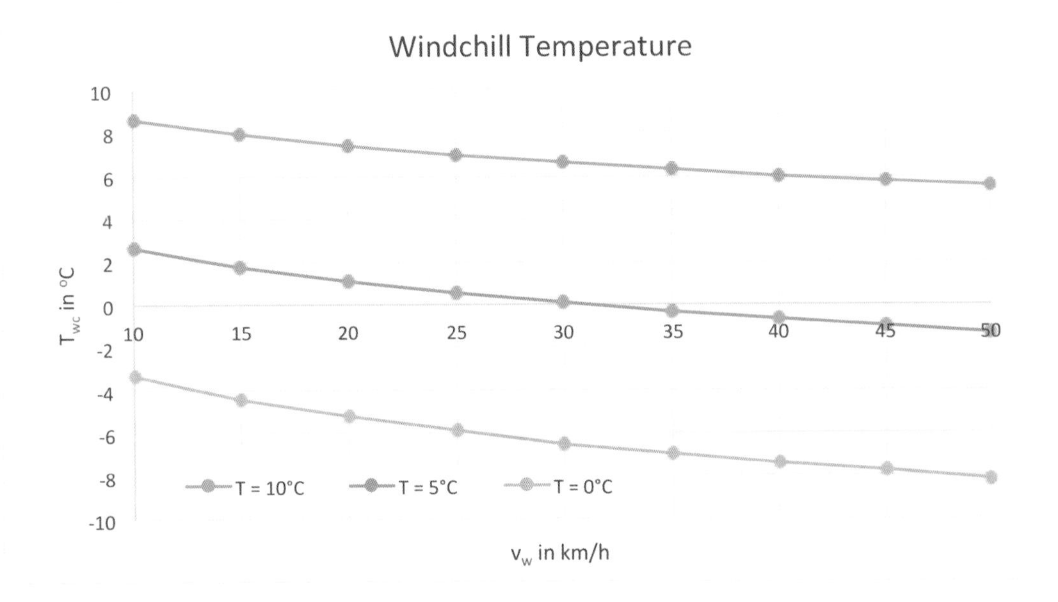

Obviously, when we cycle at a speed of 40 km/h, we are faced with a wind speed of at least 40 km/h, even in windless conditions! This means that the windchill temperature in cycling can easily be 10°C lower than the air temperature!

The Rain May Cause Hypothermia

In the rain, our skin gets wet. This prevents the insulating layer of air from forming around our skin. This is a very serious drawback, as air insulates 26 times better than water! In literature, experiences on rainy conditions during the Glasgow Marathon have been reported[5]. The air temperature was 12°C and the wind speed 16-40 km/h (4-6 Beaufort). Many runners dropped out with hypothermia, some of them with a rectal temperature as low as 34.3°C!

Wear Protective Clothing and Use Protective Skin Oil

A main function of cycling wear is to maintain the insulating layer of air around the skin. In cold conditions, it is wise to wear multiple layers of lightweight porous and breathable cycling wear that will not absorb moisture and will ensure an optimal insulation. In literature[5], guidelines can be found on the number of insulating layers as a function of the windchill temperature and the speed. At windchill temperatures around the freezing point, at least four layers are required, particularly when the cloths can get wet and lose their insulating properties. An extreme example are the Inuit at the North pole; they need ten layers of insulating clothes!

Nowadays, you can also use protective skin oil. This will form a thin insulating layer on the skin, limiting the heat loss. This oil is used by many cyclists. Be aware that the rain may wash off the oil, so the insulating properties are lost!

Small and Skinny Cyclists Are More Vulnerable to the Cold

The fourth and final factor is the sensitivity of the cyclist to the cold. Literature states that small cyclists are more vulnerable. This is caused by the fact that they have relatively more skin surface area as compared to their body weight. Consequently, their heat balance is less favorable. Cyclists with a low body fat level are also more vulnerable, as body fat has insulating properties. Tim Noakes, the author of The Lore of Running, concluded that the vulnerabilty to the cold is the inverse of the vulnerabilty to the heat. In the heat small and skinny cyclists have an advantage, but in the cold the reverse is the case.

Especially in the rain small and skinny cyclists are more vulnerable to the cold.

61. HOW FAST COULD YOU RUN, ICE SKATE AND CLIMB STAIRS?

Everything you need is already inside. –Bill Bowerman

In this chapter, we will illustrate a fun application of our models: calculating which performance you could achieve in other sports (besides cycling). We can do this by using your FTP, which is of course the amount of power that your human engine can maintain for one hour. For other durations, we can calculate the power from the FTP with Riegel's formula.

In an earlier chapter, we saw that Fast Eddy has an FTP of 4 watts/kg. As his body weight is 75 kg, his human engine can maintain a power output of 4*75 = 300 watts during one hour of cycling. In this chapter, we will assume that he can mobilize the same amount of power for other sports as well. We will study the examples of running, ice skating and stair climbing. The laws of physics apply to all of these sports, so we can easily modify the cycling formula and calculate the performance in these sports as well. Of course, our Fast Eddy is a cyclist and he will have to train sufficiently in order to master these other sports. Also, he might be more talented in cycling than in these other sports. Nevertheless, we believe that our method can be used to predict his potential performance in other sports as well, as the power of the human engine is the driving force in all sports.

Running

We can calculate the running speed with the running formula[3]. This formula says that the total power of the human engine should be equal to the sum of the power required to surmount the running resistance, the air resistance and the climbing resistance ($P = P_r+P_a+P_c$). The result is that your speed depends on the distance and time (because your power decreases with time) and the resistances such as wind, hills and so on. As an example, the figure gives the race time at the 10,000 meter as a function of the specific power (in watts/kg) in ideal (i.e., windless) conditions. We see that Kenenisa Bekele ran with a specific power of 7.04 watts/kg to set his world record of 26:17. Fast Eddy can run a time of 44:04 with his specific power of 4.08 watts/kg (which is slightly more than his FTP of 4 watts/kg as the duration is less than one hour).

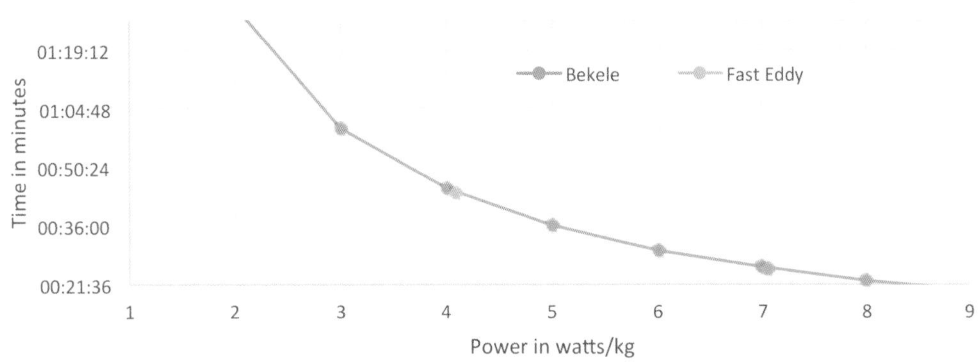

The Ethiopian 10,000-meter men's Olympic selection trials for the 2016 Rio Olympic Games in Hengelo (the Netherlands). Kenenisa Bekele ran with #1.

Ice Skating

In ice skating, the total power of the human engine should be equal to the sum of the gliding resistance and the air resistance ($P = P_g + P_a$). The gliding resistance is five times higher than the rolling resistance in cycling and 6.6 times lower than the running resistance. The $c_d A$ value in ice skating is somewhat higher than in cycling due to the sliding motion in skating. Using these data and some results in practice, we have prepared the figure of the race time at the 10,000 meter as a function of the total power. According to our calculations, multiple world champion Sven Kramer needed a total power of 580 watts for his Heerenveen track record of 12:40. Fast Eddy can skate a time of 15:27 with his total power of 330 watts (somewhat higher than 300 watts as the duration is only 15.5 minutes).

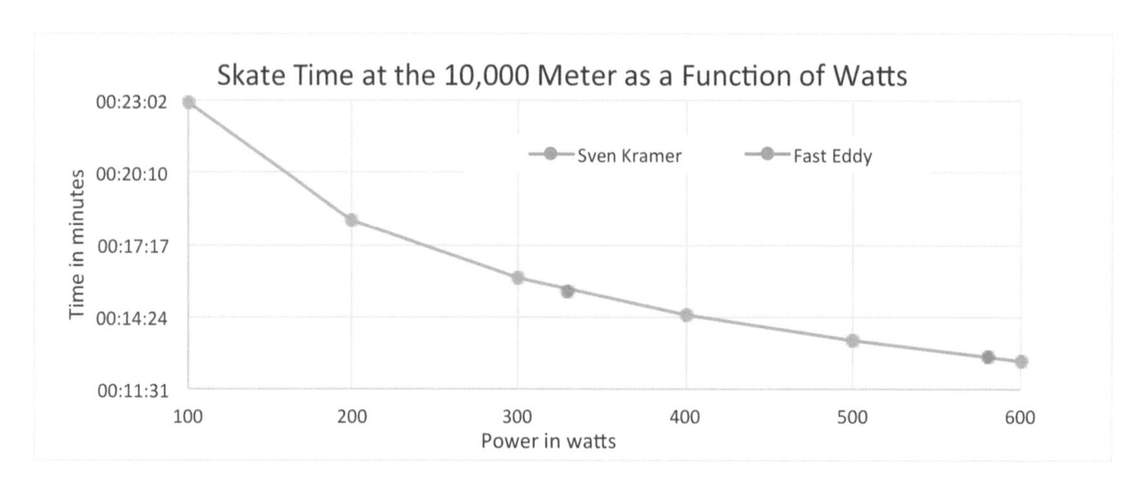

Climbing the Stairs of the Empire State Building

In stair climbing, the climbing resistance is decisive ($P_c = mgv$). Consequently, how fast you can climb follows directly from the specific power (P/m). As an example, we use the Empire State Building Run-Up (height (h) = 320 meters). The attainable race time follows from:

$$t = E/P = mgh/P = m*9.81*320/P = 3139/(P/m)$$

So far, we have neglected the power required for the running resistance. To compensate for this, we have added 25% to the climbing resistance. The figure shows the resulting relationship between the climbing time and the specific power.

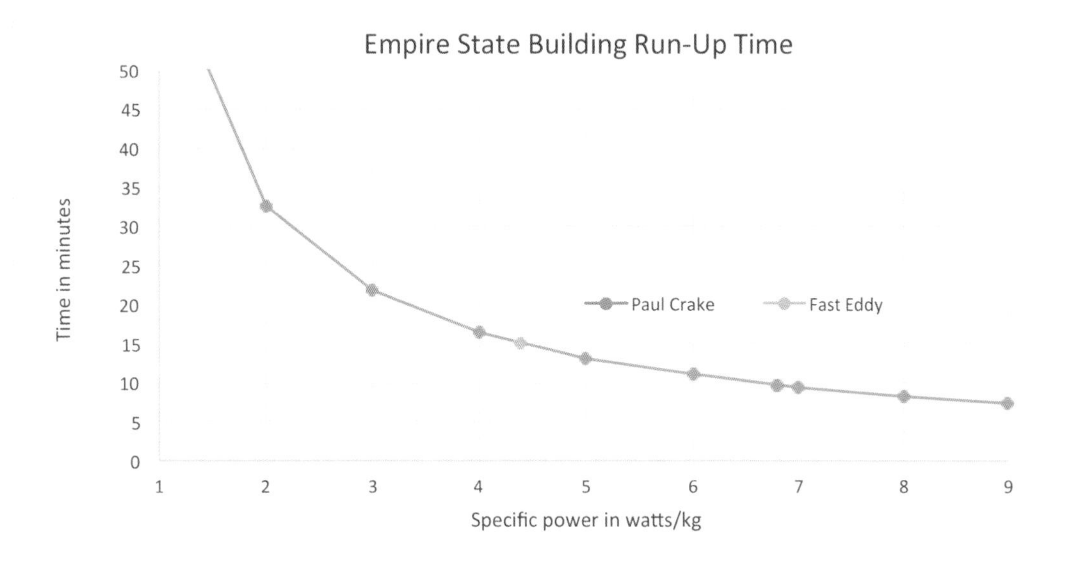

The record time of 9:33 means that the specific power (P/m) of Paul Crake must have been 6.8 watts/kg. According to our calculations, Fast Eddy could reach the top in 15 minutes with a specific power of 4.4 watts/kg (somewhat higher than 4 watts/kg as the duration is only 15 minutes).

In summary, we conclude that the laws of physics enable us to calculate the performance in many endurance sports, including running, cycling, ice skating and stair climbing. Of course, these calculations are just theory. In practice, you will have to train well to develop the muscles and skills required for the different sports. Also, you might be more talented in one sport than in another. Nevertheless, we believe these calculations will give a good estimate of your potential performance in many sports.

62. THE MAXIMUM POWER OF SPRINTERS AND ULTRA-CYCLISTS

We all have dreams. But in order to make dreams come into reality, it takes an awful lot of determination, dedication, self-discipline and effort. –Jesse Owens

So far, we have calculated a lot with the FTP, the specific power (in watts/kg) which you can maintain for one hour. We have shown that the FTP provides a good base to compare performance in different conditions and in different sports. Furthermore, we saw that the ultimate limit of human power is an FTP of 6.40 watts/kg for men and 5.70 watts/kg for women.

Now that we are approaching the end of this book, we want to look more closely at the maximum limit of human power for performances with a different time span, from short explosions in sprinting to protractive endurance power.

How Big Is the Maximum Power of the Four Energy Systems?

In an earlier chapter, we showed the table below that gives the biochemical limits of the specific power (in watts/kg) of the four energy systems of the human engine. We note that we have prepared this table with data from the thermodynamic literature[23-27], using the metabolic efficiency of 25% and an athletic body weight of 60 kg. The table clearly shows that the maximum power is very different for the four systems. On the one hand, the ATP/CP system can supply a lot of power, but it can only sustain this for a brief explosion like the 100-meter sprint. On the other hand, the conversion of fatty acids supplies relatively less power, but it can maintain this for a very long time (many hours, even days).

Power Output of the Four Human Engines	
	P/m
	(watts/kg)
FTP/CP	
FTP → ADP $C_{10}H_{16}N_5O_{13}P_3 \rightarrow C_{10}H_{15}N_5O_{10}P_2$	24.64
Anaerobic conversion of glycogen	
$C_6H_{12}O_6 + 3ADP \rightarrow 2C_3H_6O_3 + 3ATP$	13.50
Aerobic conversion of glycogen	
$C_6H_{12}O_6 + 6O_2 + 38ADP \rightarrow 6CO_2 + 6H_2O + 38ATP$	7.76
Aerobic conversion of fatty acids	
$CH_3(CH_2)_{14}COOH + 23O_2 + 130ADP \rightarrow 16CO_2 + 16H_2O + 130ATP$	2.36

Which Fuel Mix Is Used by Sprinters and Distance Runners?

Earlier, we saw that the human engine more or less automatically adapts the fuel mix. In rest and at relatively low exercise intensity, mainly fatty acids are used. As more power is required, at a higher pace in running and cycling, more and more glycogen is used in the fuel mix. At intensities above the FTP, the anaerobic breakdown of glycogen starts to kick in. Finally, near full (sprinting) power, ATP becomes the main fuel in the mix. Obviously, you cannot maintain fast paces for a long time, so the fuel mix depends also on the duration of the exercise. Sprinters use mainly ATP while distance runners rely on a mix of glycogen and fatty acids. Earlier, we also learned that the gradual change in the fuel mix is the reason for the gradual decline of power with time, as described by Riegel's formula. The table and figure below summarize the fuel mix as a function of the time in minutes.

Fuel mix				
	Anaerobic	Anaerobic	Aerobic	Aerobic
Time	FTP	Glycolysis	Glycogen	Fatty acids
(minutes)	(%)	(%)	(%)	(%)
0	100	0	0	0
1	10	65	20	5
5	2	8	80	10
10	0	0	90	10
20	0	0	84	16
40	0	0	78	22
60	0	0	75	25
120	0	0	69	31
240	0	0	64	36

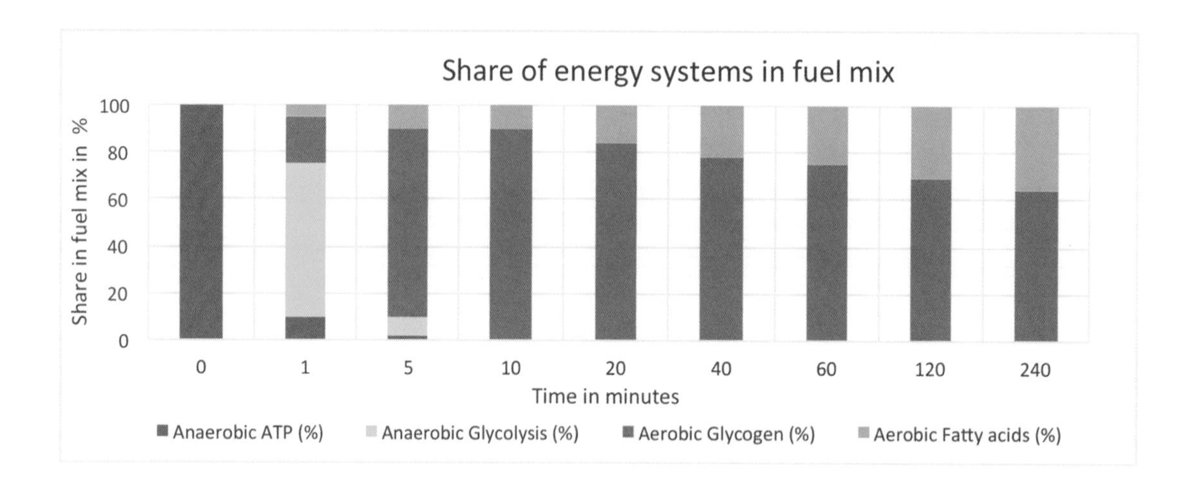

How Big Is the Maximum Human Power as a Function of Time?

When we multiply the share of the four energy systems in the fuel mix with the specific power from the first table, we can calculate the maximum human power as a function of time. The result is given in the table and figure below.

Limits of Human Power	
Time	Specific power
(minutes)	(watts/kg)
0	24.64
1	12.91
5	8.02
10	7.22
20	6.90
40	6.57
60	6.41
120	6.09
240	5.82

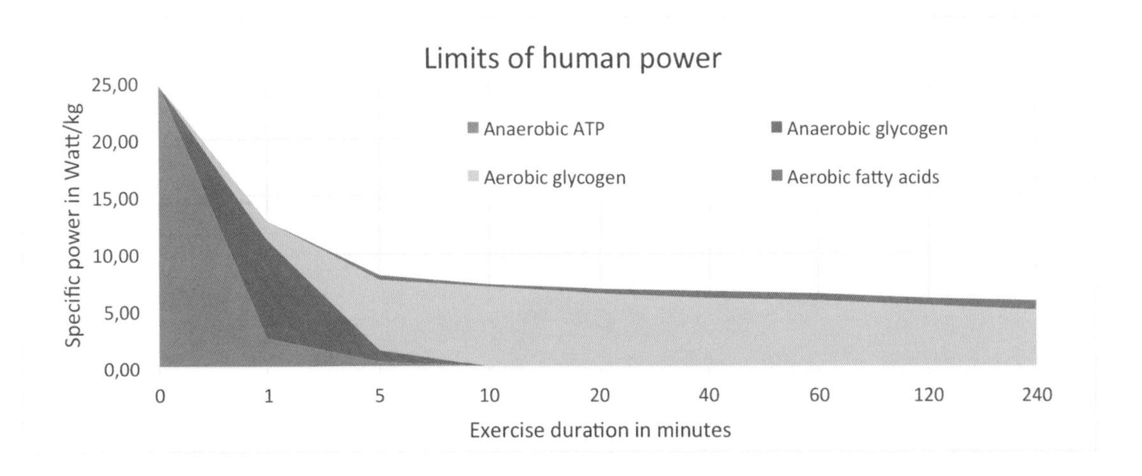

Can These Limits Be Confirmed in the Real World?

Earlier, we confirmed that the maximum level of the FTP (the specific power that can be maintained for one hour) is indeed 6.4 watts/kg for elite male athletes. This value is corroborated by the power profiles in cycling and we also found that the current world records in athletics are equivalent to an FTP of 6.35 watts/kg.

We have also calculated the equivalent specific power for other times than one hour. The table below gives the results of our calculations on various world records. Almost all calculated power values are based on our model, which uses the equilibrium condition, without the power required to accelerate from the start. The exceptions in the table are the data on the 100-400 meter, where we obviously had to include the additional power for the acceleration from 0 to 10 m/s during the first four seconds after the start. This is equivalent to an acceleration of 2.5 m/s^2. This acceleration requires an additional power (P/m = av) of 25 watts/kg. As the acceleration lasts only four seconds, the impact on the average power of Usain Bolt is 4/9.58*25 = 10.5 watts/kg. We have added this value to the equilibrium power of 12.0 watts/kg. For Michael Johnson (400-meter world record) the average acceleration power thus becomes 4/43*25 = 2.3 watts/kg, which we have added to his equilibrium power of 10.6 watts/kg. All in all, the results of these calculations match the theoretical limits very well.

Relevant Performances and Equivalent Power	
Time (minutes)	**Examples**
0	Bolt: 100 m, 22.5 watts/kg, power profiles 25 watts/kg
1	Johnson: 400 m, 12.9 watts/kg
5	Daniel Koomen: 3,000 m, 7.32 watts/kg
10	Bekele: 5,000 m, 7.06 watts/kg
20	Bekele: 10,000 m, 6.74 watts/kg
40	Koomen: 15 km, 6.41 watts/kg
60	Tadese: 21.1 km, 6.36 watts/kg
120	Kimetto: 42.2 km, 5.99 watts/kg

In summary, we conclude that the limits of human power can be based on the biochemical maximum values of the power of the four energy systems. The result is that the maximum power for a short explosion such as the 100-meter sprint is 24.6 watts/kg. The maximum power that can be maintained for one hour (the FTP) is 6.4 watts/kg. These data are confirmed by our analysis of the performances of elite athletes in running, cycling and ice skating. The values for women are some 11% lower, at 5.7 watts/kg. We believe that this difference is caused primarily by the higher body fat level of women.

The maximum power for a short explosion such as the 100-meter sprint is 24.6 watts/kg.

PART V

THE MYTHS OF CYCLING

63. NUTRITION, SUPPLEMENTS AND BEET JUICE

I don't ride a bike to add days to my life, I ride a bike to add life to my days!

Regularly, new items or books are published on products or diets that are supposed to make us more healthy or fit. Most of these reports fall in the categories of humbug or scam. The scientific literature on nutrition[6-12,41] concludes that there is no such thing as a miracle product. Moreover, a normal healthy and varied diet suffices to prevent deficiencies, even for the elite athletes. Supplements are required only in exceptional cases or extreme efforts like the Tour de France or Ironman triathlons.

What Constitutes a Healthy Diet?

In an earlier chapter, we learned that first and foremost a healthy diet should be lean and varied. As the general Western diet contains too much fat and calories, the following recommendations can be made:

1. Eat plenty (five to six portions daily) of vegetables and fruit.
2. Eat whole-wheat bread (with lean or fruit filling) and oatmeal porridge as required.
3. Eat one portion of potatoes (no fries), pasta, rice or other grain products daily.
4. Eat one portion of lean meat, fish, poultry or tofu, or another source of protein (like eggs, beans, nuts) daily.
5. Replace butter with olive oil or another liquid oil.
6. Eat or drink lean dairy products, like skin milk, yoghurt or cheese as required (maximum of three portions daily).
7. Drink plenty of water and tea and as little as possible of sodas, beer, wine and sports drinks.
8. Avoid fried products, snacks, refreshments and salted or fried cookies.
9. On occasions you may eat gingerbread, pancakes and low-fat cookies.

This diet will contain the proper amounts and shares of the energy sources (carbohydrates, proteins and fatty acids), but also of the vitamins, trace elements and antioxidants that you require. Be careful to buy fresh products and vary the menu as much as possible. Avoid using ready-made products containing flavoring additives, emulsifiers and salt. Weigh yourself regularly to make sure your weight remains stable and at the desired level.

As was stated above, supplements like sports drinks and energy gels are unnecessary. They should be avoided as they contain a lot of calories, so you will gain body fat!

The only exception to the rule of the above diet should be made in the last 2-3 days before a long race. Then you should apply carbo-loading by increasing the share of carbohydrates in your diet to 70% and reducing the share of proteins and fats to 15% each. This will increase the glycogen stock in your muscles, which will help to avoid hitting the wall in the final stages of the race. On the morning of the race, you should take an alimentary breakfast and during the race you should eat and drink to supplement the glucose and glycogen used during the race. More details on this have been given in an earlier chapter.

Supplements

As stated above, supplements are unnecessary and even unwanted in normal circumstances. We should realize that the human body is capable of synthesizing almost all required compounds from the elements which are present in our nutrition. In our intestines, most of our food is broken down to small and simple compounds. An example is the fact that carbohydrates from potatoes or pasta are broken down to glucose. The glucose is adsorbed by the blood and transported to the cells, where it is used to synthesize glycogen. Finally, the glycogen can be used by the cells to produce the energy and power we need for our cycling.

We should also realize that our body has ample stores of many compounds that can be mobilized when needed. As an example, both authors Hans and Ron have experienced that a large amount of their body fat was slowly mobilized and dissolved during the six months in 2012 when they lost weight (in both cases some 10-15 kg). In this period they ate fewer calories, while continuing their training. Consequently, their bodies needed to mobilize their body fat in order to provide the energy and power required for the training. So, contrary to popular belief, you do not have to eat a lot to supply the energy and power needed for cycling. The human body has ample stores of fat which it can mobilize.

The only exception to this rule applies to some vitamins and trace elements, which our body cannot synthetize itself. These components need to be present in our nutrition. However, also for these components the body usually has some stock available. This means that we just have to make sure that in the long run (months) our nutrition contains sufficient amounts of these components, hence the importance of sufficient variation in our nutrition. Vegetables and fruits contain a lot of vitamins, trace minerals and antioxidants which are very healthy.

After this clarification, the reader will probably understand that there is no such thing as a miracle sports nutrition or supplement. The only proven miracle products are doping substances, like EPO and anabolic steroids. These are mostly injected and influence the hormone system. When consumed orally, EPO is broken down in the intestines and loses its function. Some anabolic substances can be consumed orally, but they are much less effective.

Review of Popular Supplements

Below we will give a review of the impact and the side effects of some popular supplements, based on the scientific literature[5,6,10,11,39-41].

1. **Caffeine**
   Caffeine is not really considered a supplement, as it has become an accepted part of the normal diet. However, it does have a proven ergogenic effect (i.e., a positive impact on the performance in sports). How big the impact is, however, remains uncertain. Different studies have given different results. The small positive impact found in most studies is explained by the fact that caffeine stimulates the conversion of fatty acids. As a result, the glycogen stores are somewhat spared which will help to avoid hitting the wall. Caffeine also is known to have a stimulating effect on the brain and the nervous system. Since 2014 caffeine is no longer on the WADA doping list, but it is recommended that the consumption is limited to 5 mg/kg of body weight. For a cyclist with a body weight of 60 kg, this means consuming no more than 300 mg or 3-6 cups of coffee or 5-10 cups of tea. In view of the expected small positive impact and because coffee and tea are harmless products, it is recommended to drink some 2-3 cups of strong coffee or tea two hours before the race.

2. **Sodium bicarbonate**
   Sodium bicarbonate increases the pH of the blood and improves the buffering capacity. As a result, the negative impact of lactic acid, which is produced at speeds above the anaerobic threshold, will be neutralized. In literature a positive effect of a few percent has been reported at middle distance races, but there have been mixed results with a dose of 0.3 mg/kg, consumed a few hours before the race. An awkward side effect is that 50% of the test persons got abdominal discomfort. Sodium bicarbonate is not yet on the doping list, but this may change. It could be traced easily on account of the impact on the urine pH. Using it would be pointless for most cyclists, except perhaps for a short (track) race.

3. **Creatine**
   Creatine is present in meat and is produced in the liver. Creatine phosphate is used in the synthesis of ATP in the muscles. Some studies have shown that supplementary intake of creatine (3-5 g/day) improves the recovery process in interval training. Creatine is used in power sports, swimming and

cycling. Objections are the possible contamination of the product (e.g. with nandrolone), and the resulting weight increase.

4. **Glycerol**
   The consumption of glycerol may lead to a temporary increase of the blood (plasma) volume. Consequently, it has been used to mask the use of EPO since it results in lower levels of hemoglobin and hematocrit. However, proof of a positive impact on the cycling performance is lacking.

5. **Triglycerides**
   Theoretically, the consumption of triglycerides should improve the conversion of fatty acids. However, several studies failed to prove any positive impact in practice.

6. **Branched chain amino acids/L-Tryptophan**
   Serotonin is synthesized in the body from the amino acid tryptophan. As a neurotransmitter serotonin has a positive impact on your mood. During exercises, like running and cycling, serotonin is produced which makes you feel good. However, during protracted exercise the serotonin level can rise to levels which cause fatigue. Theoretically, the level of serotonin could be mitigated by the intake of branched chain amino acids like valine, leucine and isoleucine. In practice, mixed results have been found. This also applies to studies that looked into the direct intake of L-tryptophan. Based on current science, the use of these supplements cannot be supported.

7. **Vitamins/antioxidants (A, B1 t/m B15, C, D, E)**
   For almost all vitamins it is known that a healthy and varied diet will supply the necessary amounts, so supplementary intake is not necessary. The only exceptions to this rule can be for special sensitive groups, like babies, children, pregnant women, vegetarians, elite athletes and senior citizens. In these cases supplements of vitamin D (discussed in the next chapter) or on occasions vitamin B11 (folic acid), B12 or K may be recommended. In the 1980s there was a lot of interest in vitamin B15, which was thought to boost performances. However, later studies failed to prove any positive effect.

8. **Trace elements (Ca, Cr, B, Fe, Mg, Zn)**
   Also for all trace elements science tells us that a healthy and varies diet will supply all the necessary amounts, so supplementary intake is not necessary. For special groups, including pregnant women, vegetarians and elite athletes, supplementary intake or iron may be recommended to avoid anemia. The recommended daily intake is 10 mg for men and 15 mg for women. Some distance runners have the experience that supplementary intake of magnesium helps to prevent or reduce muscle cramps in the final stages of the marathon. In summary, there is no harm in taking a daily iron pill and occasionally a multi-vitamin pill as a precautionary measure.

9. **Phosphate**

   Phosphate is necessary for the synthesis of ATP, so theoretically supplementary intake could boost recovery. However, in practice no positive impact has been found.

10. **Carnitine**

    Theoretically, carnitine could stimulate the conversion of fatty acids. However, no effect was found in practice.

11. **Spirulina and ginseng**

    No scientific studies have been published that prove a positive effect of these formulations.

Beet Juice

In recent years, the use of beet juice has been more or less a hype in the media. The consumption of beet juice was said to improve the performance in running and cycling[69]. Some studies reported a boost in performance of 3-5%. This would be very significant indeed: no other product besides EPO and anabolic steroids could boast such an impact!

Theoretically, you could expect some positive impact of the high nitrate (NO_3-) level of beet juice. The oxygen from the nitrate might play a role in the aerobic processes in the muscles. So, you could hypothesize that it might increase the oxygen uptake capacity and thus improve performance.

However, we should approach this topic critically, as the reported results were obtained with only a limited number of test persons. This means that the results could easily have been influenced by random differences or a placebo effect. Another reason for a critical attitude follows from the mass balance. In the reported studies the total dose was 1000 mg NO_3- (0.5 liter beet juice per day during 3 days). We have compared this (on a molar base) to the amount of the oxygen used during 2 hours running or cycling. The result is that the nitrate dose is a factor 1600 smaller than the oxygen uptake! We believe that it is most unlikely that such a small dose could have such a big impact, particularly as the processes in our body are based primarily on oxygen and not on nitrate.

An argument in favor of beet juice, is the fact that nitrate will be reduced to nitrite and nitrogen monoxide in the stomach. This may lead to some dilation of the blood vessels, which will improve the circulation and reduce the blood pressure.

In view of the above, authors Hans and Ron could not resist the temptation to test it themselves. On the occasion of the 20K running race at Alphen aan den Rijn in 2013, they functioned as guinea pigs. During the 3 days before the race, they took a dose of 1800 mg of NO_3-, by drinking beet juice and eating spinach, Turnip stalks and beets. Unfortunately, during the race they did not notice any impact at all! Their race times were exactly as could be expected from their training and previous races. Of course, this can hardly be called scientific proof, so we do not want to exclude the possibility that other runners or cyclists may benefit from beet juice. So if you don't mind the taste of beet juice, feel free to try it. We have not repeated the test, as we don't believe we will benefit from it.

Authors Hans and Ron could not resist the temptation to test beet juice themselves.

64. AVOID A VITAMIN D DEFICIENCY!

Nothing will work, unless you do. –Maya Angelou

In winter, the risk of a vitamin D deficit is significant, especially in Northern countries like the Netherlands. Consequently, supplementary intake of vitamin D can be necessary and prudent, particularly for athletes. Authors Hans and Ron (and physician and distance runner Karel Bos, who co-authored this chapter) take a daily vitamin D pill to prevent any negative impact on their performance. What do runners need to know about vitamin D and how may it affect your performance? These questions will be answered in this chapter.

The History of Vitamin D

Historically, vitamin D deficiency[70] has been associated with Rickets, a bone disease which was commonly found in industrial areas in Northern Europe in the 19th century. In the 1920s research showed that it could be treated effectively by:

1. Exposure to UV light and sunlight
2. Intake of codfish oil, butter and milk

After World War II, the Dutch government set up holiday camps to increase the exposure of children to sunlight. Since 1961 vitamin D is also added to margarine in the Netherlands.

Recommended Daily Intake of Vitamin D

The European Food Labelling Guideline states a recommended daily intake (RDI) of 5 microgram (μg). However, this does not take into account the risk groups, like senior citizens, pregnant women and breastfeeding women. In the Netherlands a vitamin D deficiency is quite common, in particular amongst groups who remain indoors most of the time, people with dark skin and women wearing burkas or veils.

The Dutch Food Center recommends a daily intake of a supplement of 10 µg for the following groups:

1. Children under the age of 4 years
2. Persons between the ages of 4-50 years with dark skin
3. All pregnant women and breastfeeding women
4. All women over the age of 50 and men over the age of 50
5. All women under the age of 50 wearing veils

They also recommend a daily intake of 20 µg for the following groups:

1. Persons suffering from osteoporosis or living in a nursing home
2. Women over the age of 50 and men over the age of 70 who remain indoors most of the time

Women over the age of 50 wearing veils

Sources of Vitamin D

Sunlight

The human body can synthesize vitamin D when exposed to sunlight. People who live in tropical areas produce an estimated 250 µg/day—much more than the RDI. When the skin takes in the sun, the vitamin D production decreases, so the level of vitamin D will never become excessively high. In countries like the Netherlands, only in summer is the UV index of the sun high enough to produce a sufficient amount of vitamin D (some 25 µg after 15 minutes sun exposure of the face, arms and upper body without sun screen). Also, in many Western countries most people stay indoors most of the time or cover their skin, which limits the vitamin D production. Finally, the production of vitamin D reduces with age as a result of skin aging.

Nutrition

Our nutrition generally contains insufficient vitamin D. Only a few products contain vitamin D, in particular codfish oil, fat fish (15-25 µg/portion), some mushrooms and egg yolks. In the Netherlands vitamin D is added to margarine.

Relationship Between Vitamin D and the Performance in Sports

The scientific literature[72] contains many dozens of papers on the relationship between vitamin D and the performance in sports. The following positive effects of vitamin D have been reported:

1. Prevention of injuries, like stress fractures
2. Prevention of diseases, like infections, inflammation and osteoporosis
3. Increased muscle power
4. Improved performance in sports (sprint, swimming, gymnastics, tennis)

In a recent review paper[71], the following recommendations were made regarding the optimal vitamin D blood level:

1. Prevention of Rickets 25 nmol/L
2. Prevention of stress fractures 100 nmol/L
3. Improved performance in sport 125 nmol/L

Positive proof that vitamin D will improve the cycling performance is still lacking, This would require a study with a large number of test persons and a professional scientific methodology (e.g., double-blind, randomized).

Experiences of Hans, Ron and Karel

For many years, Hans has been supplementing his diet with 10 µg/day of vitamin D in summer and 15 µg/day in winter. Also, he regularly spends time outdoors, running, gardening and hiking. In May 2014 and in December 2014, he had his blood level checked in the laboratory. The results are given in the table and show that the level of vitamin D in his blood was adequate. The somewhat lower level of December will have been caused by the reduced sunshine in winter.

Vitamin D Data: Hans		
	Blood level	Intake
	(nmol/L)	(μg/day)
May 2014	95.2	10
December 2014	91.8	15

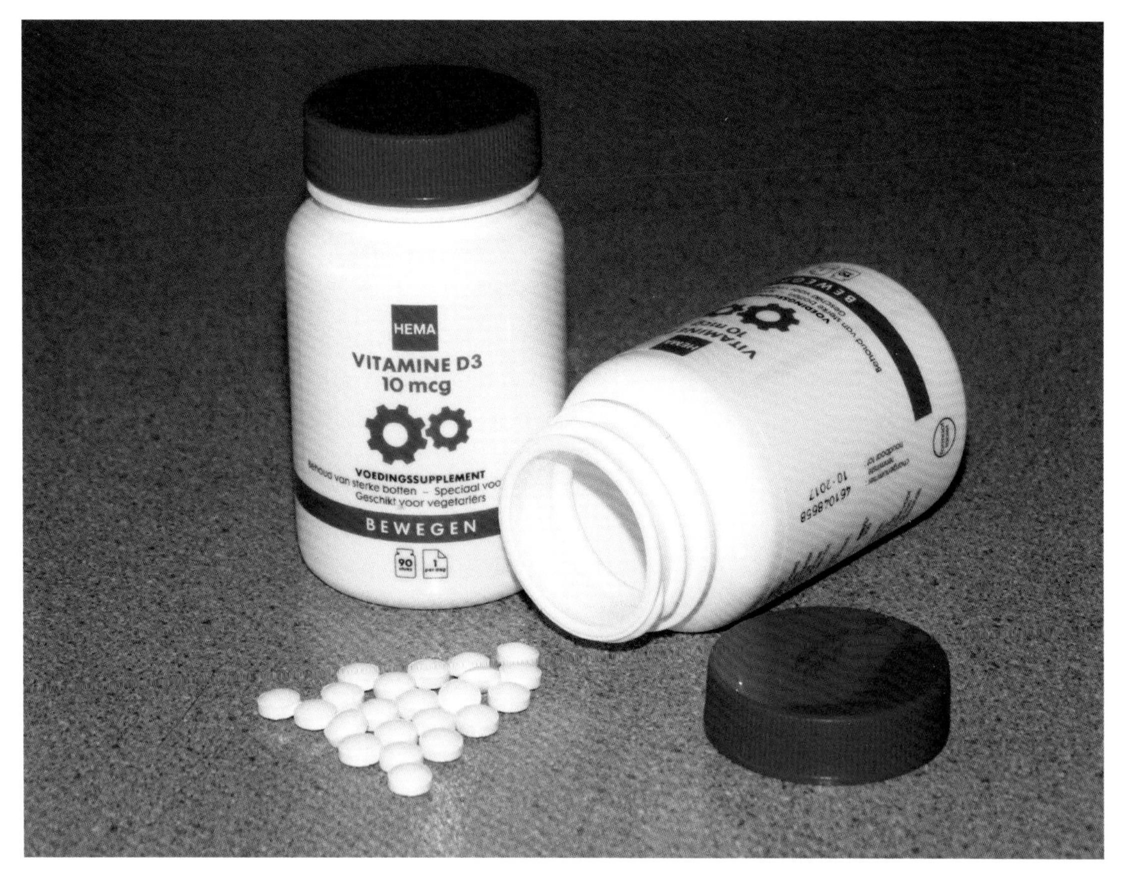

Supplementary intake of vitamin D can be necessary and prudent, particularly for cyclists.

Previously, Ron did not take vitamin D pills. Also, he spends more time indoors as compared to Hans. When he had his blood level checked in June 2014, it was found to be rather low. From then on, he started supplementing his diet, too. As a result, his blood levels increased as shown in the table.

Vitamin D Data: Ron		
	Blood level	Intake
	(nmol/L)	(μg/day)
June 2014	55.5	-
July 2014	84.5	50
September 2014	82.7	25
November 2014	71.8	20
January 2015	77.2	30
March 2015	81.8	30
April 2015	61.1	20
July 2015	69.5	20

Based on the data of Ron's table, we drew up a mass balance of vitamin D. We found that around 20 μg/day were broken down or excreted (in summer less, in winter more). So, we concluded that a supplement of 30 μg/day in winter and 20 μg/day in summer would be adequate for Ron.

Co-author Karel has been taking 20 μg/day in winter for many years. He cycles one hour every day and runs three times a week.

Conclusions and Recommendations

1. Vitamin D deficiency is prominent in the Netherlands and may have a negative impact on health and performance in sports.
2. It seems wise to take precautionary measures: take a regular sunbath in summer (a few times per week for 15 minutes; don't overdo it as too much sunshine can cause skin diseases) and supplement the diet with a vitamin D pill.
3. Risk groups and persons with complaints should have their blood level checked, so that informed additional measures can be taken.
4. Runners and other athletes should certainly take the precautionary measures mentioned above to avoid the risk of a negative impact on their performance.
5. The toxic levels of vitamin D are very high (blood level higher than 325 nmol/L), so taking some additional vitamin D does not lead to any risk of intoxication.

The human body can synthesize vitamin D when exposed to sunlight.

65. DON'T TAKE TOO MANY PILLS!

A man's health can be judged by which he takes two at a time: pills or stairs. –Joan Welsh

Earlier we learned that the scientific literature on nutrition and supplements tells us that there is no such thing as a miracle product. Even for elite athletes a normal, healthy and varied diet is sufficient and will supply all the necessary elements. Supplements are only required in exceptional cases, such as for specific deficiencies or extreme efforts (Tour de France or Ironman triathlon). Some vitamin formulas can even be dangerous! As an example of such potential problems, we will discuss vitamin B_6[73] in this chapter.

How Vitamin B_6 May Harm Your Health (The Burning Feet Syndrome)

An overdose of vitamin B_6[73] can cause neurological complaints, including tingling and burning feet (burning feet syndrome). In the Netherlands, vitamin B_6 intoxication is diagnosed frequently. One of the reasons is the fact that pills containing a high dose can be bought without prescription. Physician and co-author Karel Bos regularly sees patients with vitamin B_6 intoxication in his medical practice.

The History of Vitamin B_6

Vitamin B_6 was discovered during research into pellagra, a skin disease which is still prominent in developing countries. In 1934, the Hungarian microbiologist and biochemist Paul György traced a substance that was able to prevent pellagra in rats. One year later, he managed to isolate vitamin B_6. The molecular structure was discovered in 1939. Vitamin B_6 comprises of three compounds including pyridoxine. This name is also used as the general denomination for vitamin B_6.

Vitamin B_6 Deficiency Symptoms

Prolonged deficits may lead to anemia, lack of appetite, diarrhea, nervous conditions and a weakened immune system. In the Netherlands deficits are rare, as the normal diet contains sufficient vitamin B_6. Deficiencies are only seen in special cases, such as alcoholism and persons with a reduced kidney function.

Recommended Daily Intake

The RDI has been set at 1.5 mg/day by the Dutch Health Council. For special groups, like pregnant women, the RDI is slightly higher, 1.9 mg/day. The maximum acceptable safe intake is considered to be 25 mg/day.

Sources of Vitamin B_6

Nutrition

In our food, vitamin B_6 is mostly bound to proteins. Very rich sources are chicken and liver. Good sources are meat, fish, eggs, milk and cheese. Vegetable sources are legumes, bananas, nuts, beans, cauliflower, raisins, bread and corn. The normal Dutch diet will easily supply the RDI of 1.5 mg/day.

Vitamin pills

In the Netherlands, vitamin B_6 can be bought without a prescription. Pills are sold with a mega dose of 50, 100 or even 250 mg. The bottle instructions recommend a daily intake of 2-4 of these pills! Consequently, it seems likely that in the Netherlands, just like in the USA, many people will use a dose of 1,000 mg This is equivalent to 40 times the maximum recommended safe intake and even 666 times the RDI! So, it is obvious that people who take these pills regularly run the risk of an overdose and intoxication of vitamin B_6!

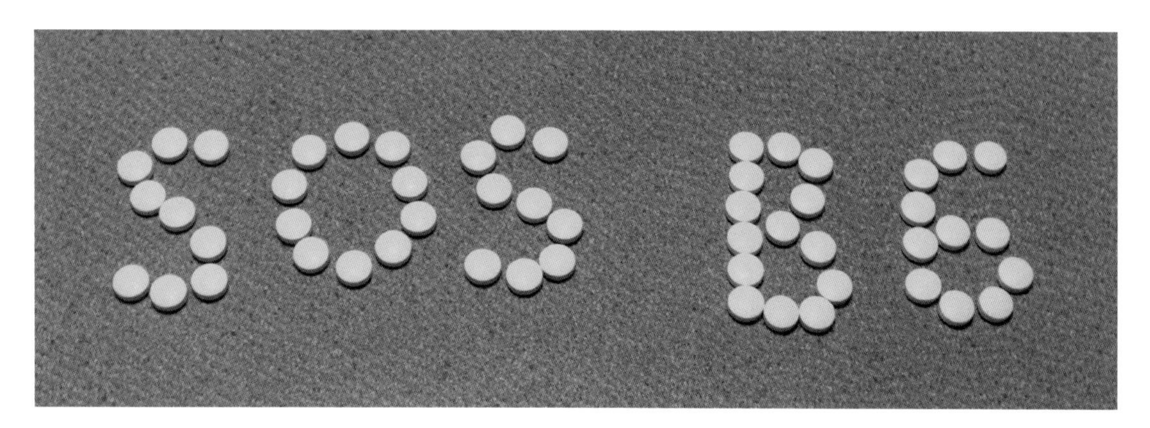

In the Netherlands, vitamin B_6 intoxication is diagnosed frequently.

Risks of an Overdose of Vitamin B_6

The scientific literature contains many papers on the risks of an overdose of vitamin B_6. It may lead to a degeneration of the peripheral nervous system and parts of the spine (peripheral neuropathy). These effect have been proven clearly at doses of 500 mg/day; patients suffer from tingling and idiosyncrasy of the arms and legs (burning feet syndrome). At lower doses of 50 to 300 mg/day, the symptoms are less obvious.

An Increasing Problem?

Vitamin B_6 intoxication is often not recognized, as physicians are not aware of the toxicity of vitamins. For a proper diagnoses it is necessary to analyze the blood level in the laboratory. The normal blood level of vitamin B_6 is 35-110 nmol/L. A hospital in the Netherlands issued a warning recently that they were seeing a significant increase in excessive blood values. Some 50% of all samples were higher than the upper limit of 110 nmol/L, with an extreme value of 12,525 nmol/L! They strongly advise not to use any vitamin B_6 pills.

Conclusions and Recommendations

1. Vitamin B_6 deficiency occurs only rarely in the Netherlands, so it not necessary to take supplementary pills, even for elite athletes.
2. Vitamin B_6 intoxication occurs regularly in the Netherlands. It is caused by the intake of pills with a mega dose and can lead to tingling and idiosyncrasy of the arms and legs (burning feet syndrome).
3. Persons having complaints should have their blood level checked in consultation with their physician. If the level is too high, they should stop taking pills immediately. The complaints may continue for as long as a year.
4. To limit the risk of overdosing, it is strongly recommended to reduce the maximum dose of vitamin B_6 from 250 to 25 mg/pill. Also the bottle instructions should warn against the risk of overdosing and intoxication.

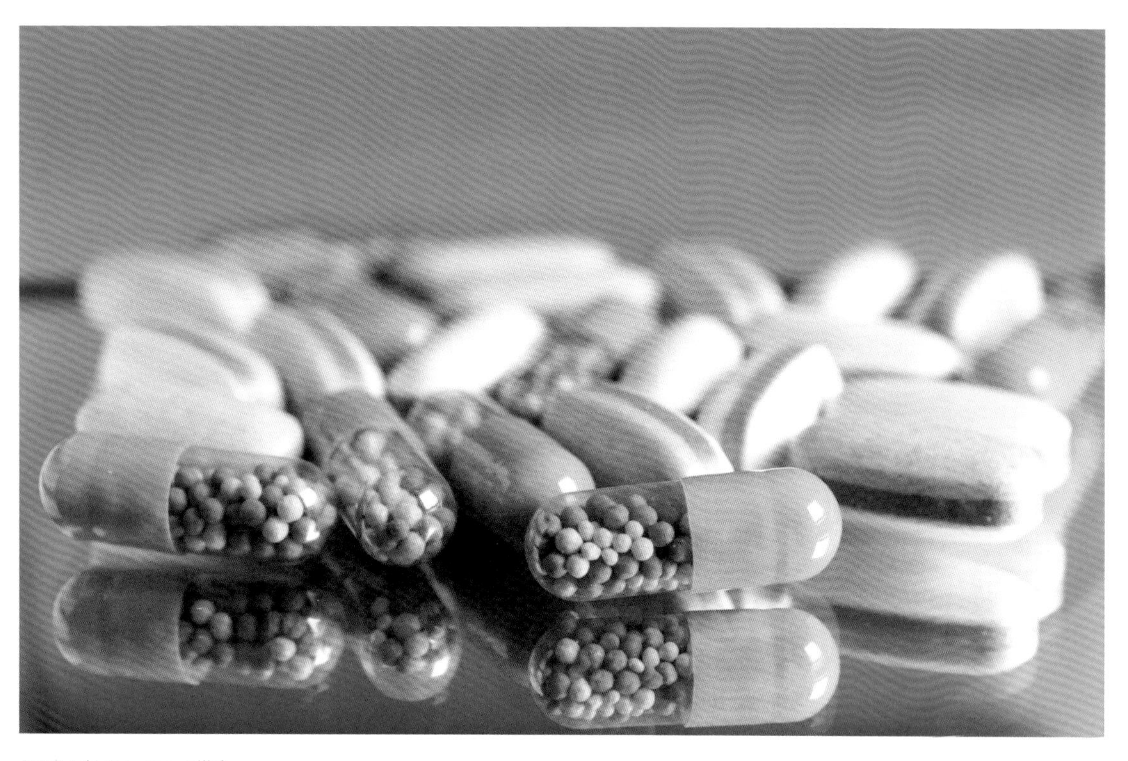

Don't take too many pills!

66. THE IMPACT OF DOPING

I was not a doper, I told myself. I just injected myself and needed pills to sleep. –David Millar

Doping is as old as sport itself. The ancient Greek used fermented honey and cheese containing the ergogenic substance tyramine. The battle between dopers and anti-doping agencies will never end. In spite of the severe sanctions and the worldwide condemnation of dopers like Lance Armstrong, some athletes will still be tempted to gain an illegal edge. In recent years[5,6], we have seen that blood doping and EPO have been the most widespread and effective doping agents. How do they influence performance and how big is the impact? In this chapter, we will answer these questions. Other doping agents will also be discussed briefly.

Blood Doping and EPO

As we learned in an earlier chapter, the oxygen transport capacity of the blood (VO_2 max) is equal to the blood flow (in l/h) and the hemoglobin level of the blood (in g/dl, see the box). Blood doping involves injecting concentrated blood in the arteries, thus increasing the hemoglobin (Hb) level and consequently the VO_2 max. A similar effect can be obtained by dosing EPO. The Hb level may be increased to 18.5 g/dl or even more and the hematocrit (Hct) value of the blood to 50% and higher. As a result of this the blood becomes thick and may clot. It has been presumed that this caused the death of several professional cyclists during the 1980s, when EPO was being introduced. In recent years, the number and quality of the doping tests have increased significantly. This has resulted in a decline of the number of positive tests.

We can explain the impact of blood doping and EPO by comparing the oxygen transport capacity of the blood. The oxygen transport capacity of the blood of a doper with a Hb level of 18.5 g/dl and a Hct value of 50% will be 15% higher than that of a clean athlete with a Hb level of 16 g/l and a Hct value of 43.5%! In the scientific literature[5,6], effects in the order of a 10% increase of VO_2 max have been reported. In the earlier chapter on the Alpe d'Huez we calculated that the record climbing time of Marco Panatani was equivalent to an FTP which was 8.8% higher than the maximum limit of 6.4 watts/kg. Obviously, a 10% impact in performance makes it more or less impossible for a clean cyclist to compete with a doper!

Blood Levels

Hemoglobin (Hb) is the protein in the red blood cells which serves to transport oxygen (O_2). Normal levels of Hb are between 14-17 g/dl for men and 12-15 g/dl for women. In relation to blood doping the maximum limit for men has been set at 18.5 g/dl. Sometimes the lab reports Hb in mmol/l. As the molecular weight of Hb is equal to 16,114, you can calculate the Hb level in g/dl by multiplying by 1.61. One gram of Hb can transport 1.34 ml of O_2. Consequently, blood with a Hb level of 15 g/dl can transport 15*1.34 = 20.1 ml O_2/dl (or 20.1 vol. %).

Hematocrit (Hct) is the percentage by volume of the red blood cells in the blood. Normal values are between 43-48% for men and 38-44% for women. In relation to blood doping, the maximum limit for men has been set at 50%. Hct can be approximated by multiplying the Hb level by 3.

EPO is the natural hormone Erythropoietin, which is produced in the kidneys and stimulates the production of new red blood cells. Since the 1980s, EPO is produced artificially and used as a doping agent. As a result of using EPO, the levels of Hb and Hct increase significantly.

Anabolic Steroids and Growth Hormones

Anabolic steroids have become notorious as a result of the widespread use in the German Democratic Republic (GDR, former east Germany) between 1960 and 1989. Anabolic steroids are derivates of testosterone which reinforce the primary sex characterics such as hair growth, appearance, voice and libido. The female GDR athletes were known for their masculine appearance. Well-known brand names are Stanolozol and Nandrolon. Anabolic steroids and growth hormones are most effective in weight lifting (providing as much as a 20% increase in performance) and they promote recovery. The most infamous user of anabolic steroids is Ben Johnson, who tested positive for Stanozolol after winning the 100 meter in the 1988 Olympic Games in a world record time of 9.79. He was stripped of his title and his record and banned from competition for two years.

The impact of anabolic steroids and growth hormones on the performance of endurance athletes is much less than that of blood doping and EPO. Moreover, severe health risks have been associated with the use of steroids, including reduced fertility, liver diseases, coronory diseases and mental illnesses.

Amphetamines and Ephedrine

Amphetamines stimulate the central nervous system and mask feelings of fatigue. A well-known brand name is Benzedrine. Amphetamines became notorius worldwide as a result of the death of cyclist Tommy Simpson in the Tour de France. The positive impact of amphetamines is much smaller than that of blood doping and EPO. Some amphetamines, including Ephedrine, are prescribed as a cure for asthma. Several health risks have been associated with the use of amphetamines, including insomnia and mental illnesses.

Race Time at the 40-Kilometer Time Trial

Once again, we calculated the impact with our model and using the standard conditions. We have assumed that the use of doping increases the FTP of Fast Eddy by 10%.

The results are given in the table. We see that the attainable speed of Fast Eddy at the 40-kilometer time trial increases from 40.41 km/h to 41.83 km/h, by 3.53%. Obviously, this is less than the 10% increase of his FTP, as the required power increases by the cube of the speed. His total gain on the time trial would be 121 seconds, putting him in a different league of cyclists.

Impact of Doping on a Flat Course: Fast Eddy

	v	T 40 km	Difference
	(km/h)	(min)	(sec)
Base	40.41	59.4	-
Doping +10%	41.83	57.4	-121

Race Time to the Top of the Alpe d'Huez

Once again, the results of our calculations are presented in a similar table. We see that that the speed of Fast Eddy increases from 15.58 km/h to 16.98 km/h, by 9%. This is almost the same as the 10% increase of his FTP. Obviously, the air resistance plays only a minor role on the climb. Eddy reaches the top after 51.1 minutes, gaining no less than 275 seconds at the climb.

Impact of Doping at Alpe D'Huez			
	v	T Alpe	Difference
	(km/h)	(min)	(sec)
Base	15.58	55.6	-
Doping +10%	16.98	51.1	-275

We end this chapter on the note that we absolutely oppose the use of doping in cycling. These calculations are meant to illustrate the magnitude of the advantage that a cheating doper may have as compared to an honest, hard-training cyclist. The results shoud definitely not be used to encourage anyone to seek such an illegal and potentially dangerous path.

We hope that the readers of our book will continue to enjoy the many benefits of cycling, just like we have, in a clean and healthy way! Cycling will enrich your life with fun and fitness, so enjoy the many benefits without cheating and jeopardizing your health!

Hans, Ron and Guido passionately support the anti-doping campaigns.

REFERENCES

1. Hans van Dijk en Ron van Megen, Het Geheim van Hardlopen, april 2014 (2e druk), NedRun, Leusden, ISBN 978-90-821069-1-6
2. Hans van Dijk, Ron van Megen en Guido Vroemen, Het Geheim van Wielrennen, juni 2015, NedRun, Leusden, ISBN 978-90-821069-4-7
3. Hans van Dijk en Ron van Megen, Hardlopen met Power!, april 2012, NedRun, Leusden, ISBN 978-90-821069-7-8
4. I. Min-Lee et.al., Effect of physical inactivity on major non-communicable diseases worldwide: an analysis of burden of disease and life expectancy, The Lancet, 380 (9838), 219-229, July 2012
5. T.Noakes, Lore of Running, 2002, Cape Town, Human Kinetics, ISBN 0-87322-959-2
6. M. L. Foss, S.J. Keteyian, Fox's physiological basis for exercise and sport, McGraw-Hill, 1998, ISBN 0-697-25904-8
7. H. Allen and A. Coggan, Training and racing with a power meter, 2010, Velo Press, Boulder Colorado, ISBN 978-1-934030-55-4
8. R.P. Lamberts, The development of an evidenced based submaximal cycle test designed to monitor and predict cycling performance, PhD-thesis, University of Cape Town, 2009, ISBN 978-90-9024959-9
9. D. Morris, Performance cycling, training for power, performance and speed, 2003, McGraw-Hill ISBN 0-07-141091-0
10. J. Friel, The Cyclist's Training Bible, Velo Press, Boulder, Colorado, 2003, ISBN 1-931382-21-2
11. A.E. Jeukendrup, Carbohydrate intake during excercise and perfomance, Nutrition 2004: 20, 669-677
12. M.Fitzgerald, Racing weight; how to get lean for peak performance, 2009, Boulder, Velo Press, ISBN 978-1-934030-51-6
13. Kris Verburgh, De voedselzandloper, Bert Bakker Uitgeverij, Amsterdam, 2012, ISBN 978-90-351-3758-5
14. www.esbnyc.com/event/2015-empire-state-building-run-up-info
15. www.fiets.nl/2015/06/08/wiggins-werelduurrecord-geanalyseerd/
16. www.fiets.nl/2015/07/25/hoe-snel-gaat-froome-alpe-dhuez-op/
17. Junghsen Lieh, Determination of Cycling Speed Using a Closed-form Solution from Nonlinear Dynamic Equations, Human Power eJournal, December 2006, www.hupi.org/HPeJ/0010/Closed-form-Vmax-bike.pdf
18. J. Martin, D. Milliken, J. Cobb, K. McFadden and A. Coggan, Validation of a mathematical model for road cycling power, Journal of Applied Biomechanics, 1998, 14, 276-291
19. en.wikipedia.org/wiki/Cubic_function

20. P. Skiba etal., Modelling the expenditure and reconstitution of work capacity above critical power, Medicine & Science in Sports & Exercise, 2012, DOI: 10.1249/MSS.0b013e3182517a80
21. P. Riegel, Time predicting, Runner's World, August 1977
22. P. Riegel, Athletic records and human endurance, American Scientist, 69, May-June 1981
23. B.I. Rapaport, Metabolic factors limiting performance in marathon runners, PLoS Comput Biol 6 (10): e1000960, doi:10.1371/journal.pcbi.100960
24. hyperphysics.phy-astr.gsu.edu/hbase/biology/atp.html
25. books.google.nl/books?id=v9HL5VyRmZcC&pg=PA292&lpg =PA292&dq=gibbs+energy+from+atp&source=bl&ots=DPSLVfLzSe&sig= z8dV3U1ppOH1S6Pbso4KtT5
26. www.rpi.edu/dept/bcbp/molbiochem/MBWeb/mb1/part2/bioener.htm
27. www.chembio.uoguelph.ca/educmat/chm452/lecture1.htm
28. A. Coggan, Power profiles, home.trainingpeaks.com/blog/article/power-profiling
29. A.V. Hill, The maximum work and mechanical efficiency of human muscles and their most economical speed, J Physiol, 1925, 01737-0025
30. en.wikipedia.org/wiki/VO_2_max
31. home.trainingpeaks.com/blog/article/what-is-threshold-power
32. E. Sterken, Fron the cradle to the grave: how fast can we run?, Journal of Sports Sciences, 2003, 21, 479-491
33. en.wikipedia.org/wiki/Body_mass_index
34. en.wikipedia.org/wiki/Body_fat_percentage
35. P. Deurenberg, J. Weststrate and J. Seidell, Body Mass Index as a measure of body fatness: age- and sex-specific prediction formulas, British Journal of Nutrition (1991), 65, 105-114
36. A. Schmidt, Das grosse Buch vom Radsport, 2007, Meyer & Meyer Verlag, Aachen, ISBN 13:978-3-89899-237-4
37. M. Glaskin, Cycling science, how rider and machine work together, University of Chicago Press, 2012, ISBN 12:978-0-226-92413-7
38. D.G. Gordon, Bicycling science, MIT Press, 2004, Cambridge, Massachusetts, ISBN 13:978-0-262-23237-1
39. E.W. Faria, D. L. Parker and I.E. Faria, The science of cycling, factors affecting performance- part 1, Sports Med 2005: 35 (4) 285-312
40. E.W. Faria, D. L. Parker and I.E. Faria, The science of cycling, factors affecting performance- part 2, Sports Med 2005: 35 (4) 313-337
41. A. E. Jeukendrup (ed.), High Performance Cycling, 2002, Human Kinetics Publ., ISBN 0-7360-4021-8

42. en.wikipedia.org/wiki/Heart_rate
43. www.welovecycling.com/wide/2016/05/06/kind-muscles-used-pedal-stroke/
44. www.cyclingpowerlab.com/PowerModels.aspx
45. www.velofilie.nl
46. www.bestbikesplit.com/
47. fredrompelberg.com/NL/wereldrecord
48. A. Baker and W.G. Hopkins, Altitude training for sea-level competition, www.sportsci.org
49. nl.wikipedia.org/wiki/Hematocriet
50. en.wikipedia.org/wiki/Altitude_training
51. www.ncbi.nlm.nih.gov/pubmed/10589872
52. P. Cerritelli, Limiting factors to oxygen transport on Mount Everest, J. Appl. Physiol. 40: 1976, pp 558-667
53. A. Baker and W.G. Hopkins, Altitude training for sea-level competition, www.sportsci.org
54. C. Capelli and P. di Prampero, Effects of altitude om top speeds during 1 h unaccompanied cycling, Eur J Appl Physiol (1995) 71: 469-471
55. nl.wikipedia.org/wiki/Werelduurrecord_%28wielrennen%29
56. S. Padilla, I. Mujika, F. Angulo and J. Goiiena, Scientific approach to the 1-h cycling world record: a case study, J. Appl. Phyiol 89: 1522-1527, 2000
57. D. Basset, C. Kyle, L. Passfield, J. Broker and E. Burke, Comparing cycling world records, 1967-1996: modelling with empirical data, Medicine & Science in Sports & Exercise, 1999, 31(11), p 1665
58. nl.wikipedia.org/wiki/Schaal_van_Beaufort
59. en.wikipedia.org/wiki/Alpe_d%27Huez
60. www.fietsica.be/
61. J. Martin and W. Spirduso, Determinants of maximal cycling power: crank length, pedalling rate and pedal speed, Eur J Appl Physiol (2001) 84: 413-418
62. J. Brotherhood, Heat stress and strain in exercise and sport, Journal of Science and Medicine in Sport, (2008), 11, 6-19
63. El Helou N, Tafflet M, Berthelot G, Tolaini J, Marc A, et al. (2012) Impact of Environmental Parameters on Marathon Running Performance. PLoS ONE 7(5):e37407. doi:10.1371/journal.pone.0037407)
64. Will Le Page, Optimum Temperature for Elite Running Performance, University of Tulsa, USA, April 2011
65. M. Ross et al. , Novel Precooling Strategy Enhances Time Trial Cycling in the Heat, Medicine & Science in Sports & Exercise, 2010, DOI: 10.1249/MSS.0b013e3181e93210
66. en.wikipedia.org/wiki/Wet-bulb_temperature

67. R. Still, Wet-bulb temperature from relative humidity and air temperature, Journal of Applied Meteorology and Climatology, 2011 (50), pp 2267-2269
68. en.wikipedia.org/wiki/Wind_chill
69. fellrnr.com/wiki/Beetroot_and_Running_Performance
70. en.wikipedia.org/wiki/Vitamin_D
71. www.vitamindwiki.com/tiki-index.php?page=Sports&redirectpage=
72. www.vitamindwiki.com/Sports+benefits+from+up+to+50+ng+of+Vitamin+%25E2%2580%2593+meta-analysis+-+Nov+2012
73. en.wikipedia.org/wiki/Vitamin_B6

CREDITS

Photo

Thanks to the following agencies and individuals for their kind permission to use their photographs as reference:

- Caroline Arends: p. 20
- Saskia Berdenis van Berlekom: p. 13
- Christie Brouwer: p. 79
- dpa Picture-Alliance GmbH: p. 58, p. 131, p. 141, p. 147, p. 355, p. 369, p. 373
- Atty van Dijk: p. 163
- Geert Hakze: p. 71
- Ingrid van Heteren: author Guido Vroemen
- iStockphoto: p. 10, p. 67, p. 144, p. 233, p. 238, p. 260, p. 292, p. 295, p. 317, p. 345, p. 363
- Raymond Kerckhoffs and Fred Rompelberg: p. 231
- Erik van Leeuwen: p. 65
- Leontien Total Sports; p. 227, p. 239, p. 252
- Ron van Megen: p. 19, p. 27, p. 43, p. 56, p. 73, p. 99, p. 101, p. 105, p. 110, p. 155, p. 177, p. 197, p. 205 p. 209 (three photos), p. 211, p. 219, p. 243, p. 270 (both photos), p. 277, p. 287, p. 314, p. 315, p. 347, p. 367, p. 371, p. 377
- Bas de Meijer: p. 236
- Cor Vos Fotopersburo: p. 23, p. 49, p. 109, p. 121, p. 123, p. 127, p. 135, p. 151, p. 225, p. 247, p. 255, p. 273, p. 275, p. 281, p. 291, p. 319
- Pioneer: p. 29, p.171, p. 182, p. 195, p. 216 left (crank only), p. 216 right, p. 267
- Quarq: p. 53 (both photos), p. 181 (middle)
- Pieter Riegel p. 86 (both photos)
- Team Roompot-Nederlandse Loterij: p. 39, p. 165, p. 299, p. 326
- Desirée Schippers: author Hans van Dijk, author Ron van Megen
- Huub Snoep: p. 62
- SRAM: p. 303, p. 305 (both photos)
- SRAM/Cyclephotos: p. 157, p. 187, p. 193
- Team4Talent fotografie: p. 33, p. 331, p. 341
- Guido Vroemen: p. 22, p. 178 u/i 181 (except p. 181 middle), p. 189, p. 266, p. 271

Graphics

Hans van Dijk, Ron van Megen and Guido Vroemen

Design

Cover design, inside layout: Sannah Inderelst

Typesetting: Katerina Georgieva

Editing

Editing: Anne Rumery, Kristina Oltrogge